Technological Change and
Economic Development

Technological Change and Economic Development

The Manufacturing Experience of Mexico and Puerto Rico

W. PAUL STRASSMANN

Professor of Economics
Michigan State University

Cornell University Press

Ithaca, New York

For EOS, IWS, *and* KLW

For LOT, JWS, and BTW

Preface

In this book I have tried to chart some of the topography of our ignorance about technological change in manufacturing during early industrialization. Nothing at all could have been accomplished without the help of numerous persons who have probed the terrain of technology in various places much longer than I and who have acquired great skill and experience. I wish to record here my gratitude for their help. First I should mention the officials of Mexican, Puerto Rican, and American manufacturing enterprises, consulting firms, and research institutes who provided the basic data with astonishing generosity and undue trust. They answered interminable and impertinent interview questions and follow-up letters with good will and no regard for sensible cost criteria.

When originally defining the scope of the project and developing research procedures, I benefited from incisive suggestions by Dr. Hans Singer and Dr. Samuel Lurié of the United Nations Secretariat; by Professors Everett E. Hagen and Richard S. Eckaus of the Massachusetts Institute of Technology; by Professor Benjamin Higgins of the University of Texas; and by Professor Einar Hardin of Michigan State University.

For invaluable counsel and criticism in Mexico, as well as for introductions to experts in person and in print, I am heavily indebted to Lic. Victor L. Urquidi, Banco de México; Lic. Ifigenia M. de Navarrete, Universidad Nacional Autónoma de México; and Dr. Miguel S. Wionczek, Centro de Estudios Monetarios Latinoamericanos. Their judicious and penetrating comments on early drafts of several chapters have saved me from errors of both fact and interpretation. They are not, however, in any way accountable for remaining errors and shortcomings. Nor is anyone else besides myself.

I also owe thanks for hospitality and indispensable help in Mexico to Lic. Jorge Aguilar, Secretaría de Hacienda; Sr. Guillermo Camargo; Dr. Cornelius A. Cannegieter, Lic. Consuelo Meyer, and Lic. Manuel Rodríguez Cisneros, all formerly of the Universidad de Nuevo Leon; Sr. Jesús Rivero Quijano and Ing. Pedro Herrera, Centro Industrial de Productividad; Dr. Robert Cuba Jones, Villa Jones Centro Cultural Internacional; Sr. Carlos Maldonado, President, Cámara de Industria de Nuevo Leon; Lic. Oscar Mendez Napoles, Secretaría de Educación; Lic. Joseph Moscarella, U.N. Economic Commission for Latin America; Lic. Victor Navarrete, Lic. Ignacio Navarro, and Ing. Carlos Quintana, Nacional Financiera; Ing. Alanís Patiño, Ing. Gonzalo Robles, and Lic. Fausto Urencio, Banco de México; Lic. Edgardo Reyes Salcido, Centro de Productividad de Monterrey; and Ing. Francisco Vera, Instituto Tecnológico y de Estudios Superiores de Monterrey.

In Puerto Rico, I am particularly indebted to Professor Rexford Guy Tugwell, University of Puerto Rico and former Governor; Dr. Vernon Esteves, Banco de Fomento; Mr. Enrique Martínez Rigán, Mr. Morris Moses, Mr. Jorge Rosado, Mr. Pedro R. Sola, and Mr. Leo Suslow, Economic Development Administration; and to Mr. A. Alecia, Mr. Jesús Figueroa, and Mr. Lorenzo García Hernández, Department of Education.

As the manuscript took shape, I benefited from many discussions in graduate seminars and with colleagues at Marshall Hall. Seven individuals who must be specially mentioned are

Professor Bert Hoselitz, University of Chicago; Professor Raymond Vernon, Harvard University; Dr. James Bausch Hendry, International Bank for Reconstruction and Development; and Professors Subbiah Kannappan, Anthony Koo, Herbert Kisch, and Thomas R. Saving, of Michigan State University. Their actions contradict the Chinese proverb that men are good-natured until asked for help. Professor Thomas Mayer of the University of California read the entire manuscript with exceptional care and tightened the analysis at many points with skeptical and occasionally zany comments.

The project began in 1960–61 with a Social Science Research Council fellowship supplemented by a grant from the Rockefeller Foundation. Later support came from Michigan State All-University Research Grants, College of Business Released Time, a 1962–63 Ford Foundation Faculty Fellowship, and a remarkably flexible Michigan State University International Programs–Ford Foundation grant. For all this generosity, I record my gratitude.

My warmest thanks go to my wife for her unfailing help, especially with the most gruesome tasks, and for her capacity to enjoy or tolerate whatever comes along, her fine blend of a Stoic and Epicurean outlook.

Portions of Chapter 2 were presented in a paper at the 1962 meetings of the American Academy for the Advancement of Science and later printed in *Symposia Studies Series.* Appendix A is partly based on an article I wrote for *Inter-American Economic Affairs.*

W. PAUL STRASSMANN

East Lansing
August 1967

Contents

Contents   *xiii*

List of Tables

Technological Change and
Economic Development

I

Introduction

Applause marks the end of a speech about inspiration and future achievement. The President of a tropical country pulls a brass electrical switch. An orange light gleams and a needle moves to the middle of its dial. Machines drone in the factory hall.

If that event occurs often enough—at times with the mayor or the owner's retired uncle substituting for His Excellency—a country will cease to be poor and technologically backward. To equate industry with progress and to call unprocessed materials birthrights frittered away are mercantilist overstatements. But what change is more conspicuous than the rising share of manufactured goods in national output? The share in fact ranges from about one-eighth at the lowest per capita income levels to one-third or so at the highest. Factories are especially helpful when they draw on resources with little alternative use, such as underemployed labor and waste materials, while generating new resources: capital through plowed-back profits, skilled operators through in-plant training, and entrepreneurship through trial and error. Manufacturing can breed social groups with the modern outlook needed for a secular, progressive society and weaken traditionalism. The analysis by economists of nonmanufacturing sectors has often progressed only through analogies from manufacturing, by quantifying intangible outputs with units of time into quasi commodities subject to production functions.

This book is about technological change in poor countries and concentrates on manufacturing. Technology refers not only to tools, a stockpile of utensils, but to a kind of tool-using behavior, a set of methods for making specific goods. Technological change is the discovery and application of new or previously ignored or rejected production methods. The process has social and economic repercussions, but these are not the subject of this book. Instead, the targets here are the character and roots of technological change. These roots, however, go far into problems of changing social organization, education, and the process of inquiry. If technology were only a stockpile of utensils and, therefore, a part of the physical environment, the analysis could be left to engineers. Anyone able to compare the efficiency of two proposed machines would be competent. Where aggregation raises problems, economists with a narrow approach could fill in as pseudo engineers. They could talk about technological change as "shifting production functions" that create lower ratios of general input to general output levels. Lags, diverse gestation periods, durability, divergent expectations, and discounting of the future, among other matters, would complicate the analysis. In this approach, indivisibilities, interdependencies, uncertainties, and noneconomic goals of management, labor, and government would either be grafted on at the end as "constraints" or ignored altogether as unfathomable "random variables."

A things-first, psychology-last study of technological change sometimes has the disadvantage of presenting elements in the reverse order of importance. The last additions prove hard to incorporate as fundamental, for they neither fit the framework nor support preliminary approximations. Better to return to the Greek concept of techne with its connotation of man's combined intellectual, moral, and physiological ability to make a product;

thus the integration of person, rational procedure, and object is implied. Technology becomes coextensive with research, education, organized work, and with the way these three are instituted in society, external to the individuals participating only in the sense that decisions and rules must purport to be validated by empirical tests, by consistency with scientific investigation generally, by principles of evidence which coerce acceptance.[1]

[1] If technology were less complex and changed in simple and uniform patterns, then simple models could point toward simple cures for backwardness. Suppose that the level of technology in developed countries grew at such a rate that r would always be the ratio of any technological level to that of the preceding year. If the growth rate were 5 percent, r would be 1.05. Suppose that underdeveloped countries were either unwilling or unable to apply that level of technology until a uniform number of years, L, had passed. How could the gap between the level of technology, D_t, in the developed country and the level, U_t, in the underdeveloped country in year t be eliminated?

If the level in the developed country had been measured in some initial year o, then:

$$D_t = D_o r^t$$

In that year the level of the underdeveloped country would be:

$$U_t = D_o r^{t-L}$$

The ratio of the level of technology in the developed country to that in the underdeveloped country would be:

$$\frac{U_t}{D_t} = \frac{D_o r^t}{D_o r^{t-L}}$$
$$= r^L$$

The gap between the two would disappear only if r^L becomes equal to unity, if technological growth ceases in the developed country, or if the lag falls to zero. But who could not have seen that in the first place? Nothing has been said to explain the lag in the underdeveloped country, which was the problem all along. Nor would help lie in further assumptions about the homogeneity of the production function, the capital-labor neutrality of technological change, disproportionalities in factor endowment, or variations in the product mix unless these shed light on the lag itself. Theories fail if the point at issue is left exogenous.

The remainder of this introduction surveys briefly how the general opinion of the last century that technological backwardness was not a complicated matter changed over the years. Chapter 2 is concerned with the international network for diffusing and adapting technical knowledge and serves also as an introduction to the many technological agents from managers to research institutes. The willingness and ability of management to direct, and of labor to operate, new processes is the subject of Chapter 3. Only then do three chapters deal successively with capital and labor intensity; relative factor prices; possibilities for substitution; the role of scale, flexibility, multiple shifts, durability, maintenance, and second-hand equipment. The last substantive chapter analyzes innovation and stresses its dependence on both prior scientific advances and government support.

Most assertions in the book were tested by, or derived from, field work in Mexico and Puerto Rico among a sample of seventy firms. During the period 1940–1965 these two areas were among the world's leaders in rapid industrialization, and their experience will be relevant elsewhere, though obviously not everywhere. Appendix A reviews the political and economic setting of Mexican and Puerto Rican development with emphasis on trends and policies in manufacturing. Appendix B shows how Mexican labor productivity would have compared with that of the United States in forty-four industries around 1960, given equal capital-labor ratios and the assumption of conventional Cobb-Douglas production functions. Appendix C describes the structure of the sample of firms. Appendix D is the questionnaire used in the field work to probe for antecedents of investment decisions, instructions to designing engineers, finance, markets, labor relations, and experience with plants in operation.

I. Early Views of Technology and Development

During the nineteenth century the transplanting of technology from country to country was seldom looked on as unusually problematical. The "right" strategy was simply that which spread it from region to region or from generation to generation. On the Yangtze or the Nile, as much as on the Clyde or the Meuse, spending wisely on given apparatus and learning meant similar rewards. Repeal of British prohibitions on emigration of skilled workers in 1825 and on export of machinery in 1842—neither had been effectively enforced anyway—seemed to grant the same chance to all countries, modified only by varying physical resources. The pace of growth in the United States and Germany even suggested that latecomers had an advantage: New designs did not have to be compromised to mesh with habits and equipment on hand.[2] If entrepreneurs were lacking, suitable princely decrees and concessions would bring them down the gangplank of next month's steamboat.

Among all types of contemporary observers, economists seemed least inclined to see the possibility of countries developing along different technological paths. After all, their discipline had gained autonomy and momentum only with the claim of the underlying planetary uniformity of "the correct principles of political economy," as Ricardo called them, laws that neither moral zeal nor the fossilized history of any nation could violate. Adam Smith had already stated that the luxurious courts and dense populations of Asia proved China, at least, "a country

---

[2] An elaborate analysis did not appear until 1915 with Thorstein Veblen, *Imperial Germany and the Industrial Revolution* (republished, New York: Viking Press, 1939). See also, "The Opportunity of Japan," *Journal of Race Development,* July 1915, pp. 23–38, reprinted in *Essays in Our Changing Order* (New York: Viking Press, 1934). The widespread forms of the case still persisting are analyzed by Edward Ames and Nathan Rosenberg, "Changing Technological Leadership and Industrial Growth," *Economic Journal,* March 1963, pp. 13–31.

much richer than any part of Europe," well cultivated and most industrious, and, like "Indostan," only somewhat inferior in manufacturing. Because of a home market as large as most of Europe and cheap water carriage, "very great manufactures" and "very considerable subdivisions of labor" had easily developed. If the mandarins would only widen the market with foreign trade, "the Chinese would naturally learn the art of using and constructing themselves all the different machines made use of in other countries."[3]

A century later no Western economist questioned the all-around economic superiority of the West, much less the universal serviceability of its technological recipes. Most understood that higher wages, as in North America, sped the acceptance of labor-saving devices, and that low wages reduced gains from mechanization. If anything, however, accumulation of industrial capital, not pressure from wages, was looked on as the special economic factor making possible the new technology. Poor workers seemed abundant everywhere, and more could always be imported from Ireland or Eastern Europe. Yet only some countries had a factory-building middle class. Among Alfred Marshall's less penetrating insights, but reflecting current opinion, was his view that "the greatest savings are made by those who have been brought up on narrow means to stern hard work," a discipline that could only be sustained in the "fresh invigorating air" of a northern climate. Where warm countries have developed, "the rulers have generally belonged to a race that has recently come from a cooler climate in a distant country or in neighboring mountain lands." Elsewhere sheer apathy could keep tribes from doubling income by applying "means that lie within their power and knowledge." England

---

[3] Adam Smith, *The Wealth of Nations* (New York: Modern Library, 1937), pp. 71, 95, 189, 205–6, 238, 645. See also E. A. J. Johnson, "The Place of Learning, Science, Vocational Training, and 'Art' in Pre-Smithian Economic Thought," *Journal of Economic History*, June 1964, pp. 129–44.

had "inaugurated the era of expensive implements" as well as that of "trade and technical publications of all kinds," so that "the most important improvements in method seldom remain secret for long after they have passed the experimental stage." "English mechanics have taught people in almost every part of the world how to use English machinery, and even how to make similar machinery. . . ." Small manufacturers with strong character need nowhere be far behind the "front of the race of progress." Marshall, like Friedrich List a half century earlier, saw that physical advantages favored some places and that developing skills and subsidiary industries took time. But enterprising nations anywhere would make England's headstart short-lived.[4]

The Victorian concept of progress had no room for virtue unrewarded because of small size, poverty, and a late start. Since the rays of technical knowledge were equally tonic for all deserving nations, analysis of change could easily be abstracted from conditions judged temporary. Two groups of writers either ignored differences in ratios of capital to labor or, alternatively, disparities in output levels and natural resource inputs. They did so partly, no doubt, to simplify problems, but not always explicitly, nor with subsequent relaxation of assumptions and disclaimers of universal relevance.

Economists who thought of technology in terms of capital-labor substitution alone were, in the relevant passages, mainly interested in effects on income distribution and aggregate de-

[4] Alfred Marshall, *Principles of Economics* (8th ed.; London: MacMillan, 1920), pp. 220–30, 270–4, 284–5, 674–5, 723–53. Marshall's election of stern character as the main growth-inducing variable did not run against views held in many countries with little growth. See Albert Hirschman's review of the literature of the Latin American "Age of Self-Incrimination," *Latin American Issues* (New York: Twentieth Century Fund, 1961), pp. 4–9. Cf. Friedrich List, *The National System of Political Economy,* Sampson Lloydd, trans. (London: Longman's Green, 1928), pp. 236–42.

mand. To stress these effects, the labor theory of value shifted attention away from real output effects and input heterogeneity. In an eloquent passage, "Does nature nothing for man in manufactures?",[5] Ricardo granted that output had risen with increased knowledge of natural phenomena such as: wind, water, atmospheric pressure, steam elasticity, metallurgy, chemistry, and fermentation. But their impotence, like that of land, to create exchange value was basic to his system. In a similar spirit Marx praised the way "stupendous physical forces and the natural sciences" had raised "the productiveness of labor to an extraordinary degree," but insisted that a machine "never adds more value than it loses, on an average, by wear and tear."[6] His main interest in technical advance was not in absolute physical, but in relative social, effects: the level of profits compared with wages, the rate of value accumulation, imbalances in the structure of demand, and economic crises. Apart from these social terms, there was no "general" technology of production but only specialized branches of industry. Study of their techniques as such was not part of political economy.[7] The labor theory of value therefore kept Ricardo and Marx exposed to the charge of inconclusive results about anyone's real income or poverty.[8] Addition of the omitted information would have seriously weakened the theory's uniform relevance to all countries.

Discard of the labor theory of value allowed, but did not compel, reference to real output effects and to input heter-

[5] David Ricardo, *On the Principles of Political Economy and Taxation* (Cambridge: University Press, 1951), pp. 76–7n.

[6] Karl Marx, *Capital* (New York: Charles H. Kerr & Co., 1906), pp. 422–4.

[7] Karl Marx, *Grundriss der Kritik der Politischen Ökonomie* (Berlin: Dietz Verlag, 1953), pp. 7–8.

[8] Cf. Joseph A. Schumpeter, *History of Economic Analysis* (New York: Oxford University Press, 1954), pp. 679–84; Joan Robinson, *An Essay on Marxian Economics* (London: Macmillan, 1942); and Leo Rogin's review of Mrs. Robinson's book, *American Economic Review*, March 1944, pp. 124–34.

ogeneity. Abiding concern with income shares of labor and capital, as well as instability in developed countries, kept economists pondering technological change in terms of a labor- or capital-saving essence. A. C. Pigou, J. R. Hicks, Joan Robinson, R. F. Harrod, Evsey Domar, Robert M. Solow, W. E. G. Salter and Murray Brown have been among the many writers who have continued to refine the basic propositions by adding distinctions between wage-good and luxury-good cheapening inventions, between induced and autonomous improvements, embodied and disembodied knowledge, static and dynamic effects, alternative market structures, as well as problems of depreciation, obsolescence, and limited elasticities of substitution.[9] Few of these works with their "golden rules" are useful

[9] A few references may suggest the changing scope of the discussion: A. C. Pigou, *The Economics of Welfare* (4th ed.; London: Macmillan, 1932), pp. 674–9; J. R. Hicks, *The Theory of Wages* (London: Macmillan, 1932), ch. 6; J. R. Hicks, *Capital and Growth* (London: Oxford University Press, 1965), pp. 148–59; Joan Robinson, *The Accumulation of Capital* (Homewood: R. D. Irwin, 1956), chs. 9–18; Evsey D. Domar, *Essays in the Theory of Economic Growth* (New York: Oxford University Press, 1957), Robert M. Solow, "Substitution and Fixed Proportions in the Theory of Capital," *The Review of Economic Studies*, June 1962, pp. 207–18. For further citations see M. Blaug, "A Survey of the Theory of Process Innovations," *Economica*, Feb. 1963, pp. 13–32; and F. H. Hahn and R. C. O. Matthews, "The Theory of Economic Growth: A Survey," *Economic Journal*, Dec. 1964, pp. 779–902. W. E. G. Salter, *Productivity and Technical Change* (Cambridge: Cambridge University Press, 1960). According to Brown, "It is not difficult to uncover reasons why the phenomenon of technological progress has become one of the focal areas of inquiry in economics: first, the predominant feeling that severe cyclical problems can be resolved. . . . A second reason is . . . structural unemployment. . . . There may be other reasons for focusing attention on the role of technological progress, but these two justify the resources devoted to its analysis and measurement" (Murray Brown, *On the Theory and Measurement of Technological Change* [Cambridge: Cambridge University Press, 1966], p. 2). For a bibliography of 344 items, see Lester Lave, *Technological Change: Its Conception and Measurement* (Englewood Cliffs: Prentice-Hall, 1966). The concern for measurement has been an important step forward since it has encouraged more rigorous speculation about the causes of technological change in developed countries.

guides to technological strategy for poor countries; nor has such guidance been their purpose, given deliberate disregard of various crucial international differences. Among writers in the orthodox tradition before World War II, Joseph Schumpeter was almost alone in treating the distribution and stability effects of "innovations" as incidental to more noteworthy structural transformations.[10]

Another group of writers shared certain traits yet represented a multitude of persuasions. They were unwilling to see production as anything other than physical treatment of diverse materials and they were, therefore, unwilling, in the eyes of proper economists, to analyze production at a meaningful level of abstraction. But their verdicts were just as global and often more influential.

Some like Paul Mantoux and S. C. Gilfillan saw the course of invention and diffusion as mainly solutions in response to intermediate product bottlenecks which then created new problems.[11] William F. Ogburn, C. E. Ayres, and others thought proliferation of knowledge was cumulative by itself, one solution begetting others, as it were, without the aphrodisiacs of economic needs.[12] Inevitably, these approaches begot their own hybrids.[13]

In contrast with theories of flowering diversity were others stressing similarities as industry after industry became infiltrated by standardization, process integration, quantitative

[10] Joseph A. Schumpeter, *Theory of Economic Development,* Redvers Opie, trans. (Cambridge: Harvard University Press, 1934); *Business Cycles* (New York: McGraw-Hill, 1939); *Capitalism, Socialism, and Democracy* (3d ed.;) New York: Harper, 1950).

[11] Paul Mantoux, *The Industrial Revolution in the Eighteenth Century* (rev. ed.; New York: Macmillan, 1961); S. C. Gilfillan, *The Sociology of Invention* (Chicago: Follet, 1935).

[12] William F. Ogburn, *Social Change* (New York: B. W. Huebsch, 1922), C. E. Ayres, *The Theory of Economic Progress* (Chapel Hill: University of North Carolina Press, 1944), pp. 105–24.

[13] Cf. Richard R. Nelson, "The Economics of Invention: A Survey of the Literature," *Journal of Business,* April 1959, pp. 101–27.

analysis, etc.[14] Most conspicuous among these similarities was the "emancipation from the barriers of living nature," from wood, leather, hemp, plant chemicals, and animal energy. Sombart found this transformation to be the single, fundamental principle of modern technology—a principle with a heart of coal in a body of iron.[15] Jevons had made the point in 1865: "By far the greater part of the arts and inventions we have of late contributed spring from our command of coal, or at any rate depend upon its profuse consumption." England had "the key to all the infinite varieties of change in place and kind of which nature is capable." "But when this fuel, our material energy, fails us, whence will come the power to do equal or greater things in the future?"[16]

Resource determinism appeared the dominant theory of development between World Wars I and II. To poor countries the message was simple: Technical progress was the rationalization of industries that lack of coal made impossible. Countries without coal were "cursed by the vicious circle of vegetable-animal economy," which not only "thwarts man's higher abilities and aspirations," but also meant "the coal-iron powers are predestined to rule over them."[17] As C. K. Leith quoted, "The white man's burden is partly one imposed by nature's distribution of

[14] Veblen was among the many who saw this progressive infiltration of industry by scientific procedures; but more significant to him was the reverse effect of matter-of-fact industrial habits of thought "intruded into the scholar's discipline from without." His view was that "science, and scientific theory especially, has made headway in the several departments of human life and knowledge in proportion as each of these several departments has successively come into closer contact with the industrial process" (*The Theory of the Leisure Class* [New York: Modern Library, 1934], pp. 387, 390). The idea recurs often in his writings.

[15] Werner Sombart, *Der Moderne Kapitalismus* (Berlin: Dunker and Humblot, 1955), Vol. III, pp. 97, 99.

[16] W. Stanley Jevons, *The Coal Question* (3d ed.; London: Macmillan, 1906), pp. 101, 136, 197.

[17] Erich W. Zimmermann, *World Resources and Industries* (New York: Harper, 1933), pp. 61, 430, 806.

raw materials." [18] That scarce energy resources also condemned Ireland and southern and eastern Europe to "vegetable civilization" was noted by Delaisi and others.[19]

Stoic acquiescence in this fate was hardly in line with the growing nationalism of poor countries. If access to modern technology lay through integrated steel plants, these could be built, subsidized, and run with imported coke and ore. Steel plants have in fact been built in the tropics ever since, not only for their propaganda value, but also for their supposed propagative or "linkage" effects. This approach fits nicely with Soviet experience and its rationale of autarchy and physical planning around a core of homemade capital goods of latest design. The oddity of a dynamic technology dependent on unchangeable energy sources, given steelmaking techniques, and no possibility for steel substitutes was not widely recognized as paradoxical. Stagnation clouded the industrial scene in many ways during the 1930's, and technological change was believed by some to have become a matter of catching up with a shrinking remnant of things worth trying. As capital accumulates, wrote Hicks, "clearly invention has a progressively harder task." [20]

[18] C. K. Leith, "The Mineral Resources of the Far East," *Foreign Affairs*, April 1926, p. 442. Cf. C. K. Leith, *World Minerals and World Politics* (New York: McGraw-Hill, 1931).

[19] F. Delaisi, *Les Deux Europes: Europe Industrielle et Europe Agricole* (Paris: Payot, 1929), discussed at length by Zimmermann, *op. cit.*, pp. 141–4. See also K. Haushofer *et al.*, *Bausteine zur Geopolitik* (Berlin: Vohwinkel, 1928).

[20] Hicks, *Theory of Wages*, p. 132. Cf. Robert K. Merton, "Fluctuations in the Rate of Industrial Invention," *Quarterly Journal of Economics*, May 1935, pp. 454–74. Alvin H. Hansen feared it might take a long time before innovations equal in magnitude to the railroad or automobile would appear, but far from advocating either a moratorium on invention because of presumed labor-displacing effects, he believed in a possible acceleration of the rate of scientific and technical progress, partly through restoration of competition ("Economic Progress and Declining Population Growth," *American Economic Review*, March 1939, reprinted in *Readings in Business Cycle Theory* [Philadelphia: Blakiston, 1944], pp. 378–86).

II. Technology and Development: Recent Opinions

From World War II emerged times that were different from the 1930's beyond all expectations. A wave of innovations from nylon to nuclear power and electronic industrial controls washed away technological pessimism. Colonial empires were broken. But with rising populations and falling terms of international trade, countries with the lowest standards of living developed most slowly and international disparities widened. The setting was auspicious for new diagnoses of low productivity and new cures.

As often happens, new policies were tried before many economists had thought of new questions, much less their answers. The "bold new program" of technical assistance, the Point Four of President Truman's 1949 inaugural address, stressed inexhaustibility of knowledge as a resource and, therefore, potentially unending benefits following its transfer.[21] Such optimism lasted a number of years. Shortly after the Technical Cooperation Administration was established in October 1950, one government adviser thought modern production methods were not "particularly different" and that "it should, therefore, be possible in almost any area, however rudimentary the techniques employed locally, to make the transition from primitive to more modern methods. This requires patience, sympathy, and above all ingenuity on the part of those who will lead in making this transition possible. The amount of foreign capital required would be infinitesimal."[22]

Perhaps the novelty of the Point Four Program lay precisely in the boldness of its optimism. After all, the International Labor Organization, formed in 1919, had long helped with labor training and other problems; the United Kingdom Colonial

[21] *Bulletin of the State Department,* Jan. 30, 1949, p. 125.
[22] Thomas Hibben, "The Point-4 Program," *Foreign Commerce Weekly,* Nov. 27, 1950.

Development and Welfare Act of 1929 included technical assistance provisions, as did the United States Interdepartmental
Committee on Scientific and Cultural Cooperation from 1940
to 1950. The Institute for Inter-American Affairs began in 1942
as a program of pure technical assistance, largely for raising
strategic materials production. Yet none of these, nor earlier
church and private efforts, matched the optimism of Point Four.
Moreover, the effect was contagious. Based on the hope for
about one-third of the funds appropriated by the U.S. Congress
for technical assistance, the United Nations broadened its plans
from $300,000 annually, approved in December 1948 (Resolu-
tion 200), to about twenty million dollars (Resolution 222-IX)
in December 1949. Other bilateral programs and the Colombo
Plan followed soon after the Point Four Program. In ten years
both the United Nations and the United States programs
quintupled their budgets.[23]

The willingness of governments to undertake the transplanting of technology and the requests for rationally dispensed
foreign loans and grants, at times as part of comprehensive
national plans, persuaded economists that an audience was
ready to listen. What they advised was shaped not only by the
tastes of politicians, but also by the availability of data. Were
drastic changes in the output-mix of an economy forbidden or
demanded? Was the spectrum of productive techniques bound
to methods proven in commercial operation? At what rate could
one expect productive factors to grow in quantity and quality?
Sometimes the personal likes of key ministers, regional discon-
tents, and the population and demand projections of planners
had already determined specific output targets. In these cases
the economist could only add overall feasibility tests and state

[23] In addition to annual official reports, see Richard W. Gable, ed.,
*Partnership for Progress: International Technical Cooperation, The An-
nals,* May 1959; Edwin A. Bock, *Fifty Years of Technical Assistance*
(Chicago: Public Administration Clearing House, 1954). Ch. 15 in Paul
Alpert, *Economic Development: Objectives and Methods* (Glencoe: Free
Press, 1963), is a good summary.

criteria for minimizing current costs and maximizing future growth through choice of technique in each area.

The economist's own productivity rises when he is allowed to reckon the mutual determination of output-mix *and* choice of technique. That is, ideally from a given spectrum, technique is determined as factors are shifted from industry to industry and as the output level in each is brought in line with export-import opportunities. Two well-known critical reviews of theory and policy at this level, made ten years apart by A. E. Kahn and Hollis B. Chenery, show the substantial growth of a literature on the subject together with some epitaphs for rejected ideas.[24] Around 1950 it was still necessary to prove that neither a maximum turnover of capital nor a minimum capital-labor ratio guaranteed highest growth rates. Ten years later it seemed that deficiencies in data and nonquantifiable social patterns blocked better allocation more than did the remaining confusion about suitable investment criteria.

But even the better allocation promised by new rules was seldom good enough because the given spectrum of techniques was seldom good enough. Wholesome social development was the aim of economic growth; and whatever that might mean, persistent underemployment was certainly its denial. Aggregate demand was low in poor countries, but, as various inflations proved, not the main cause of underemployment. Monetary and credit expansion added few jobs. Many people could not work because the spectrum of techniques did not cover the range of capital-labor ratios needed to equip the whole labor force with tools and tasks without net loss. Highly capital-intensive techniques seemed imperative in some sectors, while elsewhere, even with alternative technical possibilities, labor had already been hired to the point of very low marginal productivity.

[24] A. E. Kahn, "Investment Criteria in Development Programs," *Quarterly Journal of Economics,* Feb. 1951, pp. 38–61; Hollis B. Chenery, "Comparative Advantage and Development Policy," *American Economic Review,* March 1961, pp. 18–51.

Capital and labor immobilities from sector to sector worsened the dilemma between full employment and full output.[25]

If scarce capital and proliferating population had to be accepted as given, together with the structure of demand and market imperfections, then it remained to broaden the spectrum of techniques. That the Orient had its own technological path already was suggested, on the one hand, in the innumerable contrivances unanointed by doctrine in Japan and on the other, in doctrine untainted by much success in India. One could hardly prove the doctrine of one by the practice of the other. Handicraft cotton spinning, the very symbol of Indian *Swadeshi,* had no place in Japanese growth; nor had the Japanese much concern for the evils of industrialism that Gandhi sought to avoid—commercialism and inequality in wealth and power.[26] Indeed, Gandhi hardly set forth a theory of technology or economic growth as such. Machinery was a symbol of political oppression and ethical degeneration to him, and he pleaded for its removal before he could tell a loom from a spinning wheel.[27] His appeal could even be non-economic; he urged

[25] R. S. Eckaus, "The Factor-Proportions Problem in Underdeveloped Areas," *American Economic Review,* Sept. 1955, pp. 539–69; John C. H. Fei and Gustav Ranis, *Development of the Labor Surplus Economy: Theory and Policy* (Homewood: R. D. Irwin, 1964), pp. 58–150.

[26] In 1916 Gandhi gave this definition: "Swadeshi is that spirit in us which restricts us to the use and service of our immediate surroundings to the exclusion of the more remote," *Speeches and Writings of Mahatma Gandhi* (4th ed.; Madras: G. A. Natesan, 1933), p. 336. For a brief summary of Gandhi's views see V. B. Kher's introduction to M. K. Gandhi, *Economic and Industrial Life and Relations* (Ahmedabad: Navajivan Publishing House, 1957). A more thorough treatment of Gandhi's economic ideas and their influence on politics and policy through the mid-1950's is Nancy Jane Kenney, "The Gandhian Economy and Indian Economic Planning" (doctoral dissertation, Fletcher School of Law and Diplomacy, 1956). For a brief statement of the Japanese record, see Gustav Ranis, "Factor Proportions in Japanese Economic Development," *American Economic Review,* Sept. 1957, pp. 594–607.

[27] Kher, *op. cit.,* p. xliv.

people "to wear khadi even though it may not be so soft and elegant in appearance as foreign fineries, nor as cheap." [28] By 1924 he recognized that heavy machinery in some industries was unavoidable and that mechanization with electricity, as well as some other inventions, could increase output in villages without copying "the Western model."

Nevertheless, destroying industrialism "at any cost" still came first.[29]

An All-India Village Industries Association was set up in 1934 to put new life into production of hand-pounded rice and hand-ground flour, of *ghani* oil and palm gur; of hand-made paper and soap, toys, pottery, leather and horn work, coir spinning and weaving, and of *magan dipa* lanterns. Power was to come from men and bullocks alone, and no factory-made or imported materials were to be used. Novel implements and production techniques were devised by the Association's laboratory at Maganwadi, Wardha. Widespread use was sought, not only through publications, but also through fifty or sixty extension workers trained each year.

After independence, various boards and directorates for promoting handicrafts and small-scale industries shifted programs toward integration of small with large industry and toward suiting artistic crafts to export markets. During the early 1950's novel *ambar charkha* multiple spindle hand-spinning wheels, improved *chakki dhenki* hand rice-pounding equipment, and other devices in the Gandhian tradition were introduced.[30] But

[28] Mahatma Gandhi, *Harijan*, Nov. 19, 1938, quoted by A. R. Desai, *Social Background of Indian Nationalism* (rev. ed.; Bombay: Popular Book Depot, 1954), p. 81.

[29] Gandhi quoted by Kher, *op. cit.*, pp. xliii–xlviii.

[30] Kenney, *op. cit.*, pp. 306–24; S. K. George, G. Ramachandran, eds., *The Economics of Peace* (Wardha, Gram Udyog Vibhag: Akhil Bharat Sarva Seva Sangh, 1952), pp. 229–36; R. V. Rao, *The Gandhian Institutions of Wardha* (Bombay: Thacker, 1947); J. C. Kumarappa, *Swaraj for the Masses* (Bombay: Hind Kitabs, 1948).

much cottage production (including cotton spinning and rice milling) survived largely because of subsidies, guaranteed supplies and markets, and prohibitions and taxes on factory production and expansion.[31] Supplies and other resources were not only shifted away from more efficient uses, but higher priced consumer goods of lower quality may have lulled the peasants' urge to grow food for sale. The widened spectrum of techniques needed a push of a different order.

Economists disagree about the essential features of this push. In 1949, Hans Singer suggested that technological progress favored developed countries on two grounds: higher income elasticity of demand for manufactures and a rising ratio of manufacturing value added to material input.[32] By 1954 he put the case of underdeveloped countries in broader, more categorical terms: "Modern technology is not compatible with their

[31] V. M. Dandekar estimated that virtually all of the earnings of *ambar charkha* spinners were derived, directly or indirectly, from government subsidies. That is, the extra cost of distributing cotton to, and yarn from, the spinners matched the value their work added (*Economic Weekly* [Bombay], July 6, 1957, cited by W. B. Reddaway, *The Development of the Indian Economy* [Homewood: R. D. Irwin; 1962], p. 75). Cf. P. N. Dhar and H. F. Lydall, *The Role of Small Enterprises in Indian Economic Development* (New York: Asia Publishing House, 1961). According to A. S. Bhalla's calculations, *ambar charkhas* cost at least ten times as much as traditional *charkhas* but yielded less additional output, employment, or re-investment per rupee ("Investment Allocation and Technological Choice—A Case of Cotton Spinning Techniques," *Economic Journal*, Sept. 1964, pp. 611–22).

[32] Hans W. Singer, "The Distribution of Gains between Investing and Borrowing Countries," *American Economic Review, Papers and Proceedings*, May 1950, pp. 473–85. An earlier Mexican statement that "the technology needed for progress must be conceived strictly by Mexicans, controlled by Mexicans, directed by Mexicans, and destined for Mexicans," was concerned more with the nationality of technicians than divergent design (Gabino A. Palma, "Sin técnicos de verdad no es posible la industrializacíon," *El Universal*, July 27, 1946, quoted by Sanford A. Mosk, *Industrial Revolution in Mexico* [Berkeley: University of California Press, 1954], p. 271).

endowments and their natural requirements. They cannot develop a technology harmoniously unless it is their own technology."[33] The following year Edward S. Mason noted that:

The primitive techniques offer many obvious opportunities for improvement; at the same time the shortage of capital would suggest that improvement falls short of an adoption of the extremely capital-using techniques of the West. But devising methods and designing equipment adapted to eastern conditions presuppose the existing of research and development facilities and a tinkering propensity on the part of workers that the East simply does not have.[34]

Benjamin Higgins wrote in 1959:

No advanced technology has yet been discovered which is suited to the factor-proportions of underdeveloped countries. Perhaps such a technology does not exist; but it is important to find out. Meanwhile, the lack of technological advance adapted to their factor-proportions is a serious obstacle to development of underdeveloped areas—an obstacle that scarcely existed in the Western world during its Industrial Revolution.[35]

[33] Hans W. Singer, "Problems of Industrialization of Underdeveloped Countries," *International Social Science Bulletin*, Vol. VI, No. 2 (1954), pp. 220–21.

[34] Edward S. Mason, *Promoting Economic Development* (Claremont: Claremont College Press, 1955), p. 37.

[35] Benjamin Higgins, *Economic Development: Principles, Problems, and Policies* (New York: W. W. Norton, 1959), p. 258; Cf. Henry G. Aubrey, "Industrial Investment Decisions," *Journal of Economic History*, Dec. 1955, p. 340 and Benjamin Higgins' comment, "Aubrey on Industrial Investment Decisions," *Journal of Economic History*, Sept. 1956, p. 353. At a Cambridge University Conference held Sept. 6–10, 1964, E. F. Schumacher thought "Industrialization through Intermediate Technology" might be worth investigating. By "upgrading" traditional methods and "downgrading" Western techniques, consumers' goods, agricultural implements, and building materials should be able to be manufactured with no more than £70 to £100 sterling invested per "workplace." Nicolas Kaldor took the lead in opposing the suggestion. Ronald Robinson, ed., *Industrialization in Developing Countries* (Cambridge: Cambridge University Overseas Studies Committee, 1965), pp. 24–31, 91–9.

Not all writers shared this emphasis on factor-proportions. Richard L. Meier argued that science already held the promise of novel forms of energy, materials, processes, and organization to yield universal comfort at per capita spending of $331 annually—and all consistent with use of the most automatic, capital-intensive methods.[36] Clark Kerr and his associates were equally unfashionable in maintaining that, "at one moment of time there may be several best economic and social arrangements, but only one best technology. The technology can be up to date or antiquated, but there is no question which is which, and the modern is constantly replacing the ancient."[37] But few were more extravagant than Wassily Leontief:

Now automatic production, with its relatively low capital and labor requirements per unit of output, radically changes their prospects. Instead of trying to lift the whole economy by the slow, painful methods of the past, an industrially backward country may take the dramatic short-cut of building a few large up-to-date automatic plants. Towering up in the primitive economy like copses of tall trees on a grassy plain, they would propagate a new economic order.[38]

Slowly technological change in the underdeveloped world became the subject of empirical research and rapidly that of international conferences. Anticipating these trends by over a decade, the Mexican government in 1944 engaged the Armour Research Foundation to prepare a "technological audit" of four

[36] Richard L. Meier, *Science and Economic Development: New Patterns of Living* (New York: John Wiley and Technology Press of M.I.T., 1956), pp. viii, 162–3, 192–3.

[37] Clark Kerr, John T. Dunlop, Frederick H. Harbison, and Charles A. Myers, *Industrialism and Industrial Man: The Problems of Labor and Management in Economic Growth* (Cambridge: Harvard, 1960), p. 284.

[38] Wassily Leontief, "The Economic Impact," *Automatic Control* (New York: Simon and Schuster, 1955), p. 79; *Factors in Economic Development* (London: George Allen and Unwin, 1962), p. 175.

industries along with recommendations for applied research. A Mexican-American Conference on Industrial Research, held at Chicago in October 1945, was attended by scientists, bankers, industrialists, and politicians.[39] The Economic Commission for Latin America published studies of textile productivity in 1951, paper industry possibilities in 1954, and held international conferences on steel making and fabricating in 1952 and 1956,[40] all with an emphasis on technology. The RAND Corporation, the Center for International Studies of the Massachusetts Institute of Technology, the Netherlands Economic Institute, and the United Nations Division of Industrial Development, during the 1950's began measuring alternative production techniques and publishing progress reports.[41] Notable among later conferences have been the First Expert Working Group on Technological Centers, Copenhagen, 1954; the International Conference on Science in the Advancement of New States,

[39] Armour Research Foundation, *Estudio Teconológico de Varias Industrias Mexicanas, Con Recomendaciones Sobre la Investigación Industrial, Problemas Agricolas e Industriales de Mexico,* Vol. I, No. 4.

[40] United Nations, *Labour Productivity of the Cotton Textile Industry in Five Latin-American Countries* (New York, 1951); United Nations, *Possibilities for the Development of the Pulp and Paper Industry in Latin America* (New York, 1954); United Nations, *A Study of the Iron and Steel Industry in Latin America* (2 vols.; New York, 1954); United Nations, *Problems of the Steel Making and Transforming Industries in Latin America* (2 vols., New York, 1958).

[41] These works and others are discussed and cited in later chapters. The general status of research on "Technological Change in the Less Developed Areas" is summarized by R. S. Eckaus, *Development of the Emerging Countries: An Agenda for Research,* ch. 4. See also Jack Baranson, "National Programs for Science and Technology in the Underdeveloped Areas," *Bulletin of Atomic Scientists,* May 1960, pp. 151–4; "Un Programa de Tecnología Creativa Para Ayudar al Desarrollo Economico de los Paises Menos Industrializados," *El Trimestre Económico,* Jan.–March 1963, pp. 33–68; and Jack Baranson, *Technology for Underdeveloped Areas: An Annotated Bibliography* (Oxford: Pergamon Press, 1967). It contains 319 items.

Rehovoth, Israel, 1960; the United Nations Conference on the Application of Science and Technology for the Benefit of the Less Developed Areas, Geneva, 1963; and the Conference on the Application of Science and Technology, Santiago, 1965.

The 1965 conference followed the establishment of the U.N. Advisory Committee on the Application of Science and Technology (UNCSAT) in August 1963 under the Economic and Social Council of the Secretariat. The Advisory Committee does not itself carry on research but tries to raise the volume, quality, and dissemination of research by other United Nations and national agencies. Its biannual meetings are attended by leading officers of specialized divisions of the United Nations. Most of its work has so far been the selection of a short list of high priority targets for "concerted attack." Fifteen types of existing knowledge have been identified for accelerated transfer, and new knowledge is sought in twenty-seven other fields. Most of these targets—weather forecasting, tsetse fly control, turnaround of ocean shipping—are highly specific. The proposals for industry mention use of agricultural byproducts, leatherworking, and substituting concrete for metal in machine tools. But otherwise the industrial proposals are general suggestions for better management, standardization, factor and scale adaptation, maintenance, location, marketing, local research, subregional coordination, training, and an international conference of equipment manufacturers. All targets were to be approached through a "World Plan of Action for the Application of Science and Technology to Development." [42]

Perhaps one major premise behind the eagerness to confer and to coordinate efforts internationally is that many pieces of the technological puzzle do not have to be newly fashioned,

[42] "Third Report of the Advisory Committee on the Application of Science and Technology to Development," May 1966, Official Records of the Economics and Social Council, Forty-first Session, Supplement No. 12 (E/4178).

but already exist, although quite separately, and that assembly of the parts will show surprising fits. Indeed, such is one of the bases for this book. Less ambitious is the hope of tempering the crudeness of the boldest questions and widening horizons of the most timid.

2

The Network for Diffusing
Manufacturing Technology
among Nations

Technological information can range from advice for improving performance of a given installation to recommending a daring invention using newly discovered principles of nature. The bulk of activity today in technological transfer is diffusion of routine advice about standard processes. Information flows to newly industrializing nations so that managers can arrange the layout of machinery, adopt preventive maintenance schedules, forecast and plan production properly, control inventories and quality, reduce scrap, use proper depreciation methods, improve hiring and training practices, and balance work incentives. A harder transfer occurs when new equipment is not to be installed or used according to standard foreign or local practice. If the equipment is to be redesigned, even more knowledge is needed; and information flows must increase, especially if redesign first calls for scientific exploration. An interesting order of flows is the diffusion of knowledge about information channels themselves.

Information about manufacturing processes is immensely complex and heterogeneous, and it is sent only sporadically to widely separated places in poor countries. If enormous libraries were shipped abroad, the knowledge would get there physically but with no effect on productivity. The books would need readers who require training, and therefore schools; the schools need teachers—and, in any case, not all is clear from books, for not enough combinations of circumstances can ever be covered. Books must be complemented by experience, and experience in operating modern industry is precisely what underdeveloped countries lack and seek. This experience is itself no mysterious attainment but a function of the heterogeneity, complexity, and scattered applicability of the information. Experience is embedded as "judgment" in the human tissues of those who have long participated in a species of events, but (by definition) this knowledge has not warranted the cost of electronic or literary recording. This condition is always subject to review but not inevitably to removal.

I. Markets, Migration, and Schools

Where motivation and experience are a problem, economic self-interest and the price system point to a solution. There are, in fact, international markets where entrepreneurs of poor countries can buy information from efficient suppliers. Technical information is bought and sold across frontiers in thousands of transactions per day. But is the volume at an optimum? Would the output generated by additional sales still cover the cost of transfer? Can a competitive price system divert just the right amount of resources into transfer of knowledge?

A number of limitations arise. The will to maximize profits is not enough; economic self-interest, like other urges, does not come in a common package with the knowledge of its own best pursuit. Resource allocation, especially with respect to buying information, is a technique to be learned, not an instinct. Above all, how can prices channel information when the bids that create prices will almost certainly be wrong ones if not based on the information bid for?[1] As the circumstances change, most entrepreneurs must be taught again and again that there is something new to be learned and that learning "pays." But as the entrepreneur learns and becomes a client for as yet undiscovered knowledge from research institutes, no one will henceforth be able to tell him exactly how much any given expenditure on learning will pay. Nor can he simply keep spending until net marginal gains vanish. For discoveries never pass in review prearranged according to merit[2] like the nobility at a coronation.

Additional characteristics of information which limit the effectiveness of the market as a transfer mechanism are inappropriability and increasing returns. For an entrepreneur to appropriate a better wheelbarrow design based on information imported from across the ocean might cost a thousand dollars, but first use would show its features to all. Without militant patent protection, what craftsman could then recover his transfer cost by adding to wheelbarrow prices? If, alternatively, protection permits prices to rise, fewer wheelbarrows will be sold and some purchasers may have to accept a less expensive, outmoded design, possibly keeping these in production. Yet it would have cost nothing to use the best knowledge on all out-

[1] Kenneth Arrow has referred to this phenomenon as a "fundamental paradox" in the determination of the demand for information ("Economic Welfare and the Allocation of Resources for Invention," *The Rate and Direction of Inventive Activity: Economic and Social Factors,* National Bureau of Economic Research Special Conference Series No. 13 [Princeton: Princeton University Press, 1962]). George Stigler evaded the paradox by limiting the quest for information to canvassing buyers or sellers for their price quotations at constant quality ("The Economics of Information," *Journal of Political Economy,* June 1961, pp. 213–25). As early as 1937 F. A. von Hayek suggested that formal equilibrium analysis must remain tautologous in the absence of "definite statements about how knowledge is acquired and communicated" ("Economics and Knowledge," *Economica,* Feb. 1937, p. 33).

[2] H. B. Malmgren, "Information, Expectations and the Theory of the Firm," *Quarterly Journal of Economics,* Aug. 1961, p. 419, n. 2.

put. A dilemma is thus presented which is familiar to economists: Either less than the optimum flows in or the inflow is used to a suboptimal extent.

Uncertainty, however, is the more fundamental problem of the transfer of information. Inappropriability and increasing returns open a case for public subsidy, but one must expect government to be as uncertain (that is, ignorant) about allocating subsidies or taking over, as entrepreneurs are about purchasing. If one looks at the profitable ways in which technical information has in fact been transferred internationally, one can see that all somehow meet this problem of uncertainty —that is, the circuity of needing knowledge to buy knowledge well and of the needed knowledge being ultimately inseparable from experience reposited in human tissue.

In fact, nearly all transfers involve journeys by individuals. Immigration of whole communities such as that of the Huguenots into England, Germany, and the Netherlands during the sixteenth century[3] is at one end of the spectrum, and at the other end is the apprenticement of one's youth abroad. Both immigration and foreign apprenticement minimize the need for training at home and are most suitable where learning depends on participant experience. Since the early nineteenth century, however, the proportion of such cases has fallen greatly. Practice in English factories at that time was poorly understood by managers and workers alike, training methods were poor, and the export of technology and capital was commonly associated with emigration of workers.[4] As knowledge became systematized, and therefore teachable in schools, and

[3] Warren C. Scoville, "Minority Migrations and the Diffusion of Technology," *Journal of Economic History*, Fall 1951, pp. 347–60.

[4] Until emigration of skilled workers was legalized in 1825, recruitment of British workers by American and European agents was subject to heavy fines and imprisonment but nevertheless flourished (W. O. Henderson, *Britain and Industrial Europe 1750–1870: Studies in British Influence on the Industrial Revolution in Western Europe* [Liverpool: Liverpool University Press, 1954], pp. 5–8).

as machines needing operatives of little or no skill appeared, first skilled workers and then foremen were no longer indispensable migrants. Later, professional schools solved the dependence on outside operating managers and technicians, which left organizing and evaluating experts as the foreigners most difficult to replace. Migration, of course, retains great importance in the *internal* spread of technical information.

Schools not only increase the absorptive capacity of a population, but, through their libraries, foreign fellowships, and other contacts, can be instruments for procuring technical information. Disdain for practice, however, or just poor liaison with industry tends largely to blunt their effectiveness. In addition, liaison itself implies some industry already in existence. Education, it is plain, is not excluded from the circular paradox already expressed. Eventually, however, liaison can be expected to shape programs from on-the-job training and management development seminars to formal professional education and university research.[5]

The task of formal education in industrialization will not be further explored here except to note generally the possibility of marginal trade-offs between such expenditures and those on the import of foreign practitioners and instruments. Complicated artifacts and disembodied information related to industry can only be absorbed by functioning organizations of trained people. The more impersonal but potent the information-generating

[5] Mary Jean Bowman and C. Arnold Anderson speculate that subsidized, enterprise-linked training may be developed into "the most effective methods of transferring higher level know-how . . . including in the process the adaptations that are needed for successful transplantation" ("The Role of Education in Development," *Development of the Emerging Countries: An Agenda for Research* [Washington: The Brookings Institution, 1962], pp. 179–80). Frederick Harbison, in a similar vein, has warned planners "not to replace such systems by costly vocational schools" ("Human Resources Development Planning in Modernizing Economies," *International Labor Review*, May 1962, pp. 13, 17, 22).

import—a technical handbook, a viscosimeter, a computer, a shipment of isotopes—the greater the need for evolving complementary activities through training.

As a leading public advisor on the matter put it, "Training is, of course, the overriding objective of all technical assistance activities. . . . It must, through various methods of joint operation, build new institutions."[6] International divisions of corporations are builders par excellence of these institutions. Usually the corporation imports the institution embodied in the persons of immigrant executives but sometimes they are transfused into a wholly national crew of "company men" well inculcated with the methods and spirit of a distant parent.[7] To absorb more technology the industrial structure must change, thereby becoming both means and goal of the transfer.

II. The Relay System

Thoroughly educated immigrants and national "company men" are not the rule, however, in manufacturing industries of underdeveloped countries. Industrialization depends mostly on the performance of partially educated entrepreneurs and their access to information through a network beginning with machinery suppliers, consultants, trade journals, and government advisors. Increasing the flow of technical information rests largely on understanding this network in order to promote greater skill in its use and possibly to strengthen a few components. A total overhaul of the network may not be impossible,

---

[6] Philip M. Glick, "The Choice of Instruments for Technical Co-operation," *The Annals*, May 1959, p. 64.

[7] John C. Shearer evaluates such policies with approval in *High-Level Manpower in Overseas Subsidiaries: Experience in Brazil and Mexico* (Princeton: Princeton University Press, 1960). See also, Simon Rottenberg, *Technical Cooperation in Latin America: How United States Business Firms Promote Technological Progress* (Washington: National Planning Association, 1957), pp. 44–57.

but it might take longer than industrialization itself based on the present system.

Essentially the network consists of a series of relay stations through which information flows in both directions. At each station some information is filtered out and some added. Manufacturing quality after each station is usually higher so that the probability of losses are lower. But, due to flaws in the stations, quality is not refined by every bit of information added or filtered. Stations are not qualified to interpret every component of an information bundle. They lack the time or have interests divergent and perhaps inconsistent with the ultimate purposes of the information, and will, therefore, filter what should be retained and add what distorts. If each station discriminated perfectly, distortion would not occur, but all intermediate stations would disappear. Their purpose, after all, is not to boost a fading signal from sender to distant receiver, but at each step to render the signals intelligible through screening and gap-filling and therefore to make communication possible at all.[8] Not all types of relay stations need be involved in every transfer of information, and most transfers can be handled by alternative circuits, though not equally well. At some points successive stations may be merged, and some links can be bypassed. In most circuits there are alternative stations at any given stage, more or less in competition.

Trade journals and other standard sources of information are perhaps the most direct and least complex circuits. They are often near monopolies in the country of origin, reflecting the falling cost of allowing wider use of collected information. Doubling the use of information does not double costs (beyond that of transfer itself) because information is, of course, not "used up" when used. Trade journals and catalogues to a certain

[8] Communication within formal organizations is often subject to the same imperfections (James G. March and Herbert A. Simon, *Organizations* [New York: John Wiley, 1958], pp. 166–71, 186–99).

extent bypass the relay stations and to about the same extent lack effectiveness as stimuli to action. In his study of Puerto Rican businessmen, Cochran found American trade literature widely read but apparently of little effectiveness unless combined with a variety of personal contacts.[9] On the other hand, in Mexico I found plant design engineers not only bitterly resentful of the excessive price to foreign subscribers of American technical magazines but hampered by the distribution of catalogues by the looseleaf page instead of by the volume.

III. Entrepreneurs as Information Seekers

At one end of the relay system is the entrepreneur curious about modernizing, expanding, or building a factory. If he is an importer obstructed by a new tariff or an artisan with some clients, he almost certainly will not view himself as an agent for the diffusion of technology, a role he would think fantastically pretentious. He wants to run his enterprise the way it should be done, and that is all. His layout might be copied from one he has seen, whether right or wrong, and adapted to an available building. If sales rise, new machines are put in the least crowded corners, possibly disrupting production flows.[10] If anything differs from the routine suggested by the equipment maker's manual, it will not be designated proudly as "technological progress," but rather as a regrettable compromise forced by stingy banks, bizarre materials, incompetent workers, and greedy distributors.

His secretive and suspiciously uncertain attitude toward information tends to minimize flows. "We know from experience what to buy," is one typical phrase, and "secrecy is the soul of

[9] Thomas C. Cochran, *The Puerto Rican Businessman: A Study in Cultural Change* (Philadelphia: University of Pennsylvania Press, 1959), pp. 135–48.

[10] For additional description of such firms, see James J. Berna, *Industrial Entrepreneurship in Madras State* (Bombay: Asia Publishing House, 1960), p. 169.

business" is another. He may prefer to keep his workers only partially trained to reduce their mobility.[11] Like one Mexican leather-goods maker interviewed, he may even limit expansion to avoid training that potential competitor, an outsider to the family.[12]

Greater receptiveness to new ideas may come gradually or dramatically, perhaps when a son returns from engineering school or through sales lost to a modern competitor. In any case, machinery sellers are likely for a while to be the main technical contact, and the first problem of communication is for them to gain the trust of the entrepreneur. Establishing trust not only involves much face-to-face contact, but even face-to-machine contact, or at least face-to-photograph. "I never order anything from a slick illustration like this," the manager of a sugar mill said, brochure in hand: "Why should I believe they ever built this model? Give me a photograph under operating conditions or nothing."

Indeed, face-to-face contact to establish trust appears to be a need throughout the technical transfer network. Lack of full trust invariably means some concealment of information which impairs perception of needs at subsequent stations. Moreover, a sense of insecurity may blur the transmitter's vision as well, making him incapable of stating his problems, even on paper, and of reaching decisions. To see faces is to see confusion, satisfaction, or antagonism; to gauge whether status is being,

[11] P. N. Dhar and H. F. Lydall, *The Role of Small Enterprises in Indian Economic Development* (New York: Asia Publishing House, 1962), p. 78.

[12] That restricting outflow and inflow go together has been observed throughout the world; for example, in Britain, C. F. Carter and B. R. Williams saw a "clear correlation between secrecy and unprogressiveness" (*Industry and Technical Progress* [London: Oxford University Press, 1957], p. 117). Managers of such firms also insisted that "whatever may be the case in other industries, in *their* industry it is experience which counts. They know all the reasons why it is impossible to strike out in new ways" (pp. 108–9).

or should be, granted or withheld. The conversational setting from time to time allows the release of tensions through small talk, jokes, and laughter. The urge to conceal as well as the fear of concealment weakens.[13] In this context, as a dramatic example of the need for confrontation are the principal users of the "see-as-you-talk" service between New York, Chicago, and Washington, which began in June 1964 with a six-inch screen—at a cost of $27 for the first three minutes. They were salesmen and personnel interviewers.[14]

IV. Machinery Suppliers

To the machinery wholesaler or manufacturer's agent, the diffusion of knowledge is incidental to the diffusion of goods. Within limits, the smaller the market the greater the variety of machines handled by one importer, and the less competent the explanations and demonstrations. Often the crucial transfer of information occurs through the machinery manufacturer's follow-up service. Failure by Japanese paper machinery builders to provide these services, according to Rosen, once meant widespread losses by the Japanese of Indian sales to sales of equivalent English and Swedish machinery which was priced over twice as high.[15] Among other examples I found a Mexican mattress manufacturer who claimed he had paid a 56 per cent higher price for a new machine in preference to a one-year-old machine in order to obtain the manufacturer's manuals and technical assistance which went with the new one. Moreover, it appears important for the machinery seller to take an active rather than passive role in maintaining the flow of information.

[13] C. F. Carter and B. R. Williams, *Science in Industry: Policy for Progress* (London: Oxford University Press, 1959), p. 25, emphasize the rapid clearing up of obscurities in personal contact.

[14] *New York Times*, Jan. 3, 1965.

[15] George Rosen, *Industrial Change in India* (Glencoe: Free Press, 1958), p. 107n.

A Mexican paint manufacturer typically rejected any supplier who had no more than a "send-us-your-problems" service.

The quality of follow-up services necessarily varies with distance and density of use. Widespread sales in many areas make superior instruction and maintenance programs feasible for Mergenthaler Linotype, United Shoe Machinery, Singer Sewing Machine, and others. Access on a regular basis to the manufacturer's representatives serving Houston, Dallas, and San Antonio was frequently mentioned to me as a significant advantage for locating an industry near Monterrey instead of close to Mexico City. By contrast, a pharmaceutical branch plant reported that it had succeeded in getting a packing machinery expert flown to Puerto Rico only after direct pressure from its home office, a tactic clearly not available to locally-owned firms.

Salesmen and manufacturer's agents may well be the most extensive carriers of technical information,[16] but transactions done through this channel tend to be off-the-shelf, not based on creative reformulations of problems. Horizons are widened to include all available models, but little more. The prevalence of monopolistic profits and "satisficing" habits of accepting the first working alternative often blunt the entrepreneur's critical faculties so that he does not supply much information that could be transferred to machinery builders for use in redesign. In a way, this condition extends to branch plants. A survey of American branch plants in Brazil showed that variations in production techniques from those of the parent reflect more than any other factor the lower need for refinements in a "seller's market."[17] Higher standards and accompanying ex-

[16] Cochran, *op. cit.*, p. 138.

[17] Claude McMillan, Richard Gonzalez, with Leo G. Erickson, *International Enterprise in a Developing Economy* (East Lansing: Michigan State University Bureau of Business and Economic Research, 1964), pp. 157–77.

pertise may, however, occasionally be induced by sellers of quality components to manufacturers, such as roller bearings or instruments; or, if the manufacturer is himself a components maker, his monopolistic buyer may provide the impetus for better quality and greater knowledge.[18]

V. Staff Engineers

Engineers on the staff of a firm do not necessarily help in the definition of problems and the pursuit of information. Most engineers are trained to go by the handbook, not to experiment or to question fundamental assumptions. Indeed, the foreign textbooks used in production engineering are likely to encourage thinking in terms of large volumes, mechanization, and standard materials, rather than of conditions encountered in underdeveloped countries. The shifting of university courses away from current practice and formulas toward basic science, started by M.I.T. in the late 1950's, can be only partially applied in countries without extensive in-service training activities. In any case, without economic realism on the part of engineers, scientific vision may be sterile at the plant level. Engineers now complain about miserly bankers and owners who refuse to make money available for improvements and who force the use of the second-hand, the make-shift, and the manual. "They should work a few days in that plant," one Mexican engineer said, closing his private door. "They should see the daily problems, what it's like to deal with the kind of workers we have, to try to get production of good quality out on schedule." To him low wages were not an opportunity but a curse that let greedy owners postpone use of correct methods.

[18] For example, the Minneapolis Honeywell Regulator Company conducts instrument training courses in Mexico. Branches of Sears Roebuck furnish suppliers with designs and information about manufacturing methods from material testing to accounting systems. See Rottenberg, *op. cit.*, pp. 61–5, 70–5, for others.

In a similar vein a German engineer reported attempts to instill in his Brazilian employers a sense of thoroughness—the courage to reject doubtful or comfortable methods and an appreciation of true quality. He regretted that "The different educations, diverse mentalities, and completely divergent traditions of the partners, entrepreneur and engineer, create circumstances which are not easy for the engineer who cares to assert himself. In my circle of acquaintances, the number of cases in which the engineer could maintain the upper hand is very small." [19]

This engineer was particularly offended by improvisors using ideas from *Popular Mechanics*. Yet developing the willingness and ability to improvise and providing the opportunities to do so are probably good signs that self-sustaining industrialization is under way. Behind most ingenious adaptations of machines to local conditions one can find a man, undazzled and perhaps unfamiliar with lavish technical standards abroad, usually an outlander to highest society, who has been carried away with enthusiasm for the technical details of his industry. He tinkers and reads *Popular Mechanics* after midnight, is exasperated at difficulties, and smiles with vengeful delight at the competitor who miscalculated the market and over-mechanized. He may be the man who had his start repairing torpedoed ships in San Juan, an ambitious East European draftsman in a Mexican factory, or the ex-foreman of a mine or railroad repairshop in Africa or Asia.

VI. Management Consultants

Staff engineers, especially if foreign or foreign-educated, often encourage contact with consulting firms and foreign manufacturers willing to license in order to lend weight to their

[19] William Rudolf Batorffy, "Ethik und Praxis erfolgreicher Ingenieurarbeit in Übersee," *Der Ingenieur und seine Aufgaben in Neuen Wirtschaftsräumen* (Düsseldorf: V.D.I. Verlag, 1959), p. 124.

recommendations for capital expenditures to clear away the worst inconveniences. The contact is often agreed to by the owners because they suppose that the engineer knows how to communicate with the consultants and knows what to expect from them. Otherwise they might have little confidence that the firm would benefit.

Not all the technical information bought from outsiders leads to capital expenditures, of course. Management consultants often concentrate only on improving the internal organization of a firm. They ask whether production is properly planned and forecast, whether clerical procedures could be simplified, if costs are correctly budgeted, if inventory control records are up-to-date and accurate, whether workers are well trained and incentives balanced. They apply no esoteric knowledge but in a humdrum, systematic manner generate the internal information that the firm should have been producing all along. If there is high labor turnover, in which department is it concentrated? Is it among old or new employees? What are relative wage rates and responsibilities? Given this information, solutions are usually obvious. But many purely organizational reforms are difficult to introduce unless they are physically required by the production process.[20] The more intangible the reasons for new responsibilities, the less acceptable they will be to inexperienced workers. Managers of several firms in Central Mexico reported that savings which might have resulted from recording hours and output in detail, as recommended by their consultants, were actually more than eaten up by the delays that resulted from the process of keeping the records. Moreover, so much of the data was distorted for various reasons that, worse than no data, it led to confusion and incorrect plans for management.

[20] A. O. Hirschman has emphasized this point, especially with respect to maintenance procedures (*The Strategy of Economic Development* [New Haven: Yale University Press, 1958], pp. 139–49).

VII. License Agreements

The problems of personnel, accounting procedures, and organization in general are precisely those omitted in agreements with foreign licensors. The wish to avoid them may have been what kept the foreigner himself from organizing production in a branch plant. A prospective licensee, therefore, seeks information specific to the industry: how to choose materials and use equipment to make a given product. A patent, rather than a simple technical-assistance agreement, is commonly chosen for the transfer. The patent promises access to specific technological advances, lends itself to better guarantee and payment provisions than does the agreement, and gives legal and tax advantages.[21] But as a permit to apply foreign ideas, a license is almost always either insufficient or unnecessary. Legal patent descriptions do not have to show every trick of application and may therefore be nearly useless to all but experts in an industry. A study of ninety American companies by J. N. Behrman and W. E. Schmidt showed that 72 per cent of their patents had not been filed abroad outside of Canada.[22] Since the major reason for patenting abroad is the protection of foreign sales, patent activities tend to be product-, not process-oriented. Mexican manufacturers who had duplicated a wide variety of specialized equipment from dry-kilns to bag-machinery without patent formalities were sure they were not worth the bother of patent suits. Moreover, chemicals and pharmaceuticals were not pat-

[21] For details see J. N. Behrman, "Licensing Abroad Under Patents, Trademarks, and Know-How by U.S. Companies," *Patent, Trademark and Copyright Journal of Research and Education*, June 1958, pp. 185–6, 190–201, 230–48; and *The Role of Patents in the Transfer of Technology to Developing Countries*, Report of the Secretary General (New York: United Nations, 1964) E/3861/Rev. 1.

[22] J. N. Behrman and W. E. Schmidt, "New Data on Foreign Licensing," *Patent, Trademark, and Copyright Journal of Research and Education*, Winter 1959, p. 358.

entable at all. In other words, the lack of knowledge, not legal hindrances limit the flow of information.[23]

Technical assistance between firms, whether associated with patent and trademark licenses or not, may take a variety of forms. Access may be provided to everything from secret formulas, working drawings, operating cards, machine times and costs, to advertising copy. The right to observe production in the licensor's plant is important, as is the freedom to discuss, sketch, and photograph the process. Representatives of the licensor may help to initiate production abroad; he may also inspect periodically and send out samples of output for testing. The licensee is usually given the right to all improvements in the product or process covered, but not to entirely new developments.[24]

According to most agreements, however, the licensor initiates and controls the flow of information. He is allowed to choose what developments should be communicated, at what time, and in what manner. The rationale is that to leave discretion in these matters to the licensee who lacks adequate knowledge would lead to useless and poorly-organized transmittal.[25] In terms of the foregoing relay-stations analysis, it is clear that this practice is a rather drastic method of filtering. The licensee is granted the benefits of a continuing, unilaterally-determined, unmodulated flow of information. The clearly limited interchange does not encourage fundamental readjustments of pro-

[23] César Sepúlveda, "Current Developments in Industrial Property Rights in Mexico and the Relation thereto of Antitrust and Trade Practice Laws and Policies," *Patent, Trademark, and Copyright Journal of Research and Education,* Spring 1963, pp. 286–92.

[24] Behrman, *op. cit.,* pp. 256–7; Rottenberg, *op. cit.,* pp. 75–8.

[25] Behrman, *op. cit.,* p. 251. To the licensing flow from the United States one must obviously add the licensing and re-licensing by other countries. The Tokyo Shibaura Electric Company is a licensee of General Electric and licensor of the Indian Radio and Electricals Manufacturing Company. Lawrence Olson, "The Japanese in India Today," American Universities Field Staff *Reports Service,* East Asia Series, Nov. 14, 1961, p. 14.

duction methods or redesign of products. The same pattern applies in the relationship of parent to branch plants. Given the object to be produced, standard routing cards are used in the home engineering department to see what processes are involved. The choice of machinery, which is somewhat scaled down for lower volume, is determined in this way. Out of thirty subsidiaries in Mexico and Puerto Rico, I found only one that could choose its own equipment. In that one, the manager automatically questioned any machine that replaced a worker at a cost of $5,000 or more, compared with the $50,000-to-$100,000 scale used in the home plants.

I found almost no significant adaptations among the eleven firms and licensing agreements, the managers of which I interviewed, but this number is too small to support any generalization. The flow of knowledge that licensing agreements generate is undoubtedly great. But they are not conducive to the kind of spirit expressed by one technical director: "In this country you don't build your tools around your product, analyzing how to make each part. You build your product around the tools. You make the design fit the tools you have." [26]

VIII. Consulting Engineers

Consulting engineers assume responsibility for setting up a workable enterprise or profitable modernization and therefore tend to show more interest in adaptations than patent licensors. The difference should not be overstressed, however, since a large part of a licensor's return will be a percentage (anywhere from 1 to 10 per cent, but typically around 5 per cent) of net sales, in addition to income from selling component parts. But

---

[26] A perceptive analysis of foreign licensing in Mexico has been prepared by Dr. Miguel S. Wionczek, "Transfer of Technology to the Developing Countries through Enterprise-to-Enterprise Arrangements: Issues Arising in the Case of Mexico," (mimeographed paper prepared for the Fiscal and Financial Branch of the U.N. Secretariat, Oct. 1966).

the licensor's hope of sharing in success is not reinforced by a similar sharing of responsibility in case of failure. He can argue that the information conveyed is already in successful use in the home plant, so failure abroad must be due to the incompetence of others.

A greater sense of responsibility and more receptiveness to information about local problems by consulting engineers does not guarantee highly adaptive behavior. When planning the lay-out, supervising construction, and initiating production, the consultants usually consider familiar patterns to be satisfactory if they are feasible at all. Technologically, consulting engineers tend to be "satisficers" with the familiar, not optimizers from among possible alternatives. And what is familiar to them is the practice in an industrialized country. Yet the very reason for the existence and use of overseas consulting is that industrial peculiarities are more crucial than geographical differences. Since economies of specialization and scale in information run along specific industrial lines, the centers of expertise will be near the greatest centers of specific industries, that is, in the developed countries. Superior expertise in underdeveloped countries may at times be developed in conjunction with industries based on peculiar mineral resource clusters, vegetation, and consumer tastes but expertise seldom grows from general experience with low wages and scarce capital. Industries that are not strongly shaped by specific local resources and tastes can usually benefit from foreign consultants, even those slow to redesign in terms of local prices and business arrangements.

In many cases, failure to adapt beyond the minimum is due to pressure from business managers. These, as previously mentioned, are likely to have neither time nor stomach for experiments. They want old and reliable experience quickly embodied in a plant. They would not have endorsed the project at all if profits had not looked high enough to withstand some maladaptation. Fast establishment promises recovery of investment within the time that government policy and the rise of competition appear predictable. But such short time horizons cannot be attributed to all enterprises, nor to government agencies promoting industrialization such as the Economic Development Administration in Puerto Rico. An examination of consultant reports to such agencies reveals the basic approaches of engineers when unhurried. In reports shown to me alternative markets, materials, and transport—but not production methods —were considered. At this stage capital and labor costs are applied to a conventional layout, perhaps submitted by a machinery manufacturer, often with standard times and productivities. Since projects accepted presumably would be profitable by these standards, later adjustments in production methods can easily be viewed as embellishments rather than as pressing necessities. This procedure is fairly satisfactory if machinery builders are in the habit of supplying underdeveloped countries and have appropriate standard layouts on hand, but it is not conducive to initiating adaptations.

Once a contract has been awarded, designing and building a plant is essentially an assembly operation not unlike building a house. The less a plant involves an integrated, continuous-flow process, the more its output consists of discreet, multiple-component objects, the more alternative sub-installations will be feasible, and the more the engineering firm will subcontract either design or construction work. The engineering firm will view its job as the ordering of electrical, pumping, shaping, handling, and other equipment from manufacturers and the assembling of a workable whole in a suitable structure with proper space, lighting, electrical circuits, and plumbing for the desired volume of output. Its adaptations are most likely to consist of the acceptance or rejection of components developed by manufacturers, not of invention or redesign of methods. Its contribution is "know-where," far more than know-how. In this it is assisted by the diversified sales networks of an industrialized area in which an electrical manufacturer, for example, will quickly make an expert in motor starters, switch gear, or any other detail, available to a design engineer. Nor is it unusual for consulting engineers to confer at length with experienced workmen when substantial redesign is contemplated. But as gaps in space, language, and education widen, the corresponding increase in the difficulties of doing this further handicap adaptation to conditions in underdeveloped countries. As the case studies of Chapter 7 will show, where major adaptations or innovations were brought about with the assistance of foreign consultants or manufacturers in Mexico, their development was the explicit goal from the beginning. Ambition and perseverance by the clients not only made time-consuming experiments acceptable but inspired the search for novelty and creative channels of information in the first place.

IX. Research Institutes

Direct contact with American or European industrial research organizations implies channels particularly sensitive to possibilities for adapting knowledge to local conditions. An American or European laboratory may have direct contact with an overseas manufacturing enterprise; may be affiliated with a laboratory abroad, "backstopping" its services; or may even be commissioned to organize one of these laboratories. The activities of these organizations in underdeveloped countries thus run the gamut from impersonal transfer to education.

A random sample of consulting laboratories, surveyed by Rottenberg, showed that 130 out of 353 had served Latin American customers. Many of these were not manufacturers—dental colleges sought information about properties of metals, planters about fungicides, mining companies about ore treatments, oil companies about prospecting services, builders about analyses of structural materials, and a steamship line wanted information about boiler water conditioning.[27] Much of this work as well as that performed for manufacturers was routine testing and analysis. Properties and composition of materials were observed without testing novel hypotheses for altering production methods. Pioneering, of course, requires first of all a search of the literature and investigation of current practice. Some larger laboratories not only supply library and laboratory work, but also economic surveys, management counseling, and engineering design. Ease of communication among workers at various stages makes possible quick recovery or removal of anything filtered or added at any stage that should not have been.

If an underdeveloped country already has a sizeable research institute affiliated with another one abroad, the tasks transmitted internationally are least likely to be laboratory experiments. Once the frontier of knowledge has been discerned, the steps beyond can often be made with relatively simple and inexpensive methods, requiring above all, mental fertility and stamina. But an established research institute in an old industrial area is likely to have better facilities than its counterpart in an underdeveloped country for quickly sifting a vast literature, sampling expert opinion, and finally evaluating alternative approaches to installation. After processing patterns in manufacturing have been determined in general, related industrial experience is less available in laboratories than in producing enterprises in developed countries. At this stage, the established research laboratory can find companies using processes of interest and, given some personal contacts and institute prestige, open doors and files. They can often calm the impatience of inexperienced sponsors with assurances of the soundness of work in progress. In addition, usually they will not hesitate to press for a reorientation of activities toward a definite economic goal

[27] Rottenberg, *op. cit.*, pp. 81–4.

when the research appears to have reached the point where that is feasible. The Armour Research Foundation, for example, succeeded in redirecting scientists in the Philippines from interesting but diffuse activities into a team effort to develop an integrated coconut product industry.

To help an affiliate is useful; to establish a laboratory where none exists obviously is even more important. While the proposal for a laboratory is still under consideration, advisors from an experienced research institute can indicate possible research projects, methods of organization, personnel needs, layout, and sites. If proposals are accepted, they can provide an acting director and other assistants to supervise installation, set up administrative procedures, establish training programs (including scholarships and work at the home laboratories), and to initiate specific research projects. In a third phase, these individuals from the home laboratory and their guidance of both administration and research are gradually withdrawn.[28] Few institutions can match the potential of research institutes as intermediate relay stations in technological transfer. They can be superb as problem recognizers and definers, local information seekers, and selectors of best sources of information abroad. Their output of knowledge and knowledgeable people, like that of schools or weather stations, is valuable in part because it reaches into countless economic activities sometimes in subtle but still influential ways. For that very reason, identifying and settling accounts with beneficiaries is out of the question. Industrial research institutes in underdeveloped countries, therefore, warrant public subsidies, a need easily recognized but also apt to present an impasse. The vanity of the public official meets the wariness of the businessman. If the institute is to succeed, it must keep begging industry for contracts for which

[28] *Manual on the Management of Industrial Research Institutes in Developing Countries,* U.N. Department of Economic and Social Affairs (New York: United Nations, 1966).

purpose it develops elaborate promotional activities; yet it must keep every droplet of information about a firm a holy secret. If the public officials on the board see the industrialist as a tax evader perhaps even supporting a political opposition group, they will find this asymmetrical information flow unpalatable.

Most businessmen recognize the value of the institute, but they tend to treat research and innovation like price competition. They are for it in a vague, ideological way, but are frightened of its practice. Frederick Harbison has concluded that in a modern corporation with all its expert advisors, "a tremendous amount of energy must be devoted to 'selling' the line management on new ideas. . . . The consumption of this energy . . . can never be completely eliminated." [29] A staff member of a British technical advisory service reported that even a free service must be heavily promoted: "A high proportion of the time of the staff has been spent visiting firms and telling them what can be offered. As soon as this process is reduced the number of enquiries falls, so that a continuous effort has to be made." [30] Non-profit research institutes in the United States do not circulate brochures and wait hopefully. They employ professional sales methods to obtain clients and plan each new contact and follow-ups with elaborate care. Such efforts, with the possible addition of free demonstrations of the power of research, are even more needed in underdeveloped countries. Each Indian national laboratory of applied research has its own liaison unit for finding industrial problems and "selling" solutions.[31] The words of one Puerto Rican manager probably fit the typical response to a first contact:

[29] Frederick Harbison, "Entrepreneurial Organization as a Factor in Economic Development," *Quarterly Journal of Economics*, Aug. 1956, p. 377.
[30] Quoted by C. F. Carter and B. R. Williams, *Science in Industry: Policy for Progress*, p. 31.
[31] *Science and Technology for Development* (New York: United Nations, 1963), Vol. VII, p. 35.

Then these development boys come and ask if they can help me or other managers with our problems. Now isn't that ridiculous? I spent years building up this business. I've lived with these problems day after day and know them like my own children. Maybe I had decades of experience before. And these characters come and say "Let me solve your problems." They never saw a plant like this before!

To try to persuade such men is not an activity compatible with the traditional attitude of many governments toward private business; an attitude once compared with that of an "occupation army in a defeated country." [32] None of the four government-sponsored industrial research laboratories that I visited in Mexico and Puerto Rico solicited private contracts with zeal remotely comparable to that of research laboratories in the United States. In at least one, this lack had long been a subject of controversy among board members. Fears of disclosure of research results or other company secrets also discourage full private use of public research institutes. For over ten years two Puerto Rican laboratories were not authorized to keep research results secret after a process had been brought into commercial production. The laboratories also reported that official policy had at times discouraged patent applications which were viewed by some board members as leading to restrictions on the use of knowledge. As a result, in a decade only two research projects, both relatively minor, had been conducted on private account. *The Instituto Mexicano de Investigaciones Tecnológicas* guarantees strict confidence and assigns patents to sponsors, but nevertheless remains identified as an agency of government. Since it must test and certify officially the quality of textiles for export, among other duties, this government iden-

[32] Hernán Echavarría Olózaga, *El Sentido Común en la Economía Colombiana* (Bogota: Imprenta Nacional, 1958), p. 301, quoted by A. O. Hirschman, *Latin American Issues* (New York: Twentieth Century Fund, 1961), p. 26.

tification is not surprising. If it is felt within a private firm that the firm has something to conceal from the government, the firm will avoid sharing information with such an institute, regardless of its scientific excellence. At higher cost, they consult foreign laboratories.

The difficulty with foreign research institutes is that they cannot work closely with their distant client firms. Yet research, like vocational education, must be linked closely to the firm. The economies of scale in problem-solving of a sizeable industrial research institute should be linked to the in-plant knowledge and problems of the firm. Granted moderate guarantees and incentives, a research institute could "adopt" a firm, acquire access to its records over a period of time, exchange personnel, communicate apparent technical and scientific possibilities to it, and develop production methods that the firm will be committed to demonstrate to outsiders under a subsidized technical-assistance contract. These technical advances would lead to others based on the wider knowledge both of problems and performance in factories, as well as of equipment and solutions from all sources which the consultants would have acquired. Personnel in firms should be taught and paid to use standardized equipment record cards from which a documentation center, preferably international, could derive cost curves and assemble total plant records so that attention could be called to odd deviations. Attempts to innovate are justified if cost deviations of any plant are not mainly due to organizational defects and if correction is not apparently possible with equipment and processes available from consolidated international catalogues. In rapidly changing industries, such catalogues must use a system that avoids the lags of editing, printing, and ordinary distribution.[33]

[33] Guidelines may be found in *Coordination of Information on Current Federal Research and Development Projects in the Field of Electronics*, U.S. Senate Committee on Government Operations, Sept. 20, 1961; Inter-

X. Government Assistance

The United Nations and governments of both developed and underdeveloped countries, under various slogans and programs, have assumed much responsibility for international transfer of technology. But with respect to manufacturing, their agencies do not usually add a new variety of channel. Public industries use the same consulting engineers and make the same licensing agreements as other enterprises. Most international technical assistance to private industry consists of subsidizing all the activities already described. The difference is that the manufacturer does not approach the transmitters of knowledge directly with his problem or idea; he goes instead to a productivity center, a ministry, or the foreign technical mission. If a program in his industry is under way, he may easily be added to the list of clients to be served by experts already under contract. If no program exists, the agency approached must draft a proposal evaluating significance, cost, and alternative legal arrangements for obtaining consultants. In the case of American aid, after contracts had been duly reviewed by A.I.D., financing was usually provided, but only for the experts' salaries and for expenses in the United States. The "host country" paid international transportation and local costs, including interpreters and secretaries. In view of all the requirements of negotiating and coordinating, security clearances, and Washington orientation sessions for consultants, internationally subsidized technical assistance is hardly suited for quick action on new projects. There is, consequently, a tendency to put programs on a wider basis than the firm so that consultants will be available to entire

agency Coordination of Information, *Hearings before the Subcommittee on Reorganization and International Organizations,* U.S. Senate Committee on Government Operations, Sept. 21, 1962; and *Documentation and Dissemination of Research and Development Results,* U.S. House of Representatives, Select Committee on Government Research, Nov. 20, 1964.

industrial sectors, for example, foundries or cotton mills, for a certain period of time. To be effective, these programs clearly require careful promotion among possible clients.

The incredible heterogeneity of manufacturing industries renders direct government assistance difficult. Few technical problems—quality control, fuel economy, by-product use, mechanization criteria—are of common interest to a substantial majority of industries. Even progress toward solution of these cannot be explained in management seminars at productivity centers and then made compulsory like small-pox vaccination or D.D.T. sprayed from airplanes. Adoption in thousands of major and minor branches and sub-branches of industry depends on technicians who can work out strategies in terms of each situation. Few governments of underdeveloped areas, however, can afford to have such specialized technicians on the permanent staff available solely for consulting.

Nevertheless, some governments, such as that of Puerto Rico, try to fill the need. The Economic Development Administration of Puerto Rico has an Industrial Engineering Section in its Department of Puerto Rican Industries (locally-owned industries), an Industrial Research Department, and a Department of Industrial Services for plants of mainland United States ownership. These departments provide liaison with the rest of the government; help to get permits, public credit, and utilities for plants; organize in-plant training for workers; subsidize training of foremen in the United States; and periodically visit new plants to uncover difficulties that managers consider too trivial or hopeless for official complaints.

The Industrial Research Department will test minerals, water, air purity, and the like for prospective investors. The Industrial Engineering Section advertises its ability to plan complete plant layouts for food products, apparel, graphic arts, furniture, metal, and plastics industries. Much of the Section's work is of a trouble-shooting character—it will attempt to reorganize plants where the entrepreneur wrongly thought he could "squeeze production out of old junk or hobby-shop equipment," as one official put it. The Economic Development Administration also has a variety of large consulting firms on retainer so that specialized expertise can be brought to bear on unyielding problems without delay. All these activities could be interpreted as mere subsidies in kind that could just as well be given in cash which would then leave allocation of the money to the judgment of the entrepreneur, that is, to the market. But the very essence of fostering entrepreneurship where little exists is the provision of judgment where entrepreneurs have developed none. By assuming responsibility for specific problems, rather than subsidizing manufacturing income in general, the Economic Development Administration not only insures the pig in the poke but reassuringly implies that porcine ailments are minor, anyway, and responsive to routine cures.

India has also emphasized direct government technical assistance. Demonstration vans with modern equipment are sent to villages where there are artisans; public workshops help manufacturers with difficult operations like forging or electroplating; and Small Industries Service Institutes provide extension workers to solve other problems. P. N. Dhar and H. F. Lydall have criticized this program as often lacking either quality or relevance. General extension technicians are unable to give good advice on many problems, and specialized programs find too few takers. Dhar and Lydall recommended that government should retain private consultants for unraveling knotty problems in their various specialties after preliminary screening by "generalists." [34]

[34] P. N. Dhar and H. F. Lydall, *The Role of Small Enterprises in Indian Economic Development* (New York: Asia Publishing House, 1961), pp. 65–9. An experiment worth watching, however, is the Indo-Japanese Prototype and Training Center near Calcutta established to develop machines especially suited to Indian conditions. Similar centers near Bombay and Delhi already have American and German assistance, respectively,

XI. *Interdependence and Local Adaptation*

The preceding, lengthy and yet incomplete, description of the components of the international communications network may recall Kuznets' view that no theorist "exercised in spinning out inferences, could even approach the variety of experience encountered even in a first approximate review of the empirical evidence." [35] But one nevertheless can try to add a few generalizations about the working of that system.

To begin, is repudiation of "technological colonialism" and dedication to "national technological independence" possible and desirable? If technological colonialism means widespread preference for distant sources of information, it is likely to grow with industrialization as experience increases in buying information abroad. As firms expand they develop increased sensitivity and access to information, regardless of source, first by hiring technicians, followed by foreign specialists, and finally through contracts with foreign licensors, consulting engineers, and research institutes. Table 1 is consistent with this chronology. Sixteen of eighteen large firms visited in Mexico and Puerto Rico had formal contracts for obtaining information abroad, and none lacked personnel with technical training

---

but adaptation of modern production to small-scale, low wage conditions is uniquely an achievement of Japanese industrialization. Twenty Japanese instructors with a million dollar's worth of equipment were given the task of teaching 250 trainees how to make and, if possible, redesign wire-drawing, die-casting, and thermoplastic extrusion machines. But it may well prove to be that cultural differences, including the discipline that permits coordinated, interdependent small-scale organizations in Japan, are more significant than economic similarities (Lawrence—Olson, *op. cit.*, pp. 7–11).

[35] Simon Kuznets, *Six Lectures on Economic Growth* (Glencoe: Free Press, 1959), p. 122.

Table 1. Highest direct source of technical information from abroad: Forty Mexican and Puerto Rican firms other than foreign subsidiaries

Size, ownership and location	A Consulting engineers and/or research institutes under contract	B License and/or technical assistance contract with foreign manufacturer	C Personnel with technical training abroad, but not A or B	D Neither A, B, or C: chiefly machinery and material distributors and visits to suppliers abroad	E Undetermined	Total
Small (5–99 employees)	1	2	1	5	—	9
Medium (100–499 employees)	1	5	3	2	2	13
Large (above 500 employees)	9	7	2	—	—	18
Government-owned	2	2	1	—	—	5
Immigrant-owned	1	3	4	1	—	9
Other	8	9	1	6	2	26
Nuevo Leon (mostly Monterrey)	6	5	1	4	2	18
Central Plateau (mostly in or near Mexico City)	4	8	4	1	—	17
Mexico (total)*	10	13	5	5	2	35
Puerto Rico	1	1	1	2	—	5
Total	11	14	6	7	2	40

* This equals the sum of Nuevo Leon and Central Plateau.

abroad. Government-owned firms were no exception. Small firms were the most willing to operate with only a little foreign contact, either by choice or by necessity. They had, however, a strong relative preference for new equipment in order to obtain the assistance and guarantees of suppliers and because they did not trust, nor know how to repair, second-hand equipment.

But growth of international technological interdependence does not mean importing all knowledge above a certain level of novelty the way a country might import all highly capital-intensively produced commodities. It is easy to disagree with the Mexican official who, referring to a research institute, said, "Research like that should not yet be attempted here. It is the last phase of economic development. It should come at the end." To import the known techniques as much and as fast as possible is still the highroad to better productivity and living standards. The capacity to import is limited, however, and must proceed selectively in response to most insistent problems and opportunities. Where a particular problem will lead is often unpredictable. Adjustment of a valve may be the solution in one case and biochemical experiments in another. If laboratory experiments have to be exported in all cases, the country probably lacks the kind of technical community that can recognize the need for experiments at all. Ways of approaching technical problems make up a continuum. Within a country (at best, within each organization)[36] there must be people skilled in all

[36] Professor Robert Solo has shown with great clarity how technological adaptation at three levels of complexity takes a corresponding "structure of cognition," meaning a hierarchy of problem-solving competence ("The Capacity to Assimilate an Advanced Technology," *American Economic Review*, May 1966, pp. 91–7). In the postwar period Yugoslav research institutes were instructed to earn part of their income by contract research. They found industry disinterested in paying for other than routine short-term investigations. Lack of research facilities in factories meant no

parts of the continuum so that practitioners at the most applied levels will have a sense of personal contact with the most far-ranging basic approaches and, therefore, a feeling of confidence that permits them to view problems in all relevant perspectives. Scientific originality must therefore be encouraged so that it will be possible for these countries to take best advantage of foreign research.

Nevertheless, developing the original must be regarded as supplementary, to be used for important special opportunities and peculiar bottlenecks, not as a way of avoiding something alien or of creating a unique technological road for the country that imported expertise would prevent. The language of technology is universal in a vast preponderance of happenings and not legitimate prey for ethnic parochialism.

Manufacturers have a large stake in mastering local opportunities and bottlenecks, but change tends to come more readily through linkage forward from researchers and process consultants pushing their wares rather than backwards from demand, reflecting the manufacturer's precise circumstance. Where the manufacturer's accountants and engineers transmit an accurate local-opportunity signal to consultants, the final installation, even if novel, may not reflect much of this signal after selective filtering and adding at each of the relay stations. Each stage must consider elements unknown to the original customer—complementarity with other work, legislation of all sorts, professional reputation, etc.—so that consideration of

---

"logical link between the official research institutes and plant production departments . . . no practical means of converting scientific discovery and achievement into industrial processes and new products" and inability to "brief the official institutes on the problems it wishes them to study" (*Science and Technology for Development* [New York: United Nations 1963], Vol. VII, p. 30, based on B. Rakovic, "Formulating of Research Policies and Programs: The Relative Place of Applied Research," E/Conf. 39/1/19).

the total original signal, including its local-opportunity component, diminishes.[37]

Added to the "vertical" hindrance to innovation through relay-station attenuation, there is a "horizontal" problem. This problem comes from the uncertainty, lack of appropriability, and decreasing costs of information production, referred to in Section I, above. Because of uncertainty, consultants asked to generate an innovation will price their services at cost plus a fixed fee. Payment is related to effort rather than to achievement; "best judgment," not a predetermined innovation is sold.[38] The manufacturer does not know how expensive his innovation will be, but he could sharply reduce the cost by sharing it with firms in similar industries, especially non-competitors in other countries. But arranging this kind of syndicate is itself complicated, expensive, and uncertain. His co-manufacturers abroad will prefer to wait and pay royalties if necessary. But once contrived the innovation may be so obvious, containing such a large component of unpatentable knowledge, or so inaccessible to outside control within copying factories, that, like

[37] If there are n relay stations in a set, and s is the sensitivity (percentage of signal retained) at each, then the attenuation factor a equals sensitivity raised to the nth power.

$$a = s^n$$

If local-opportunity signals are reflected with 80 per cent accuracy, a four-relay station system will yield only 40.96 per cent conformity to it. Moreover, the relative efficacy, R, of one set, f, compared with another, g, is the ratio of their sensitivities raised to the nth power.

$$R = \left(\frac{s_f}{s_g} \right)^n$$

A four-stage system with twice the sensitivity at any station compared with another will have sixteen times the efficacy. Thus, conformity to an original signal with four stations of only 40 per cent sensitivity drops to 2.56 per cent.

[38] Arrow, *op. cit.*, p. 624.

Whitney's cotton gin, it will be paid for by one and free to others without payment of royalties. Machinery manufacturers, consulting engineers, or research institutes with vision could undertake innovation on an underdeveloped-world-wide basis, which would sharply reduce some of these problems. Actually, these groups have usually worked on a job-order basis, laboriously ferrying each customer across the stream instead of building a bridge. No one customer will finance the bridge; each appears without others in sight, and is eager to cross in a hurry.

XII. Summary and Conclusions

Technological information is not an ordinary commodity, and ordinary markets will not transfer it efficiently from developed to poor countries. The uncertain value of information not yet owned, the difficulty of owning information exclusively, and its inexhaustibility in use, have led to a complex and still imperfect network for its international diffusion to manufacturers. In part this network consists of schools, libraries, technical periodicals, and trade journals. In part it consists of inquirers and responders who have been compared to a system of relay stations. Entrepreneurs pose the problem of how to buy and run manufacturing equipment. Their engineers, machinery sellers, consultants, foreign patent owners, research institutes, and government technical-assistance agencies either offer a solution or pass the problem on. Considerable misinterpretation of questions and distortion of answers is inevitable because of uneven specialization and conflicts in outlook. Such "vertical" attenuations mean less productive answers to problems. Lack of "horizontal" coordination among different groups at the same stage can be an additional source of waste.

More educated and versatile individuals would be better at posing and solving problems—a counsel of perfection. But at least a few more strategically placed scientists and engineers could develop a flair for economic realities and make better designs come off the drawing boards. On the other hand, more technologically competent and scientifically keen entrepreneurs and managers would mean a more receptive clientele for these designs.[39]

A general feature of international technical transfer is that the relay stations are not closely coordinated. This lack has the advantage of flexibility but means that a given problem is solved piecemeal at the various stages; the problem is defined from the point of view of each in turn, that is, always narrowly. A top-level scientific agency monitoring performance as a whole might occasionally see that the sum of aspects filtered out as irrelevant indicates a different solution, the filtered aspects being more important *in toto* than what is sequentially retained.[40]

During 1965 the United Nations Advisory Committee on the Application of Science and Technology to Development (UNCSAT) considered setting up groups that might carry out this monitoring and stimulating activity in "concerted attacks" on selected problems. In the field of building, one problem was sharply defined: the provision of better roofing materials and roofing designs for the tropics. But in the manufacturing area the Committee had not yet gone beyond general support for techniques that should be relatively small scale and labor-intensive, using indigenous raw materials and versatile equipment. A narrower project was to follow proposed pilot projects

---

[39] For a strong case in favor of using scientists in administration, see C. F. Carter and B. R. Williams, *Industry and Technical Progress* (London: Oxford University Press, 1957), pp. 34–6, 129–35. The Center for International Studies, Massachusetts Institute of Technology, has tried to interest the engineering faculty in identifying "crucial problems" and appreciating "the inapplicability of existing technologies" (R. S. Eckaus, "Technological Change in the Less Developed Areas," *The Development of the Emerging Countries*, pp. 143–4).

[40] This point is an application of a general principle of organization. (March and Simon, *op. cit.*, pp. 197–8).

in "technology transfer centers" and to make case studies of present transfers in selected industries.[41]

The foreign subsidiary of a large manufacturing corporation is an example of a thoroughly organized channel of transfer, one that appeared flexible in minor, but not in major, ways in Mexico and Puerto Rico. Communication was typically maximized for detailed bureaucratic control, not for the encouragement of imaginative adaptation. By contrast, some European machinery builders are staffed to provide full services in consulting engineering, an arrangement that increases flexibility in machinery design, but requires more trust by the customer and his bank. A German engineer reported that this flexibility provided an important competitive advantage over British and American consultants who were limited to the standard equipment that some machinery builders insisted on supplying exclusively.[42] Savings through standardization must not be forestalled, but can standardization not be tailored more closely to conditions in underdeveloped countries?

The variety of measures that can improve the transfer system does not drip from its most abstract formulation like stalagmites rising below stalactites. Rather, the transfer system must be built up like a coral reef, largely for and by its participants. Some channels which prove to be well worth encouraging are unforeseeable from abstract generalizations.

One problem mentioned at virtually every meeting of United Nations expert working groups is lack of data owing in part to industrial secrecy based on distrust of the tax collector and fear

[41] United Nations Advisory Committee on the Application of Science and Technology to Development, *Second Report* (New York: United Nations, May 1965), pp. 31–4, and "Record of the Fourth Session" (Geneva, Nov. 1965, mimeographed), pp. 30–6 and Annex E.

[42] B. Plettner, "Erfahrungen aus der Auslandsarbeit eines grossen Unternehmens," *Der Ingenieur und Seine Aufgaben in Neuen Wirtschaftsräumen*, pp. 137–8. The International Bank, among others, will not support projects without independent consultants.

of possible competitors. In Mexico fear of the tax collector appeared the most important factor. Harmless technical data are not published so that the masking of financial details can be explained as a general taste for privacy. Of course, many firms operate without careful record-keeping and have little tangible information to share. Experiments could be made with programs to encourage useful record-keeping. For example, the training of record-keepers could be subsidized and the resulting improved records would be conveyed to specified outsiders—perhaps international technicians only—in return for technical assistance and other privileges, such as fellowships for managers and the opportunity to attend specialized international industrial conferences.

But with all collectable information at hand and with full appreciation of the wisdom of subsidizing its flow, one would still be unable to say precisely how much more support dissemination deserves. The information output created and transmitted by the relay stations per minute or year is no doubt a function of various combinations of input. Unpredictable, however, are the self-reinforcing effects of channel use, especially for seemingly unrelated purposes; that is, the way the production function of information is shifted by the very act of production, not to mention the unmeasurable proliferations from knowledge as an input for industry. Nevertheless, a United Nations committee has been appointed to study the uses and limitations of cost-benefit analysis and other quantitative techniques for guiding investment in the application of science and technology to development.[43] In view of these uncertainties, the correct strategy for learning the answers will be sequential sampling of new techniques, a method applied by the Greeks in conquering Troy.

[43] UNCSAT, "Record of the Fourth Session," *op. cit.*, Annex D, pp. 1–3.

3

Technology and Skills
of Labor and Management

Chapter 2 showed how types of knowledge and men interact to link firms in less developed countries to channels of information. Within a firm, problems of communication are those of management itself. The employees of a firm are coordinated by daily two-way communication and by sporadic dissemination of basic plans, including standard operating procedures. The messages that management and labor are each capable of formulating and absorbing determine in part the type and volume of communication possible and needed, hence the type of organization. Whether a society is rich or poor, its choice of technology is limited by the kinds of organization feasible and can only be approached in such terms. Perhaps the potter's wheel came early in antiquity and the spinning wheel centuries later because spinning was a group task with an important educational by-product. There were spinning bees but not "potting" bees. Some tasks and mechanisms demand too much concentration for talk.[1]

In the eighteenth century, capitalist employers first became supervisors of every detail of the work of large numbers of

[1] Peter F. Drucker, "Work and Tools," *Technology and Culture*, Winter 1959, p. 33.

men. This change required new methods in organization because large numbers of men had previously been used either under coercion (in mines and plantations) or under privileged circumstances (public works, royal workshops, and legal monopolies). Large-scale market production within an enterprise impressed English observers around 1800 more than any acceleration in the rate of mechanical invention. In fact, a growing trickle of inventions had affected workshops in this or that industry for at least two centuries. Regrouping workers into large units under disciplinary systems that seemed modeled on prisons and pauper workhouses was new. If the society had not tolerated this change, the trickle of inventions might have remained a trickle much longer.[2]

The job here is not to choose among alternative Prime Causes but to see how characteristics of labor and management influence choice of technique in underdeveloped countries and how their characteristics may be changed. Organizational problems may lower the number of technological options; but, conversely, some technological developments may reduce organizational problems and increase a firm's range of choice in other directions. A framework for discussing these issues is developed in Section I below and, in Section II, is applied to the tasks of top executive, supervisory, and operative employees. The relevance of productivity measures at the operative level is discussed in Section III. The last six sections explore the way personnel characteristics may be improved and how improvement at lower levels depends on that of upper levels.

[2] A. Rupert Hall, "The Changing Technical Act," *Technology and Culture*, Fall 1962, pp. 501–15; Sidney Pollard, "Factory Discipline in the Industrial Revolution," *Economic History Review*, No. 2, 1963, pp. 254–71, and the literature there cited, especially, Neil McKendrick, "Josiah Wedgwood and Factory Discipline," *Historical Journal*, Vol. IV, No. 1, 1961, pp. 30–55; Sidney Pollard, *The Genesis of Modern Management: A Study of the Industrial Revolution in Great Britain* (London: Edward Arnold, 1965).

I. A Framework of Numbers and Skills

Many changes in production methods encourage or compel changes in business organization. If the entrepreneur cannot create or manage the kind of organization implied by a different production technique, then specifications of costs at various wage, interest, and output rates will be exotic to him. His decision to change methods must begin with a concern for the organization he must build, or, perhaps, rebuild. In line with his experience and that of his advisors, he may have either a realistic or a faulty idea of the cost of tuning up an organization to various levels of productivity, or, alternatively, of the divergence from the productivity norms specified by equipment manufacturers that fits the organization he is able to build.

To begin most simply, a change in technique may affect organization by changing the number of employees and their average level of skill. There are two variables, numbers and skills, and three basic values for each: more, less, and no change. One can draw a grid with nine squares for all possible combinations, as follows:

Table 2. Possible effects of changes in technique on employment and skills per worker in an organization

Number of workers	Skill level		
	Less	Same	More
Fewer	Case No. 1	Case No. 2	Case No. 3
Same	Case No. 4	Case No. 5	Case No. 6
More	Case No. 7	Case No. 8	Case No. 9

Output may rise or fall in specific cases, but the incentive to change is higher profits, and higher profits can in most cases be drawn more easily from a greater than a smaller volume. Profits need not then become a higher fraction of a shrunken total.

Organizational problems are presumably least for Case 5 in which a new technique can be operated by the same number of equally skilled workers. If one kind of skill is substituted for another in this case, and retraining is impossible, one would have problems after all. The other eight cases can be grouped into four categories:

A. *Task-simplification; Case 7.* More, but less skilled, workers are needed. As in Adam Smith's pin factory and Josiah Wedgwood's Etruria, partly trained workers replace fewer but more versatile craftsmen. A low level of mechanization is implied. I found this principle still used in setting up a Puerto Rican shoe factory in 1951 and a Mexican furniture plant in 1954. Both factories employed over 200 workers. "No, these workers aren't carpenters," said the Mexican manager, "even their supervisors can't read blueprints. Each step is so simplified, that we've actually started employing a few women. See how skillful they are? With those jigs, it's easy."

B. *Mechanization; Cases 1, 2, and 4.* In these cases, either the skill level or employment falls, or both fall. Skilled workers are displaced. In Case 2, skilled and unskilled workers are displaced in proportion to their original numbers; so that the skill level is actually unchanged.

C. *Instrumentation; Case 3.* This label suggests that the use of fewer but more skilled workers is not a reversion from the system in Case 7 to pre-industrial craftsmen. Such reversion may take place in some areas, especially in the making of luxury goods, but is less likely than the replacement of low-skilled workers in Cases 1, 2, and 4 (mechanization) by more sophisticated, self-adjusting, "automated" machinery. Productivity of labor in Case 3 depends mainly on equipment downtime and percentage of rejects. Machinery will therefore be supervised and serviced by more highly trained and versatile workers who, compared with craftsmen, understand a smaller portion of the total activities in their industry. But as industrialization proceeds, the jobs of these workers (repairing valves, coding control tapes, etc.) will exist in a larger number of industries so that skills become less industry-specific.[3]

D. *Scale-Related Changes; Cases 6, 8, and 9.* More workers, more skills, or more of both, are involved. If lower capital costs do *not* result (possible demechanization), higher total costs are implied. Higher total costs with all else unchanged are likely to be chosen in a given product line only if unit costs fall—that is, only when economies of scale can be achieved.

These four categories hardly reflect all the diverse implications of technology for organization. Noting differences in the *direction* of change is only preliminary to assessing the effects of various *amounts* of change in given directions. Difficulties may further arise from changing the *composition* of given amounts. The framework shown here can do no more than sort out some of the problems. For example, one must separate problems of changing to a new organization from problems of then running it.

II. The Effects of Change at Three Levels

By increasing or decreasing the needs for numbers and skills, a change in technology may increase or decrease the problems at various levels of an organization. For simplicity, the levels considered here will only be top executive, supervisory, and operative. Work at the executive level is the most crucial and difficult. Top executives must not only build the internal structure of the firm by recruiting workers and assigning tasks, but must make the firm part of the legal, financial, and commercial web of society. They must procure technical knowledge and

[3] Edward Ames and Nathan Rosenberg, *The Progressive Division and Specialization of Industries* (Purdue University, Institute for Quantitative Research in Economics and Management: Paper No. 39, 1963), pp. 8–12, 20; James Bright, *Automation and Management* (Boston: Harvard University School of Business Administration, 1958), ch. 12.

decide when to search for new methods; they absorb risks and settle conflicts. Above all, they work out the routines and schedules for the activities at the lower levels.

At the supervisory level, tasks are also diverse. In general, however, supervisors relay the instructions from the top level to the line workers and see to it that these workers are able to do as told. Supervisors must identify problems unforeseen at the top level and either solve or report them. The line workers, or operatives, carry out the supervisors' instructions and should solve or report problems that arise at their posts.

In underdeveloped countries, both "task simplification" and "mechanization" make it easier for operatives to understand and to carry out their tasks. At the two higher levels task simplification generally increases, and mechanization tends to decrease, problems. Insofar as both types of change allow use of inexperienced workers, however, fewer problems will be identified, reported, and solved. A general manager in Puerto Rico said, "American managers usually don't know their own business. They depend on workers to solve small operating dilemmas. And they're right. After decades, a good lathe man can do it."

Task simplification increases problems higher up because more workers must be recruited and trained and because supervisory costs per worker rise with employment. "Two do less than one, and three nothing at all," is a common saying. Fewer workers means not only fewer supervisors, but supervisors employed more fruitfully. They can spend less time rounding up truants from their homes, checking on unauthorized exits and loitering, mulling over leave applications, and the like.[4] But

[4] Subbiah Kannappan, "Labor Force Commitment in Early Stages of Industrialization" (paper presented at the meetings of the American Academy for the Advancement of Science, Dec. 1964); and Kannappan, "The Economics of Structuring an Industrial Labor Force: Some Reflections on the Commitment Problem," *British Journal of Industrial Relations,* Nov. 1966, pp. 379–404. Werner Baer and Michel E. A. Hervé have shown how a minimum of skilled labor per unit of unskilled labor can

above all, with more workers and simpler tasks, more detailed instructions must be formulated, and production schedules become more complex and easily distorted. That good management is more crucial to task simplification than to mechanization is supported by one report on India. With one shift and no special emphasis on intensive staffing, poor management and poor incentive systems would lower production in semi-automatic operations by one-fourth but by one-third in hand-fed operations.[5] Mechanization appears to simplify a firm's problems in all main areas except capital costs and maintenance.

"Instrumentation" further eases some of the problems already reduced by mechanization, but at the cost of introducing other problems. The complexity of coordinating sheer numbers lessens, but the problems of training the required few increase. Once basic decisions are made in cases of instrumentation, production schedules are more easily set up and they are executed more or less automatically. Repercussions from any disturbance, however, are likely to be widespread and difficult to correct. Higher skills are needed in large part to forestall such disruptions and, if they do occur, to resolve them quickly. Since most of the possible disruptions presumably do not occur often, possibilities for thoroughly training unskilled assistants on the job are low.

"Scale-related changes" are hard to classify in a summary way. Demanding more skills and probably more employment as well, these changes are likely to encounter in varying inten-

---

limit an economy's absorptive capacity for unskilled workers in labor-intensive processes to the rate of skill-formation ("Employment and Industrialization in Developing Countries," *Quarterly Journal of Economics,* Feb. 1966, pp. 88–107).

[5] "Choice of Capital Intensity in Operational Planning for Under-Developed Countries," paper presented by the Research and Evaluation Division, Center for Industrial Development, United Nations, at the São Paulo Seminar on Industrial Programming, São Paulo, March 1963, pp. 6–7.

sity the organizational problems of each of the other three categories. Since scale is not likely to fall in the course of industrialization, neither problems of training nor those of coordinating workers are likely to diminish. At best their solution will become a familiar routine, and at least some eighteenth-century aspects of task simplification may be skipped.

III. Measures of Productivity

Profits and the related productivity of management depend not only on organizing men and machines in production, but on choice of product line, sales methods, and strategy with respect to government, suppliers, and finance. The productivity of supervisors with a given layout is that of the men they direct. A worker's productivity depends on his "proficiency" (the time needed to accomplish each task) and his "consistency" (the number of tasks carried out correctly per day or month). The likely degrees of proficiency and consistency bear heavily on the kind of supervision needed and on the choice of task-simplification, mechanization, or instrumentation.

The difference between proficiency and consistency can be overstated. Proficiency is rarely a matter purely of muscular coordination, and more complex mental traits are not relevant to consistency alone. Complaints about poor manual dexterity in underdeveloped countries are very unusual. In one Mexican plant, parts were machined with too much measuring and polishing for the specified tolerances but were then attached with bolts half loose: The mind, not the fingers, needed training. Workers must learn something about *why* tasks and tools are arranged as they are, or as Brannen and Hodgson put it:

Local employees should be taught to relate the amount of production to the passage of time. They should also receive the instruction needed to enable them to recognize quality differentials. And they should gain a clear understanding of established standards of performance. Attention to this type of training is needed as a means of teaching local employees that their performance can be objectively evaluated by themselves as well as by their supervisors. Until local employees develop their ability to analyze and judge their own efforts they will be incapable of self-evaluation. Without self-evaluation they cannot exert self-discipline. Without self-discipline a highly efficient work force is impossible.[6]

With the psychological development of each employee that important, one may well expect proficiency to vary sharply from firm to firm. Three foreign subsidiaries in Monterrey had made fairly scientific comparisons in a specific operation of output per worker there and at home. One found proficiency 25 per cent lower than that of the home firm; one was 2 to 4 per cent lower; and one was 30 per cent above the home firm. For operations in general, seven foreign subsidiaries in the Mexican sample had measured productivity at 50 to 85 per cent of that of their home plants. Five Puerto Rican branches had measured it between 60 and 95 per cent. Whether studies had been made or not, all executives interviewed were asked to compare the productivity of their workers with productivity in the United States, or in any other industrial country, in a plant with identical equipment and the same volume of output. Many were not informed about other countries and chose not to answer. Results are shown in Table 3. About a quarter of the Mexican executives with opinions and one-third of the Puerto Ricans thought productivity was as high or higher than in the United States.

A few direct quotations may shed more light on the way managers in Mexico saw the relation between dexterity, supervision, schooling, incentives, and productivity. The American production manager of a rubber products subsidiary:

[6] Ted R. Brannen and Frank X. Hodgson, *Overseas Management* (New York: McGraw-Hill, 1965), p. 71.

The Mexican worker is equal to the American if properly supervised. But it's almost impossible to bring these semiliterate workers up to supervisory levels. They can't follow instructions.

The Mexican superintendent of a steel mill:

Our workers' problem is not lack of mechanical skills, learning how to operate a machine, though they're slower to learn. But not being high-school graduates, knowing no more than reading and writing, they don't easily learn how a particular operation fits in with other activities of the enterprise. We have a crucial shortage of people that can be trained to be responsible supervisors.

Table 3. Relative productivity between production workers in seventy Mexican and Puerto Rican manufacturing enterprises and production workers in the United States or Europe as estimated by company executives

Type or location of firm	Productivity compared to U.S. or Europe			
	Less	About the same	Higher	Do not know or no response
Small	6	1	4	6
Medium	16	4	—	6
Large	14	4	—	9
U.S. subsidiaries	18	3	2	5
European subsidiaries	1	—	—	1
Immigrant	4	1	—	4
Private national	10	5	2	9
Public national	3	—	—	2
Nondurable producers	17	4	2	12
Durable producers	19	5	2	9
Nuevo Leon	12	5	1	7
Central Plateau	13	1	—	12
Mexico (total)	25	6	1	19
Puerto Rico	11	3	3	2
Total	36	9	4	21

The general administrator of a wood products subsidiary:

We use the mechanization of the 1930's because newer equipment requires understanding that two or three years of school might make difficult to impart.

A European technician at Mexican-owned machinery plant:

We prefer mechanics with nine years of school, or else they're too hard to train, too closed-minded, just tool-pushers. . . . We can't give a worker a blueprint and expect him to make something on a lathe, as in the United States or to use several machines as in Europe. We must make a motion study for each step and gesture and write an instruction sheet in detail for even a single item—not just for high production. So we have a special planning department. It's like writing instructions for toys. Incredible! We advertised for three weeks for lathe and milling machine operators, but none answered.

The American technical director of another:

It all depends on who they're working for, how well the job is set up for them. Here productivity is 55 per cent of what it is in the States, more or less. But they could bring that to 80 to 90 per cent with adequate organization, and to 100 per cent with piece rates. Without telling them we tested two ordinary men on assembling a cotton and corn planter and found they could produce 115 to 125 per day instead of the 90 they do in the States. Productivity one-third higher! They have a sense of touch with machines and grasp things fast.

The Mexican production manager of an electronics subsidiary:

Our workers press a phonograph record in 45 seconds compared with 53 seconds in the American plant. Of course, we have a different incentive system. They also had more problems producing correct deflection yokes than we did. But on the assembly line, our girls have four or five jobs, not just one. The production run is over before they're anywhere near the top of the learning curve. A set stays with them eight to ten minutes. In the United States it's less than one. There instructions are printed with a circuit diagram. Here a model is put up to show them with nothing written.

Puerto Rican managers spoke in similar terms, but also reflected the greater tensions that exist in a more competitive, newer, and faster growing industrial setting. An executive of a textile mill that closed within a year of the interview:

The workers have much dexterity. They tie loom ends and perform manual operations better than in the United States. Their problem is consistency, keeping all the looms going. Our predecessor here gave up after eight years. And our productivity has not shown a rising trend in four years. Look at the sharp fluctuations from month to month on this chart. No American plant would have such a wobbly line. All we aim at is 90 per cent of what is standard efficiency in the United States. Our South Carolina plant has older equipment and pays wages of $1.46 an hour. Yet their labor cost per pound is only slightly more than ours here with $.87 an hour. When we send a worker to South Carolina, his productivity goes up: But it doesn't stay up when he returns.

The technical director of an elaborate plant employing 240 workers:

These people just don't make good mechanics—I mean trouble shooters. But they can do a fine job machining a part. They follow the blueprint and set their own tools. But on the main process a loose part may mar every bit of the product. The man at the end marks it all defective but doesn't investigate or correct the cause. The foreman explains it to him. "*Sí, sí.*" But next day, same thing. . . . Even with perfect foresight of our troubles, this would still be a sound investment. But personally I'm ready to pack. I'll take whatever comes along.

The general manager, a Puerto Rican, of a tobacco subsidiary:

People come to me and cry, 'The workers are no good. Productivity is terrible!' Well, I say to them, 'Did you train them carefully? And how carefully did you train their trainers?' We don't use the government accelerated training program. That just means getting money from them and we don't need their money. We have to do the training anyway. It's our job. And it's the first factory job for these girls. Many of them have never seen any place like this, this cafeteria. They're a blank slate. How we start them out is what they'll accept. They could do less and they could also do more. But why should they if that's the U.S. standard? I'm for these people. I'm on their side. They look young, but there's a drama with every one of them. An abandoned family with eight younger children. Heartbreaking stories. Organizers come from San Juan and the mainland and press hard to get a union. I'm not against that. And I'm not for it. I don't help them. I make cigars. They make unions.

Another native Puerto Rican general manager at a metal products branch plant:

Maybe a good executive can spot flaws in a machine or product at once. But how can the worker remember something that happens only three times a month? If it's missing once in ten times, you'd see how fast he'd learn it. I hear these continentals saying, 'Ah, the workers are no good.' I say, 'Wait a minute! How many times in the last six months have you explained this? Three times? On a thing that rarely comes up? What troubles would the Russians have in setting up some unusual industries of theirs in New Jersey, explaining it in Russian or broken English?' These workers are good. Work alongside them and explain the operations. Every human wants to know, 'Hey, how do you do this? Why does it work?' If you can explain it, they're your friend for life. And wages don't matter that much. The Latin has his *dignidad* and you can't treat him like a dog, no matter how inexperienced he is. But the best workers are the women. They'll do anything you say without arguing. They're docile and really appreciate favors. In all plants I've been in, they outproduce men by a big margin, even on machines where you wouldn't expect it. They've got better dexterity too. By the way, I keep some spare parts locked up to force workers to solve breakdowns by careful investigation.

According to a 1960 survey by the Economic Development Administration, Puerto Rican workers showed up well. Top officials of 61 subsidiaries employing 7,498 workers (about 10 per cent of all manufacturing) were interviewed, and workers were reported 92.9 per cent as efficient (output per unit time) as their mainland counterparts. Of 61 plants, 21 had higher and 25 lower productivity. Seventeen of the lower-productivity plants were in needle trades and leather working; and 17 of the higher-productivity plants were in electrical equipment, metal working, and plastics, the three other industries in the selected sample. To bring workers to these levels of proficiency, 47 per cent more training time was needed than is usual in the United States.[7]

In 1961 the National Industrial Conference Board received answers to a questionnaire from American companies with 70 plants in Latin America: Brazil 24, Mexico 21, Argentina 13, Venezuela 8, others 6. Using similar equipment to make a similar product, labor time per unit of output was estimated as *higher* by 43 per cent of the plants, *lower* by 5 per cent, and

[7] Juan A. Albors, "A Study of the Productivity and Training Requirements of Puerto Rican Factory Workers" (San Juan: Economic Development Administration, Sept. 1960, mimeographed). Gregory and Reynolds believe that "the evidence suggests that given comparable training, equipment, and management, there is no significant difference between the personal efficiency of experienced factory workers in Puerto Rico and on the mainland. The wage gap is not offset by any systematic productivity gap, and it does permit substantially lower unit labor costs in Puerto Rico" (Peter Gregory and Lloyd G. Reynolds, *Wages, Productivity, and Industrialization in Puerto Rico* [Homewood: R. D. Irwin, 1965], p. 20). This view contrasts with that of 50 companies that decided against locating in Puerto Rico in 1958. Two-thirds expected productivity to be so low that wages averaging 60 per cent lower would mean equal or higher labor costs (Rosemary C. Griffith, "Factors Affecting Continental U.S. Manufacturing Investment in Puerto Rico" [unpublished report to the Social Science Research Center, University of Puerto Rico, Dec. 1960, presented also as a doctoral dissertation at Harvard University, 1961], cited by Gregory and Reynolds, p. 102).

the *same* by 52 per cent. Two-thirds of the plants had a lower fraction of skilled employees, compared with American counterparts, apparently less because of a lower level of mechanization than because of the unavailability of skilled workers. The newer the plant, the lower was productivity.[8]

Another questionnaire, sent by Mordechai Kreinin in 1964 to U.S. companies with 78 Latin American plants, sought to find out how much higher or lower labor productivity might be with given equipment, volume, and organization. According to the replies, workers in 24 Mexican plants averaged 77 per cent as effective as American counterparts; those in 52 other Latin American plants averaged 64 per cent as effective.[9]

An American consulting engineering firm made a study in 1959 of seven Monterrey factories for the I.C.A. and a Mexican Productivity Center. All of the factories were in an industry that is inherently labor-intensive. The workers were described as "among the quickest and most dextrous we have ever observed," but time and methods procedures and incentive schemes were found inadequate in five of the factories. Productivity in most was less than half of American productivity in comparable jobs, but in the two exceptions it was 75 and 100

[8] Theodore R. Gates and Fabian Linden, *Costs and Competition: American Experience Abroad* (New York: National Industrial Conference Board, 1961), pp. 54, 57, 122, 207.

[9] Mordechai E. Kreinin, "Comparative Labor Effectiveness and the Leontief Scarce Factor Paradox," *American Economic Review*, March 1965, pp. 131–40. I am indebted to Professor Kreinin for having the Mexican figures computed separately for me.

Interviews at 38 Brazilian branch plants by Professors Claude McMillan and Richard R. Gonzalez found that, with given equipment, workers were more productive in 15 per cent of the plants, and less productive in 48 per cent. Loyalty and responsiveness to training and incentives were the same. The authors kindly provided more tabulations to me than were cited in their *International Enterprise in a Developing Economy: A Study of U.S. Business in Brazil* (East Lansing: Michigan State University Bureau of Business and Economic Research, 1964), p. 174.

per cent of American productivity. The top firm was described as "well-engineered," as having twice as much supervision as the others, and as deficient only in quality control. Commenting on the case, a Mexican expert said:

There's a standard for every machine, and an efficient firm simply comes up to that standard. Wages are pretty low, but it doesn't pay to have a few extra workers about or fewer machines per worker just to make sure everything keeps going smoothly. No, productivity is a frame of mind. We must do everything to develop an attitude of productivity. To have some workers with little to do destroys the morale of the others.

Most of these studies and comments did not clearly separate the proficiency from the consistency aspects of productivity. Breakdowns, maintenance problems, high turnover, and absenteeism can easily offset the quickest and most dextrous fingers. Maintenance difficulties and breakdowns affect task-simplification the least; high turnover and absenteeism are least troublesome under mechanization because training of replacements appears to be easier. One Mexican manufacturer said that, in the molding of plastics, a pressman can be brought close to U.S. productivity standards in four days but a skilled mold maker at triple the pay and with far more supervision, rarely and slowly reaches the U.S. level. Losing a good mold maker is serious.

In general, Puerto Rican managers seemed more disturbed by absenteeism than were managers in Mexico. In about three-quarters of the Puerto Rican plants, absenteeism ran higher than 4 per cent. An occasional 20 or 30 per cent did not strike some managers as unusual. An electrical manufacturer with over 400 employees found that absenteeism remained at 6 to 7 per cent in spite of new employees' contracts with threats of dismissal after the second occurrence and even after the manufacturer employed only high school graduates. This firm did not give prospective employees application blanks if they scored too low on preliminary intelligence and personality tests.

In comparison, an Economic Development Administration survey found a median level of absenteeism of between 3 and 4 per cent. Only 37.5 per cent of firms reported more, and half of these had no more than 5 per cent absenteeism. But in Gregory and Reynolds' 1954–55 sample of 67 plants, 63 per cent had more than 4 per cent absenteeism, mostly over 7 per cent.[10]

Large and small breakdowns in production are probably more important than absenteeism in lowering consistency. A Puerto Rican manager said only bottlenecks in internal supply kept his plant from exceeding the standard of its Philadelphia parent. But so far no scheme for getting workers to use initiative in solving small production problems had worked. A Mexican production manager said one of his hardest problems was getting workers to check into occasional delays in supplies to their posts.[11] Such problems seem to vary with the industry. Papermaking appeared to be especially troublesome. The American technical director of a Mexican mill said:

[10] Albors, *op. cit.*, pp. 38, 41, 44, 46, 48, 50; Gregory and Reynolds, *op. cit.*, p. 155. It may be that the workers' standards of consistency are no higher for managers than for themselves. One plant in my sample experienced a three-day delay in meeting the payroll, and no workers complained.

[11] At the other extreme was a Puerto Rican worker who, on the day of my visit, called for more materials in an insulting manner. The slow supplier responded with his fist. The first worker grabbed a pick axe. The production manager, a native Puerto Rican, stopped the fight with a brandished pistol, which he usually carried.

"You can't just fire types like that either," he said later in his office.

"You're afraid for your personal safety?"

"Afraid? No!"

"But you do consider it?"

"Of course."

In my notebook is the observation, "Management not skilled in labor relations."

Incentive pay merely leads to falsification of records. Then we can't judge performance of equipment and amount of rejects in inventory. We've tried other incentives: promoting, demoting, but no effect. The workers accept whatever we do. They don't care. We don't know what they're thinking. Do they resent us as foreigners or admire us as experts? We do know that they don't care whether or not paper is produced. If a felt tears and a machine stops, that's all right. Everyone disappears. Repairs that should take one hour, take three. If a production run is defective, steadily tearing the product, no one does a thing. And we have remarkably frequent power failures. At night we have doubled the amount of supervision. I'm getting an awful lot of experience, but I can't imagine where I'll ever use it.

IV. General Comparisons of Productivity

The measures and comparisons of productivity in the last section must not be confused with general measures of productivity that simply divide net output (value added) by the number of workers. Labor productivity in that sense is usually low in underdeveloped countries. Lack of capital, small scale, and deficient management will lower output per worker regardless of the level of labor proficiency and consistency. Mexican output per worker in manufacturing in 1961 was only about 27 per cent of American labor productivity in 1958, but the difference in quality of labor was hardly the cause of the 73 per cent gap.[12]

An upward adjustment of the 27 per cent to allow for differences in market structure, management, and scale is difficult to make because of insufficient data. Differences in capital per worker are known approximately, however, and, if allowed for under certain assumptions, seem to account for one-fifth to one-quarter of the productivity gap.

For example, one can assume that in both countries the

[12] Edmar L. Bacha, "Comparación entre la productividad Industrial de México y Los Estados Unidos," *El Trimestre Económico*, Oct.–Dec. 1966, p. 661.

relation between capital and labor inputs (K and L) and value added (Q) has the property of a Cobb-Douglas production function: Returns to scale are assumed constant and the elasticity of substitution between capital and labor is unity. Let the output elasticity with respect to capital be k in Mexico and g in the United States. Both k and g are positive fractions which are less than 1 if for any percentage increase in capital or labor, output rises by a smaller percentage, assuming other things remain unchanged.

The two production functions are:

Mexico: $$Q_m = C_m K_m{}^k L_m{}^{1-k} \qquad (1a)$$

United States: $$Q_u = C_u K_u{}^g L_u{}^{1-g} \qquad (1b)$$

In these equations C is a constant of proportionality; m and u are subscripts for Mexico and the United States respectively. Dividing equation (1a) by L_m gives the labor productivity of Mexico, and dividing (1b) by L_u gives that of the United States.

$$\frac{Q_m}{L_m} = C_m \left(\frac{K_m}{L_m} \right)^k \qquad (2a)$$

$$\frac{Q_u}{L_u} = C_u \left(\frac{K_u}{L_u} \right)^g$$

If k and g were equal, then C_m/C_u would be the ratio of Mexican to American labor productivity *if both countries had the same capital-labor ratio.* Using Bacha's data and equation, (3) below, Professor Einar Hardin and I have estimated that this ratio would be 42 per cent.

$$\log \frac{Q_m/L_m}{Q_u/L_u} = c + b \log \frac{K_m/L_m}{K_u/L_u} \qquad (3)$$

Equation (3) is the logarithmic form of the ratio of equations (2a) and (2b) if k and g are equal. The antilogarithm of the constant term c is the ratio C_m/C_u and measures how far the two production functions are apart when factor inputs are the same.

Omitting petroleum refining, as Bacha does, we calculated the following regression equation for forty-four industries.

$$\log \frac{Q_m/L_m}{Q_u/L_u} = -0.372 + 0.520 \qquad \log \frac{K_m/L_m}{K_u/L_u} \quad (3a)$$
$$\phantom{\log \frac{Q_m/L_m}{Q_u/L_u} =} (0.092)\ (0.183)$$

Converting from logarithms shows that C_m/C_u equals 42 per cent.

Unfortunately, good reasons for assuming equal output elasticities, k and g, have not yet been discovered. Hence, E, the ratio of output per worker in the two countries with equal capital per worker is given by equation (4).

$$E = \frac{C_m}{C_u} \bullet \left(\frac{K_u}{L_u} \right)^{k-g} \qquad (4)$$

If E is to be estimated for the actual capital-labor ratios in United States industries in a particular year, then the following estimate for C_m/C_u based on equations (2a) and (2b) can be substituted in equation (4).

$$\frac{C_m}{C_u} = \frac{(Q_m/L_m)}{(Q_u/L_u)} \bullet \frac{(K_u/L_u)^g}{(K_m/L_m)^k} \qquad (5)$$

As a result, all the terms with g cancel out and an assumption needs to be made only about k, the capital exponent in Mexico.

$$E = \frac{(Q_m/L_m)}{(Q_u/L_u)} \bullet \left(\frac{K_u/L_u}{K_m/L_m} \right)^k \qquad (6)$$

Using equation (6), we estimated the E's for forty-four Mexican industries. Detailed results are given in Appendix B. The unweighted average for equal-capital labor productivity was 36 per cent when $k = .3$; 40 per cent when $k = .4$; 45 per cent when $k = .5$. The last estimate and assumption appear the most plausible.[13] Nevertheless, they still merge possible short-comings in worker proficiency and consistency with other drawbacks of manufacturing in Mexico, not to mention the doubtful validity of assumptions behind the Cobb-Douglas procedure. In fact, since the late 1950's economists have tried to improve this procedure and have chosen to label residual differences in productivity as "technological" whenever specific causes remained unidentified. I shall therefore return to labor proficiency and consistency as defined earlier and consider their origins.

V. Worker Quality and Culture

Where should the impetus for the attitudes and abilities that lie behind proficiency and consistency come from? Who must do the crucial organizing and educating—management or government? How much of the problem is "cultural" and, therefore, beyond the scope of direct short-run policies? After interviewing 325 managers in ten Latin American countries during 1959–63, Lauterbach concluded that:

Managers appeared to have a predominantly high opinion of the innate ability of their workers to learn even somewhat complicated mechanical processes promptly. . . . The number-one complaint may be summed up in the word *apathy*. A good many managers felt that the combination of Indian, Iberian, and feudal influences had resulted in characteristics variously described as laziness, indifference, lack of ambition, lack of understanding for teamwork, timidity in doing business, dependence on the state, inability to look beyond the necessities of the moment and to plan ahead, even violence and destructiveness.[14]

[13] Einar Hardin and W. Paul Strassmann, "Industrial Productivity and Capital Intensity in Mexico and the United States," *El Trimestre Económico,* Jan.–March 1968, pp. 51–62.

[14] Albert Lauterbach, "Executive Training and Productivity: Managerial Views in Latin America," *Industrial and Labor Relations Review,* April 1964, pp. 373–4.

I often heard similar opinions. A general manager of a plant near Mexico City, himself a son of Central European immigrants, said:

Yes, these workers are intelligent, learn fast, and are goodnatured. But they feel deeply alien to their supervisors and to the interests of the enterprise. It's an attitude conditioned by centuries. Good workers cover up the irresponsibility of their fellows. Two years of school seems average. I've set up a school with four grades, and thirty workers attend. I pay the teacher myself. They're excellent, highly motivated students. But the regularity, the orderly progress of factory work, has not yet shaped their private lives. There you find all kinds of, you might say, irregularity: drunkenness, infidelity, wife-beatings. And the children that come out of those families will not be regular factory workers either. What can you expect? This country is very young in industry. Perhaps in the next century . . .

Such views were expressed more emphatically in Puerto Rico, still younger in industry, but they were often contradicted around Monterrey. Large-scale industry there dates back to the 1890's and has given the city its character. Anecdotes are common in Mexico about the man from Monterrey (like the man from São Paulo, Medellín, or Scotland) who is reputed to be not just thrifty, hardworking, and imaginative, but stingy, dogged, and sly. "At least our Monterrey workers are reliable," said one otherwise faultfinding manager, and added, "They don't let whatever comes along interfere with the need to get the work done on schedule." Another who had migrated to Mexico City from the north thought, by contrast, that his Central Plateau girls were neither hardworking, honest, or "noble," and he believed that high turnover proved they could earn more through vice around *cantinas* than in industry. Of course, there is no more accuracy in these stereotypes than in any others.

Without question, however, industrial and pre-industrial

societies differ in values, or, more accurately, in emphasis. A shift in what counts most has to take place in almost all under-developed countries before foreign machines can be run at low cost. Not only must occupations and tasks, once despised, be found inoffensive but tending machines with alertness, thoroughness, punctuality, hope of promotion, yet acquiescence to routine and detailed orders must be seen in total as a good and wholesome life. Campaigns to indoctrinate workers with such bourgeois values go back to the earliest British factories:

For unless the workmen *wished* to become "respectable" in the current sense, none of the other incentives would bite. Such opprobrious terms as "idle" or "dissolute" should be taken to mean strictly that the worker was indifferent to the employer's deterrents and incentives. . . . The conclusion cannot be avoided that, with some honorable exceptions, the drive to raise the level of respectability and morality among the working classes was not undertaken for their own sakes but primarily, or even exclusively, as an aspect of building up a new factory discipline.[15]

Seeking this new kind of respectability means yielding the old. It means being judged by today's performance, not hereditary inner worth or *dignidad*. In Puerto Rico, *dignidad* affected performance at highest and lowest levels. Governor Tugwell wrote in 1947, "This intense desire to be accepted at face value without examination because of the danger that an inferiority may be exposed lies behind more policies than even the most intelligent Puerto Ricans will admit." For his associates he sought "realistic" young Puerto Ricans, usually technically trained in the United States, "who recognized the difficulties and dangers of *dignidad*." "It was they who possessed the power to transform. . . . All those with . . . empty pretensions resisted examination and testing for genuine utility [and]

[15] Sidney Pollard, "Factory Discipline in the Industrial Revolution," in *op. cit.*, pp. 269–70.

fought it viciously." [16] Even at the lowest level of skills, Brameld found:

Jíbaros and urbanized ex-*jíbaros* will not willingly take abusive or domineering orders. They were said to be quite shocked upon observing for the first time a Continental fellow worker meekly accepting a 'bawling out' from some factory 'boss.' Discipline on the job cannot thus be maintained with the average Puerto Rican worker of rural background. Because he considers himself, however humble, as a *caballero* (gentleman), his way of retaliation is often to say little but then quietly to quit.[17]

A continental president-manager, whom I interviewed, agreed that Puerto Ricans were easily insulted and responded very poorly to tough talk. "Well, I switched to an ultra-patient approach," he said, "and some men broke down and cried. So what was I supposed to do then?"

Answers to that question have been attempted in a growing literature on labor commitment that cannot be reviewed here.[18] A one-sentence summary could run as follows: Managers commonly tend to underrate the economic rationality and adapt-

[16] Rexford Guy Tugwell, *The Stricken Land: The Story of Puerto Rico* (Garden City: Doubleday, 1947), pp. 489, 490. Among the associates were the future President of the Development Bank, Rafael Picó; the Economic Development Administrator, Teodoro Moscoso; the University President, Jaime Benítez; and the Secretary of State and second elected Governor, Roberto Sánchez Vilella.

[17] Theodore Brameld, *The Remaking of a Culture: Life and Education in Puerto Rico* (New York: Harper, 1959), p. 203. See also Thomas C. Cochran, *The Puerto Rican Businessman: A Study in Cultural Change* (Philadelphia: University of Pennsylvania Press, 1959), pp. 87–8, 161–2.

[18] See Kannappan, *op. cit.*; and Wilbert E. Moore and Arnold S. Feldman, *Labor Commitment and Social Change in Developing Areas* (New York: Social Science Research Council, 1960). Gregory and Reynolds were "struck not by the oddities of workers' reactions but by the extent to which they parallel those of seasoned factory workers in the United States . . . these workers' adaptation to the industrial way of life impressed us as surprisingly complete and rapid, a matter of a year or two rather than 10 or 20 years" (Gregory and Reynolds, *op. cit.*, pp. 298–9).

ability of workers while overrating their own performance, and being in turn underrated by social scientists. Obviously lacking in any case is the tradition of a foreman class. Workers often mistake intermediate supervisors as brothers with duties to their fellows or revere them and top managers as fathers imbued with all-embracing authority. Technological change may call for roles that strike all participants as baffling and unnatural.[19]

VI. Education and Training

Education may help to remove from factory routines their culturally-evoked taint of seeming unnatural. It can change values, roles, and productivity. Relative effectiveness in achieving desirable changes in these areas partly depends on the priorities given by those in charge of the education. But who should be in charge? Should education, especially vocational training, be carried on by each enterprise or by a central authority? Who benefits? Who can do the job?

Market forces cannot determine these matters well in early development because, except in cases of educating slaves or indentured servants, adequate benefits are highly uncertain for any group that pays for the training of another. In the early

---

[19] The Puerto Rican president-manager mentioned above first chose a worker almost at random to be foreman of one crew. The next day the man appeared in a white shirt, barked orders all day, and had the workers call him "Don Rafael." Finally a policy was adopted of hiring only former U.S. Army personnel—not because they had previous contact with advanced technology, but because they understood military discipline. Henceforth workers were called corporals, sergeants, and lieutenants. "We must all work together around this furnace and accept orders calmly or we might all get killed. The man who gives the orders is not a better man; he just has a different rank." In Gregory and Reynolds' sample of 539 male workers, the percentage of veterans in skilled jobs (60 per cent) was twice as high as that of veterans among all male workers (31 per cent), and their percentage in unskilled jobs was half as high (17 per cent vs. 35 per cent). Of course, acceptability for military service is associated with educational levels. (Gregory and Reynolds, *op. cit.*, pp. 203–4).

phases, employers who "pirate" workers trained by other firms, yet pay no training costs themselves, can outcompete those other firms. In response, the training firm may do but half a job, lowering a worker's value to itself (but still more to others), a loss more than offset by the greater chance of keeping him longer: [20] a private net gain and social loss. Few good reasons exist for accepting this loss or for having some firms subsidize both workers and competitors. Subsidies are best raised collectively. Subsidies in the form of education, especially when marked by economies of scale, would seem to lend themselves to central or public administration.

But economies of scale may not be large. Firms may be too diversified to be served by any vast common program aimed at more than basic literacy and arithmetic. If only a small part of the industrial sector can be served, questions of equity arise. Who should be left out? Because qualified teachers and funds for adequate equipment are scarce, public vocational education may not serve *any* sector well. For example, only twenty-five qualified craftsmen were trained by thirteen vocational schools in Uganda during eight years in the 1950's.[21] Mexican employers in 1960–61 typically said that only 10 per cent of vocational school graduates were worth hiring. Part of the problem, of course, is accurate and early forecasting of industrial needs. After extensive studies Harbison and Myers concluded that,

In many cases the vocational schools are little more than high-cost producers of nontechnical manpower, whose rather dubious contribution is to give a poor general education to students unable to get

[20] P. N. Dhar and H. F. Lydall, *The Role of Small Enterprises in Indian Economic Development* (New York: Asia Publishing House, 1962), p. 78.

[21] Robert L. Thomas, "High-level Manpower in the Economic Development of Uganda," cited in Frederick Harbison and Charles A. Myers, *Education, Manpower and Economic Growth: Strategies of Human Resource Development* (New York: McGraw-Hill, 1964), p. 56.

a better one in the academic secondary schools. It is our impression, from visits to various countries and from reports of education and training experts, that the greatest waste in secondary education is to be found in such vocational schools.[22]

Thus, the government should train but cannot; industry can train but will not do enough. The way out is a joint program, which is not a new idea even for underdeveloped areas. As early as 1919 the Indian Industrial Commission proposed "a system of organized apprenticeship for a period of four or five years, with practical training in the workshops and theoretical instruction in attached teaching institutions."[23] Today India has a large training-within-industry program. At a São Paulo meeting of steel making and fabricating experts from numerous countries, the efficiency of training-within-industry systems was agreed upon unanimously.[24] Employers may provide part of such training on a group basis either through voluntary association or through the stimulus of a tax system.[25]

The advantages of enterprise-linked training programs are clear. Unneeded skills are not likely to be created. Where training schemes are accelerated, forecasting errors will be especially low. Accelerated training for fairly comparable levels may even be relatively less capital-intensive.[26] If plants have excess capacity, as is likely in firms that build ahead of demand in small markets, their equipment may be used for training and

[22] Harbison and Myers, *op. cit.*, p. 82.
[23] East India (Industrial Commission) *Report of the Indian Industrial Commission, 1916–1918* (London: H.M.S.O., 1919), p. 2.
[24] *Problems of the Steel Making and Transforming Industries of Latin America* (New York: United Nations, 1958), Vol. I, p. 21.
[25] *Loc. cit.*; and Harbison and Myers, *op. cit.*, pp. 91, 99.
[26] G. K. Boon, *Economic Choice of Human and Physical Factors in Production* (Amsterdam: North-Holland Publishing Company, 1964), pp. 72, 76. Boon estimates savings in the Netherlands of about 23 per cent in training capital from accelerated programs.

thus will be far better than what schools could provide. One can also best relate training to acceptable standards of job performance where the trainee sees actual production.

VII. Vocational Training in Puerto Rico and Mexico

Accelerated industrial training has played an important part in Puerto Rico's Operation Bootstrap. Enrollment rose twenty times, from 423 in fiscal 1948 to around 9,000 in the mid-1950's. From fiscal 1951 to 1957 as many persons were trained in this program as had been employed in all manufacturing (excluding home needlework) in 1951: 56,000. But manufacturing employment rose by only 23,000. Many trained workers had emigrated, found nonmanufacturing jobs, remained unemployed, or had been retrained several times. By fiscal 1961 the program had become more selective: enrollment was cut by one-third but expenditures per student were doubled to $38. Accelerated training was down to 40 per cent of all vocational education enrollment, compared with 62 per cent during 1951–53.[27]

Worth noting is that training was free and limited to workers who would be at least 18 years old by the end of the one-to-three month training period. If trainees were paid substandard or no wages by prospective employers, the training center had to be separate from the production line, and none of the articles produced in the center could be sold. Instructors, paid by the Commonwealth, were usually the future supervisors or foremen. If Puerto Rican, the instructor might have been sent to the

[27] These and subsequent statistics were supplied directly by the Division of Vocational Education, Department of Education, Commonwealth of Puerto Rico. Interviews with a number of officials supplemented the data. See also the following publications by the same Division: *Vocational Education: 25 Years of Service to the People of Puerto Rico* (San Juan, 1959); *Industrial Vocational Education in Puerto Rico* (Hato Rey, 1960); and the *Annual Descriptive Report of the Vocational and Technical Education Division* (Commonwealth Board for Vocational Education, June 30, 1964, mimeographed), p. 142.

United States for preliminary training. If Continental, he could have a translator, himself a future worker in the plant. Educational prerequisites for trainees depended on the employer. Some employers were said to prefer the lower labor mobility that went with accelerated training and little education, but I found that half of the sample firms, including a majority of the subsidiaries, tried to staff their production lines with high school graduates. One executive attributed his employees' superior record to the fact that they were *all* former teachers.

Vocational education in Puerto Rico did not begin with the accelerated training program. In 1931 the Smith-Hughes Act of 1917 was extended to the island. Henceforth the Federal Government matched funds appropriated for vocational education by the legislature. In fiscal 1932, 167 students were enrolled in vocational education and 6,500 others took industrial arts courses. By the beginning of Operation Bootstrap in fiscal 1948, industrial arts enrollment had tripled to 19,100, and vocational education had grown to 3,000. Ten years later there were 13,500 in vocational education (apart from accelerated training), including 5,600 in a federally supported veteran's program.

Comments by managers shed little light on the effectiveness of the program. Where productivity is good, managers take the credit; where it is poor, they call for more and better vocational schools as the solution. Where high skills are needed, managers want schools to create them. Where work is simple and repetitive, managers fear that vocational training gets workers into slow habits and makes them think they know enough to argue. If industrialization moves from task-simplification to mechanization and instrumentation, therefore, the need for vocational education will rise.

In contrast with Puerto Rico, virtually all workers in the Mexican firms studied had been trained only on the job or in courses set up by management alone. If, as suggested by Section III, productivity with similar equipment was about one-fifth less than in Puerto Rico, fewer years in school seems the most plausible explanation other than differences in supervision. In 1950 only 54 per cent of Mexicans 25 years old or more had ever gone to school, compared with 67 per cent of Puerto Ricans (see Table 4). There had been in fact a gradual

Table 4. Amount of schooling and school attendance
Mexico and Puerto Rico: 1950

Amount of schooling	Percentage of adults, 25 years of age and over			
	Nuevo Leon	Federal district & state of Mexico	Mexico	Puerto Rico
No years	28	32	46	33
1 to 6 years	64	54	48	43
7 to 9 years	4	7	3	14
10 years and over	4	7	3	10

Age group	Percentage attending school	
	Mexico	Puerto Rico
7 to 13 years of age	41	68
14 to 19 years of age	16	38

Source: A. J. Jaffe, *People, Jobs, and Economic Development: A Case History of Puerto Rico Supplemented by Recent Mexican Experiences* (Glencoe: The Free Press, 1959), p. 255, based on *Censo de 1950: General de Población,* Tables 7 and 8, and on *1950 U.S. Census of Population, Puerto Rico,* Table 56; figures for Nuevo Leon, the Federal District and the State of Mexico from Dirección General de Estadística, *Compendio Estadístico: 1958* (Mexico, D.F., 1959), pp. 45–60, 119, 176. Of the population aged 6 to 14 in 1952, 52 per cent were enrolled in Mexico, 75 per cent in the Federal District, and 65 per cent in Nuevo Leon. In 1960 these proportions were 56 per cent, 76 per cent, and 68 per cent (Charles Nash Myers, *Education and National Development in Mexico* [Princeton: Industrial Relations Section, Princeton University, 1965], p. 85).

lowering of educational standards in Puerto Rico for unskilled and semiskilled jobs so that the earlier and more remote Bootstrap plants could bid for high school graduates with less competition from other employers.[28]

The two Mexican regions where most of the sample firms were, Nuevo Leon and Mexico City and surroundings, had a somewhat smaller fraction of adults with no schooling at all than did Puerto Rico. But very few had gone beyond primary school, and the dropout rate within primary school was high. Of the children who entered the first grade in 1951 in all Mexico, only 14.5 per cent remained in school through the sixth grade.[29]

An eleven-year program to improve general education was given priority. Teacher training was accelerated, salaries were raised sharply, and the government began a large program of building low-cost, rural schools, some with novel construction techniques. By 1962, 68 per cent of children aged 6 to 14 were enrolled—the Puerto Rican level of 1950. The program became a model for other countries.[30]

Meanwhile, during 1955–57, the Department of Industrial Studies of the Bank of Mexico had collected information about needs for technically trained workers from a sample of 838 factories. In the sample of 108,000 employees, only 11 per cent had had any technical training. After weighting parts of the sample properly and eliminating small handicraft shops, the Department estimated that 82.1 per cent of the nation's industrial employees had not had a single vocational course or any systematic technical training. Partly as a result, managers hired as few additional workers as possible, so that during this

[28] Gregory and Reynolds, *op. cit.*, p. 140.
[29] Dirección General de Enseñanzas Tecnológicas Industriales y Comerciales, *Boletín de Información*, March–April 1963, p. 19.
[30] *Loc. cit.* and *New York Times*, Jan. 13, 1965.

period manufacturing output grew at a rate one-third higher than the growth rate of manufacturing employment.[31]

Corrective steps formally began in July 1962 when President Lopez Mateos approved a national training center for technical instructors, to be set up with the aid of the United Nations Special Fund. In April 1963, after much consultation, the Minister of Education announced the establishment of ten industrial training centers and twenty agricultural centers. Ten thousand students could be enrolled at a time in the forty-week industrial courses, which offered fourteen specialties. Completion of primary school and a minimum age varying between thirteen and fifteen depending on the specialty were prerequisites for admission. (The Puerto Rican minimum age, by contrast, was eighteen years.) The maximum age was twenty-one although workers already employed in a specialty might be enrolled up to the age of forty. By late 1964, twenty more industrial centers had been set up, or were under construction, and enrollment had reached 30,000. The government had apparently learned that such centers could be useless if not tailored to the needs of industry; and in October 1964 a regional advisory committee with industrial, union, government, and productivity center (if any nearby) representation was authorized for each. Active participation, not platonic approval was sought.[32]

[31] *Boletín de Información, op. cit.*, p. 22; Departamento de Investigaciones Industriales, Banco de México, *El Empleo de Personal Técnico en la Industria de Transformación* (Mexico, D.F., 1959); and sources cited in chapter 2, note 9.

[32] *Mercado de Valores*, April 16–22, 1963, pp. 210–20; *Boletín de Información, op. cit.; El Día*, Oct. 5, 1964. This system largely superseded an earlier one started in 1923 (George F. Kneller, *The Education of the Mexican Nation* [New York: Columbia University Press, 1951], p. 137). The earlier system was not geared to the prevalence of union control of hiring and resulting stress on seniority. Early union membership and accumulation of seniority were rewarded more than additional years of education. Among the company unions of Monterrey this problem was

VIII. Foremen and Supervisors

Where labor is less trained and skilled, management may have to spend more on other factors of production to get an enterprise going. Relative factor prices, that is, lower wages, can hold up this shift in spending only as long as some elasticity of substitution remains. But workers of lower skill have less ability to replace other factors: Where this ability becomes zero, no wage cut will bring an extra man into a plant. Instead, the services of more machines or more supervision must be bought. More supervision can make up for a worker's inexpertness in materials and processes, his nonchalance about coordinating one task with another, and his disdain for long hours of gray captivity.

Unfortunately, supervisors who can do their job well are usually scarcer and harder to train than anyone and constitute perhaps the greatest bottleneck for economic development. In 1919 the Indian Industrial Commission stressed that local industries could not:

supply from the ranks of the workmen or of the educated classes connected with the industries the recruits wanted for the control of existing or future undertakings. . . . We shall therefore require special arrangements to supply candidates for supervising posts with the practical training in the factory which, in the case of so many industries in England, is obtained almost automatically.[33]

Forty years later a German engineer at Rourkela, India, reported that skilled welders and mechanics were available.

less serious (Charles Nash Myers, *op. cit.*, pp. 120–21). Technical education in Nigeria went through a similar transition. Until 1953 stress was on lengthy, isolated training of master craftsmen. Then came a series of shifts to short-term, industry-linked courses, some including supervisory techniques (Peter Kilby, "Technical Education in Nigeria," *Bulletin of the Oxford Institute of Economics and Statistics*, Vol. XXVI, No. 2 (1964), pp. 184–8).

[33] *Report of the Indian Industrial Commission, 1916–1918*, p. 99.

"Lacking, however, is that stratum of setup men and foremen (*Vorarbeiter und Meister*) that is so important to industry."[34] Other speakers at that conference (on engineering problems overseas, held in Aachen, June 1959) had similar views. According to one, newly trained workers in the tropics at times outperformed their German counterparts, and college graduates were also more or less available, but:

In general the important middle-level specialists are totally lacking, as are those practical men that have worked their way up to foreman through proper studies and apprenticeship. These people are the backbone . . . without which the best managers are helpless. The lack of this middle level leadership is the great weakness of developing countries.[35]

The survey of the *Banco de México*, cited earlier, found that manufacturers employed only one-sixth as many trained sub-professional technicians as engineers, instead of at least three times their number as is the practice in most long industrialized countries.[36] Spokesmen for 69 per cent of my sample firms said they had problems finding satisfactory supervisors, particularly if special training was important. Most supported such statements by claiming they paid a greater relative pay differential to supervisors than was their impression of common American practice. A 1961 survey of twenty-three American firms in Mexico showed they paid assistant foremen or leaders of small groups double or triple the average wage of 900 pesos monthly

[34] B. Plettner, "Erfahrungen aus der Auslandsarbeit eines grossen Unternehmens," in *Der Ingenieur und Seine Aufgaben in neuen Wirtschaftsräumen* (Düsseldorf: V.D.I. Verlag, 1959), p. 148.

[35] H. Knipping, "Technische und personelle Probleme bei der Ausführung grosser Bauvorhaben in Entwicklungsländern," in *ibid.*, p. 170.

[36] *El Empleo de Personal Técnico en la Industria de Transformación*, pp. 150, 162–3. Puerto Rican firms employed about twice as many supervisors as mainland firms of comparable size, one for every 13 workers in 1953, according to a Bureau of National Affairs study cited by Gregory and Reynolds, *op. cit.*, p. 128.

(U.S. $72). Shift foremen with assistants earned three or four times the average wage. Supervisors with technical knowledge and at least three foremen under their control usually earned five to eight times the average wage, and some were paid as high as 11,000 pesos (U.S. $880) monthly. The median hiring rate for newly graduated engineers was only 2,000 to 3,000 pesos (U.S. $160–240).[37] One Monterrey firm of my sample had only one-fourth the desired number of supervisors and lacked setup men altogether although ten were needed. To the management's considerable annoyance, the firm could not even afford to part with a Communist supervisor who circulated Party literature in the plant and "agitated" during lunch. Professor Joseph Kahl, in his intensive 1958 study of a Mexican factory, found that "the few semiskilled workers in our factory who had ambitious dreams for their children spoke either of the role of mechanic or that of a full-scale professional; even they did not look upon the foreman's role as a legitimate aspiration."[38]

In the choice of techniques, the shortage of supervisors obviously works against capital-saving task-simplification. Yet this shortage persists in the face of widespread awareness and high wage differentials primarily because the job itself is hard and not easily simplified. Three basic elements are involved: men, objects (machines and materials), and instructions from above. The task is to reduce instructions to events. The difficulty is that if one part of the job is simplified, other parts may grow harder for that very reason. If staff experts and specialists help

[37] American Chamber of Commerce of Mexico, *Salary and Employee Benefits Survey* (Mexico, D.F., March 1961).

[38] Joseph A. Kahl, "Three Types of Mexican Industrial Workers," *Economic Development and Cultural Change,* Jan. 1960, p. 168. In Gregory and Reynolds' sample, only 5 per cent of Puerto Rican factory workers wanted to be a supervisor as a long-range occupational aspiration, but 95 per cent of those with a high-school diploma did not exclude it, compared with 44 per cent of those with no formal education (*op. cit.,* pp. 127, 276).

the supervisor too much with equipment or oversimplify instructions, his ability to secure cooperation from the workers
may be lost because they may look on him as a minor figurehead
with little authority, a mere transmittor of orders.[39] The less
technical expertise the supervisor has and the less the foreman
roles are traditional in a culture, the more easily will this problem arise. If the supervisor sees himself as a man too low (a
would-be engineer who failed) or as a man too high, and, therefore, a traitor to brother workers, he may have trouble both
following and giving orders. In any case, the pay differentials
that go with the position may not matter as much as the hope
of future earnings in still higher positions. Barring the supervisor's way up tomorrow can block his emergence and performance today.

Attempts to solve the supervisor shortage fall into six categories: externalization, foreign hiring, use of graduate engineers, use of engineering dropouts, special training, and
promotion from the ranks.

1. Externalization means the elimination of at least some
managerial problems by a reduction of the size of the firm.
Since managerial intensity rises with the number of employees,
fewer workers means a greater proportionate decline in the
amount of supervision. With sufficient shrinkage (or lack of
growth) the owner and his family can run the plant directly
without status-troubled intermediaries. By the same token,
however, the amount of interfirm trading in an economy may
rise (or stay high) in greater proportion than the increase in
the number of firms. A net gain may follow where trading is a
familiar activity and large-scale supervision a new concept.

Where large-scale employment and supervision are manda-
tory, management may nevertheless externalize much of the

---

[39] Frederick Harbison and Charles A. Myers, *Management in the Industrial World: An International Analysis* (New York: McGraw-Hill,
1959), p. 30.

problem. Recruitment, training, raising productivity, discipline, and even decisions on pay rates may be delegated to labor contractors or jobbers. Such delegation of authority has been widespread in tropical mines and plantations, as well as in cotton mills and the jute industry. When conditions change, strife with the jobbers is probable and reorganization of production, especially toward less labor-intensive techniques, will be difficult.[40]

2. Although importing foreign supervisors and foremen is an alternative, it is expensive. In addition, the superior technical experience of these men may be offset by their impatience or intolerance with the shortcomings of local workers which produces resentment and loss of self-respect instead of pride in learning. In one Mexican brass mill owned by a German immigrant a switch to German foremen was made in an attempt to raise output, but morale deteriorated so much that production fell. The Mexican foremen were reinstated. The reverse, it is true, happened at a chemical plant expropriated during World War II. The German management was replaced by Mexicans with such disastrous effects that the workers petitioned (successfully) to get the Germans back. A Puerto Rican survey showed that workers not bothered by differences in language and culture found mainland supervisors preferable to Puerto Ricans because of greater "courtesy and consideration."[41] One manager told me that greater courtesy toward his men had paid off better than higher wages in keeping newly hired but experienced mechanics from returning to sugar grinding.

[40] Walter Phillips, "Technological Levels and Labor Resistance to Change in the Course of Industrialization," *Economic Development and Cultural Change*, April 1963, pp. 257–66; Reinhard Bendix, *Work and Authority in Industry* (New York: Wiley, 1956), pp. 212–15.

[41] "Workers' Attitudes toward Factory Supervisors," Manpower Resources Project, Social Science Research Center, Rio Piedras, 1956, cited by Cochran, *op. cit.*, pp. 89, 187. See also Gregory and Reynolds, *op. cit.*, pp. 137–8.

Their *patrón* of twenty years had met them unsuccessfully at the factory gates with reproaches of infidelity and ingratitude. Another manager said:

Workers prefer to get their instructions from Americans. Puerto Rican supervisors are tougher with the men, and yet won't take any responsibility. That means delays of all kinds, top management getting called out during the night shift. My four principal assistants —top men in the industry—and I put in fifty to sixty per cent more time than we would in the United States.

Of course, foreign supervisors have certain inevitable handicaps too. As a maintenance advisor from Texas said in Monterrey, "We Americans can't do a thing to ride herd on the workers because they'll charge us at once with abuse before the labor courts and get us deported. In those courts the worker always wins."

3. Using local graduate engineers as supervisors is unsatisfactory because they resent being so used and are likely to be untrained for handling either men or machines. In the words of the same Texan:

No, locally educated engineers are the worst. They've never worked in their lives. . . . If there's trouble with the equipment, they give instructions, but they don't stick around to see the work gets done right. They'll up and tell you they're university graduates and should be used in the office, not on the machines as laborers. And there they stay.

As a Mexican production manager said in idiomatic English, "All these young punks want is a dignified post and to be called *Ingeniero*."

But even where status was no problem, partly because all engineers had been given high-sounding titles, an American superintendent said, "They simply don't know what kinds of things to look for to raise production, and if they find trouble they don't know how to analyze the causes." The Banco de

México survey found that the major complaint of 49 per cent of managers was that engineers were poorly prepared to handle equipment. Among the engineers themselves, 55 per cent agreed that this had been a deficiency in their curriculum, again the complaint most often made. Want of training in production costs and human relations were the other major troubles as seen by 48 and 46 per cent of engineers. Knowledge of basic science, design, and laboratory techniques were found satisfactory by over two-thirds.[42] Those engineers who understand machines, however, are sometimes worst at handling workers. The personnel manager at a pipe mill said:

These engineers are young. They have little maturity and sympathy for the problems of the workers. They only think about production. Often they storm in demanding to have a worker removed from their department. A misunderstanding or temporary problem may turn a worker that's good into a bad, resentful one.

4. An even less satisfactory alternative are the university engineering dropouts, although they were the most common variety of foreman among the larger plants around Mexico City. In the plant studied by Kahl, mentioned above, twelve of nineteen foremen were engineering dropouts, and all were dissatisfied with their jobs. Of the remaining seven, only three were dissatisfied. The workers below and the engineers and managers above were quite content. Foremen earned more than three times as much as semiskilled workers.

But they came from middle class families or else had strong middle class ambitions, as evidenced by their general values and by their educational attainments, and they could not obtain the standard of living they sought on their present salaries. Furthermore, they had come to expect a level of responsibility on the job which they could not satisfy working under the close supervision of graduate engi-

[42] *Empleo de Personal Técnico en la Industria de Transformación*, pp. 38–9.

neers. They were frustrated men who sought positions with other companies or wanted to start businesses of their own so that they could earn more money and have more responsibility. . . . Mexico does not yet appear to have institutionalized an accepted career for the middle ranks of industrial workers. These men are neither successful members of the working class nor accepted members of a stabilized lower middle class. They are men who have failed to reach their initial goals, and they are unhappy about it.[43]

Among others, the production manager of a large public enterprise agreed: "I want none of these so-called sub-professionals. I call them half-breeds. I disagree with the *Banco de México* that we have a great shortage of these. I don't believe in half-breeds. Let me promote up from the ranks to foreman, or give me engineers. Half-breeds get dissatisfied when not promoted."

5. At the Geneva Conference on Science and Technology, Professor J. J. Morf of Switzerland rightly said that a student dropping out after half of his engineering training had very general ideas of mathematics and very broad ideas of physics, but was a poor technician. He urged avoiding confusion "between intermediate levels and higher levels, or a school which, in two years, might be expected to produce a technician and later a trained engineer."[44]

That special training for intermediate levels should be developed was by no means a unanimous view at the Conference. Dr. Joseph Ben-David of Israel thought such training had thrived "only in countries with a tradition of class differences debarring people with the necessary capacity from further study," in Europe, rather than in the United States or Soviet

[43] Kahl, *op. cit.*, pp. 166, 169; Charles Nash Myers, *op. cit.*, pp. 125–8.
[44] *Science and Technology for Development: Report on the United Nations Conference on the Application of Science and Technology for the Benefit of the Less Developed Areas*, Vol. VI., *Education and Training* (New York: United Nations, 1963), p. 101.

Union. If mobility is to be introduced in traditional societies, should or could one bring it only to the European level and no further?[45]

In Puerto Rico intermediate training is the purpose of the new terminal two-year course of the Puerto Rico Technological Institute. This program admits only high-school graduates but gives no college credit. In Communist China, similar twelve- to eighteen-month programs for turning out technicians proved inadequate and in 1957 were extended to three years.[46] In Mexico the task of training 4,500 supervisors in five years was given in 1965 to the ten-year-old (but renamed) Centro Nacional de Productividad, A.C. The program was set up with United Nations Special Fund and International Labor Organization assistance at a cost of 61.5 million pesos (U.S. $4.9 million). The job of the 4,500 supervisors was to train 135,000 workers in the program already described in Section VI, above.[47]

6. Until such programs become widespread, however, promotion from the ranks will remain the best way to get foremen. Top management can either work out a way of bringing supervisory tasks down to the capacity of best workers or train the best workers to take standard responsibilities. A Puerto Rican electronics firm tried to subdivide and simplify supervision by making some production workers "line heads" with some authority over methods and products but none over personnel matters. The Puerto Rican survey of the mid-1950's cited before showed "that where opportunities for advancement existed and a job hierarchy was paralleled by a structure of wage rates, the response of workers was always sufficient to fill job openings." In these cases, "Workers who hesitated or re-

[45] *Ibid.*, p. 106.

[46] E. H. Phelps Brown, *The Economics of Labor* (New Haven and London: Yale University Press, 1962), p. 70.

[47] *El Mercado de Valores*, June 28, 1965, pp. 409–11.

fused proffered promotions" usually yielded to "a little per-
suasion and encouragement."[48]

That energetic and talented top management could make
successful foremen out of line workers was also demonstrated
in a few very large Mexican enterprises. A foreign-owned chemical and textile firm had systematically eliminated graduate
engineers from first-line supervision in several plants over a
four-year period. A large Mexican-owned metal furniture plant
was supervised by a general foreman who had started as a
draftsman and whose assistants had also come up through the
ranks. Most of these men had no more than six years of schooling. A U.S. consulting firm had set up an incentive system,
and hourly productivity matched American standards.

IX. *The Inescapable Charge of Top Management*

The last two sections above show clearly that the systematic
backing of top management is crucial for both effective public
vocational training and a firm's internal development of good
supervisors. Unguided education and the worker's self-interest
are not enough. Management must show teachers what to teach
and workers that learning will pay. Machines and materials can
generally be bought according to specifications; but a labor
force must be developed from people with their own diverse
hopes and habits. Creating an organization is much harder
than buying its equipment.

If equipment performs poorly, therefore, poor organization
is the usual cause. At the São Paulo meeting on steel making
and fabricating, it was said that:

[48] Peter Gregory, "The Labor Market in Puerto Rico," in Moore and
Feldman, *op. cit.*, p. 163. Peter Kilby has also warned that it is easy "to
over-emphasize the importance of psychological factors; in Nigeria it is
the economic considerations which are the decisive ones" ("Technical
Education in Nigeria," *op. cit.*, p. 189).

The low productivity in machining in Latin America is fundamentally due to deficiencies in work preparation, methods, procedures and utilization of machines, all of which are related to poor management since they are almost exclusively a function of the organization and techniques introduced by managers or directors. Cutting operations are governed by basic laws, so that the relative advantages of each machining process must be about the same in all countries.[49]

Inefficiency at the Indian Rourkela Iron and Steel Works was traced to such matters as the combination of overelaborate procedures for ordering spare parts and no standardized list of what was on hand, no in-plant telephone system, overlapping responsibilities, poor disciplinary and promotions policies, and insufficient training of workers. The Solveen investigating commission of experts thought that "difficulties in the steel mill could have been avoided if during the initial period the Hindustan Steel Limited had employed a sufficient number of German personnel authorized to give instructions and carrying the full responsibility."[50] More communication, discipline, training, and effective repair systems were needed because the L–D process and a hot and cold wide strip mill were new to Indians.

International Labor Office reports from Productivity Demonstration Missions to nine countries have been analyzed by Peter Kilby. In the numerous demonstration firms simple reorganization of working methods and product flow generally saved one-fourth to one-half the labor and capital per unit of output. But with the exception of Israeli experience in 1959, demonstration firms were not copied by others. On the contrary, many demonstration firms themselves slipped back to inefficient ways. The ILO found that changing the attitudes of top man-

[49] *Problems of the Steel Making and Transforming Industries in Latin America*, Vol. I, p. 18.
[50] "Solveen Report on Rourkela Steel Plant," *The Eastern Economist*, Aug. 17, 1962, pp. 304, 307.

agement had to come first to make plant work more successful.[51]
The Israel Institute of Productivity had been started in 1950
and emphasized job analysis and training of foremen and technicians. But as elsewhere, the need for broader management
training became obvious, and an Israel Management Center
was set up.[52]

Good top management seeks and uses good sources of information, and is not generally secretive. It employs enough intermediate managers and has good recruitment and training
policies. Cost conscious, its decisions will reflect quantified
alternatives, and it will judge performance by outside standards. Good recruitment and training lead to subordinates who
can act on their own and to whom authority can and should be
delegated. Yet, quantified decision-making and standardized
measuring of performance require reporting to and complying
with a central authority. Thus, good top management must
make delegation of authority compatible with coordination. All
employees not watched in some way are apt to be money lost,
but the servant of a King still must be a king in his own more
limited realm.

The managerial decisions relevant here are those stemming
from choice of technique. A progressive management regularly
appraises performance and compares it with earlier times and
with changes in the art of an industry. Information needed for
a decision may come from detailed cost accounting, records of
physical machinery input-output, frequency of breakdowns,
repair costs, percentage of idle time, time-and-motion studies,

[51] Peter Kilby, "Organization and Productivity in Backward Economies," *Quarterly Journal of Economics*, May 1962, pp. 303–10. Kilby
supports his conclusion with evidence from five rubber-creping plants in
Nigeria.

[52] The Israel Management Center, "Scientific Management in the Service of New States," paper given at the Conference on Science in the
Advancement of New States, Rehovoth, Israel, 1960 (mimeographed),
p. 3.

and various personnel data. At best, such information is generated as part of the permanent activity of an enterprise. Those in charge will then calculate from time to time the way a process compares with its best alternatives and any appropriate changes are proposed. As shown in Table 5, about two-fifths of either large firms or foreign subsidiaries in the Mexican-Puerto Rican sample had change built into their organization in this manner.

Two other approaches involve keeping records in considerable detail but not analyzing them as a matter of routine to test the adequacy of production methods. Analysis combined with probing for additional information is attempted only at fairly long intervals, perhaps every three years, or whenever some unusual problem arises. Some firms reallocate part of the regular staff to the study while others bring in outside experts. Which approach is better depends on the firm. If the firm has a staff capable of conducting the analysis, the job may be done more often and with faster results, but less often and more slowly is better if the staff lacks the appropriate skills. Table 5 shows that medium-sized firms and those owned by native Puerto Ricans and Mexicans preferred to leave the job primarily to consultants.

Small firms were least likely to analyze their production methods thoroughly. Often records, other than inventories, cash, and accounts payable and receivable, were scarce. Managers did not consider further information worth the bother and expense. The highly-trained, record-sifting executives of large firms often admitted uncertainty about which production method was really best. Gruff or jovial, the small owner-manager who does not keep records usually thought he knew from experience what to buy. Eighty-six per cent of the small and medium-sized factories in the Banco de México survey employed no technicians. In 70 per cent of these, the owner-manager (*dueño*) solved technical problems, and 26 per cent

Table 5. Manner of analyzing production methods in seventy
Mexican and Puerto Rican manufacturing enterprises

Type of firm	Continual activity, may originate plant reorganization	Staff reallocated when analysis desired for decision	Information provided to outside analysts before decision	Operations never thoroughly analyzed, inadequate records
Small	2	4	4	7
Medium	6	7	9	4
Large	11	7	8	—
U.S. subsidiaries	10	10	6	1
European subsidiaries	2	—	—	—
Immigrant	2	2	2	3
Private national	3	4	12	7
Public national	2	2	1	—
Nondurable producers	7	12	12	4
Durable producers	12	6	9	7
Nuevo Leon	5	3	11	6
Central Plateau	8	9	6	2
Mexico (total)	13	12	17	8
Puerto Rico	6	6	4	3
Total	19	18	21	11

claimed to have no such problems.[53] James J. Berna found that
small industrialists in Madras, India, considered methods
studies inappropriate for their plants, partly because they did
not understand them and partly because they had accepted
technical problems as inevitable.[54] Engrossed in daily affairs,
they put off both basic analysis and long-run planning.

[53] *El Empleo de Personal Técnico en la Industria de Transformación,*
pp. 38, 44.
[54] James J. Berna, *Industrial Entrepreneurship in Madras State* (Bombay: Asia Publishing House, 1960), pp. 169–170. See also Jean Marie
Ackermann, *Communicating Industrial Ideas: An International Handbook
for Industrial Extension* (Menlo Park, Cal.: Stanford Research Institute,
1962); and Joseph E. Stepanek, *Managers for Small Industry—An International Study* (Glencoe: Free Press, 1960).

Besides, why plan when in the manager's view, freedom of action is what he needs and already has? Without a plan, he can reverse his decisions and happily forget about past mistakes and the possibility of his own poor judgment.[55] He will, nevertheless, be well aware of unpredictable features in his environment and may even magnify them in accordance with what personal insecurities the social frictions of rapid growth (among other factors) may have kindled. Feelings of personal insecurity can blur vision and leave the manager unable to make a decision, perhaps further heightening his insecurity.[56] Planning and technological analysis are needed so that subjective uncertainty may be reduced through learning, comparing plans with results, and trying to understand old mistakes in order not to repeat them.

X. Teaching Managers

Much of this book tries to show how managers see technological choice in the early phases of development: how they collect technical information, instruct subordinates, appraise factor costs, and size up competing machines. The gap between practice and potential gives productivity centers and management schools their task. Managers should be taught better accounting systems, production planning, maintenance procedures, quality and cost control, methods studies, training systems, personnel relations, and ways of keeping informed. The substance of these matters has either already been discussed or belongs to later chapters. Here we shall merely comment briefly on the way managers must be taught.

[55] Cf. Robert Caussin, "The Improvement of Small Business in a Developing Country," *United Nations Conference on the Application of Science and Technology for the Benefit of the Less Developed Areas*, E/Conf. 39/D/3, pp. 5–6.

[56] Albert Lauterbach, "Social Factors in Business Uncertainty," in Mary Jean Bowman, ed., *Expectations, Uncertainty, and Business Behavior* (New York: Social Science Research Council, 1958), pp. 94–95.

Some of the same principles apply to teaching managers as to turning a peasant into a skilled, and perhaps supervisory, factory worker. An odd new world may have to be unrolled before the manager without arousing too much uneasiness, for doubts and fears can block progress. The link between better performance and higher rewards, therefore, must be unmistakably clear. Largely academic exploration of broad patterns will seem unpractical, and a man's lack of interest will assure scanty application.

Most relevant for teaching strategy is a man's past experience with learning. Those with least formal training must be reached most informally: not in seminar rooms but on their own shop floor. When Mexican productivity centers limit in-plant consultation to firms with less than one hundred employees, they recognize this need for informality as much as the small firm's limited ability to pay consultants. Much remains unexplained about the origin of small factories, but a certain recurrence of general patterns from eighteenth-century Britain to the twentieth-century tropics is observable. An artisan's home workshop grows too crowded so he takes over a small building. A skilled mechanic at a mine, mill, or railway repair shop takes a few private orders, then more—and finally has enough to be on his own. In Puerto Rico work on Army bases or on torpedoed ships gave a start to some. Extra financing comes from relatives or customers, and initial machines are secondhand. Sons or sons-in-law may be sent to business or engineering school and return with plans for modernization. Meanwhile, however, better methods are almost out of the question. Studying accounts or blueprints in an office at a lonesome desk is as dreary and disheartening to the craftsman-manager as an assembly line is to the uncommitted peasant. To listen to a lecture at the productivity center, shaved and necktied, makes the craftsman-manager feel uncomfortable and the experience will seem to him ridiculous and pointless. The productivity expert must come to him. However, if the founder is a graduate engineer, as is often the case, he will not particularly dread formal courses. A third group—salesmen turned entrepreneurs and making off with a share of an ex-employer's markets or former importers goaded into production by a tariff—are not eager to grapple with new concepts. They are at least in the habit of moving about and meeting strangers. As they rarely are technicians, they usually have the most production problems.

Production reform must be suggested to managers with both drama and reassuring prudence. To gain his attention new approaches must break over his horizon with dramatic splendor; but to be tried, first steps must be cheap and safe. The trip to modern plants abroad is to the manager what an elaborate factory tour is to the new employee—dramatic, but not a personal test. When it comes to first steps, nothing seems as safe as copying others, the more closely, the better. The Indian Prototype Production and Training Centers apply this viewpoint in an interesting manner. The Centers both manufacture and assemble parts. Small firms begin by copying assembly; then gradually manufacture a few parts under supervision; then more—finally the Center withdraws from that particular product.[57]

Better than the small companies, large, established firms and foreign subsidiaries can select and develop high-level managers. They can hire well-educated and experienced specialists and release older managers for retraining with less inconvenience. But a close linking of training to job-performance to reward is as essential in these cases as for a new production worker. Where family or foreigners monopolize top positions, the excluded subordinates will *seem* incapable of absorbing and applying new knowledge. Where the way up is not blocked,

[57] A. D. Bohra, "Training for Industrial Production of Prototype Machinery," *Industrialization and Productivity*, Bulletin 6 (New York: United Nations, 1963), p. 39.

however, unsuspected energy, ambition, perseverance, and ingenuity will blossom.[58] As a Puerto Rican engineer, now the president of his company, told me: "Then, when I saw I could rise to the top, I began treating the shop as my own. It was my secret. How could I tell it to any superior? But one week I put in seventy-two hours of hard work."

XI. Summary

In terms of effect on organization, four basic types of technological change are task simplification, mechanization, instrumentation, and scale-related changes. The effect on organization is that either more or fewer men must be managed, or that more or fewer skills must be imparted, or some change in both. Needed may be either more supervisors or more intensive training. Hence, for top management the choice of technology is determined in part by ability to mount training systems and to recruit and deploy supervisors. Training systems for skills of the most widespread utility must be supported by public action. But if vocational training is too general and unrelated to needs of specific firms, it is apt to be largely wasted, especially in the early phases of economic development. Well-deployed supervisors not only need to be well trained, but also must be armed with authority. Top management itself must be trained to see supervision and organization in a way that encourages learning, teaching, and problem solving among subordinates, especially the supervisors. Above everything else, top management must make pay and promotion the rewards for good performance. Otherwise, productivity may be low in spite of astonishing manual dexterity. The worker will be unable and unwilling to

[58] For a sharp contrast in the performance of those subsidiaries that keep Americans in top positions and those that withdraw them as soon as possible, see, John C. Shearer, *High-Level Manpower in Overseas Subsidiaries: Experience in Brazil and Mexico* (Princeton: Industrial Relations Section, Dept. of Economics and Sociology, Princeton University, 1960).

judge and to better his own performance, and he will be reluctant to follow his supervisor. The supervisors in turn will seem timid or ineptly domineering. Inadequacies of supervisors and workers will seem to reflect gaps of the culture in general rather than those of one aspect: low managerial preparation.

Easier than building an organization and creating its labor force is buying sturdy, mindless, precoordinated machines—at best, self-healing instrumentation.[59] But this requires more costly hardware. Interpretation of relative prices of capital and labor is the task of the next chapter.

[59] During the 1930's fully automated plants were not yet available anywhere and David Granick necessarily concluded that "Soviet metal-working could not copy the most recent Western technology and production organization, even when relative scarcity of factors was not a dissuading force. This is because technology and production organization are inseparably linked, and because matured, intricate organizational methods cannot be 'adopted.' They must, to a considerable extent, be developed anew in each country, with the requisite bases for them being established over an extended time-period." ("Economic Development and Productivity Analysis: The Case of Soviet Metalworking," *Quarterly Journal of Economics*, May 1957, p. 232). Speaking of the 1930's he suggests that "the great product of Soviet investment in metal-fabricating industry during these early years was not physical product at all—but rather was an industrial labor force" ("On Patterns of Technological Choice in Soviet Industry," *American Economic Review*, May 1962, p. 156). Inability to subcontract efficiently kept some components from manufacture in an optimum large-scale, concentrated way; while continuous-flow, single-shift methods led to excessive scale elsewhere.

4

Labor-Capital Substitution: Relative Scarcity Signals and Their Interpretation

Compared with better information channels, better management, and possible innovations, even the most adroit factor substitution *per se* is a second-rate source of higher productivity. Yet second-rate does not mean negligible. On the contrary, among economists no topic has been given more weight. Land, labor, and capital have remained the fundamental building blocks of production theory since intermediate factors—materials, power, and other services bought by domestic firms from one another—disappear as net inputs for an economy. Applying substitution theories from advanced countries in poor ones was a natural exercise. Besides, the relative abundance of labor and scarcity of capital seemed the most obvious feature of poor countries. The strength of these accumulated theories and appearances has been great enough to keep more attention on capital-labor proportions than might otherwise be expected. The need to untangle valuable insights from needless but ingenious elaborations will take some time.

The first section of this chapter shows the limitations of theory in setting forth *a priori* conditions of optimum capital-labor intensity. Drawing away the curtains of unrealistic assumptions brings onstage the indeterminate and the subjective. Although the most abstract theories do not consider the degree of development, a few do claim special relevance, and these are stressed. The later parts of this chapter, however, suggest that much can be said about capital and labor misallocation even without knowing precisely what an optimum might be. Our theoretical gyroscopes may be imperfect, but our simple plumb lines and levels deserve wider use. The capital and labor market imperfections of Mexico and Puerto Rico will be described as distinctive in some features but typical of underdeveloped areas in others. Primarily for sizeable modern factories, do market imperfections raise the price of labor and lower that of capital. As a result, choice of excessively capital-intensive techniques is encouraged. The last section shows that this bias may be further distorted by entrepreneurial habits of improperly weighting and discounting given price tags in the reckoning of future costs. This tendency will affect employment and factory hardware, however, only to the extent that alternative techniques of production are available. The urge to substitute, whether biased or not, can find expression only through the medium of alternatives. These alternatives, the forms in which capital and labor can actually be combined in manufacturing, are discussed in Chapters 5 and 6.

I. Theories of Labor-Capital Substitution

Labor-capital substitution may change the performance of a task, the design of a factory, the structure of an industry, or the output mix of an economy. Substitution may consist of building a country's first brewery at one end of the scale, and at the other of less automatic bottle labeling. This book is concerned specifically with technological choice in poor countries, hence does not deal with the broader subject of adjustment of output mix and export-import mix. The question here is: When should a given industry change to a *known* technique that uses relatively more labor and less capital, or the reverse?

"Whenever physically possible," is not the answer. An increase in the wage bill, even at lowest hourly rates, can certainly be extravagant if only minute capital savings follow. The answer must therefore be, "whenever economically possible"—that is, when other costs are considered. Nor is adoption of capital-saving techniques an end in itself for poor countries. The aim is to raise productivity. If incidental benefits and damages "external" to the transactions of production and distribution are absent, say, no pollution or adornment of the countryside, the best technique under competition will be the most profitable. When an alternative technique is considered, what counts is the comparison of its output-raising capacity with its costs, not its relative use of capital and labor. Where volume grows, machines do tend to be substituted for labor, but that does not imply rising capital costs per unit of output. The familiar identity below shows that a rising output-capital ratio, O/K, and a falling labor-capital ratio, L/K, can go together, for example, with a given labor force whenever output rises by a larger percentage than the capital stock.

$$\frac{O}{K} = \frac{L}{K} \cdot \frac{O}{L}$$

Even if labor were released while capital is expanded, one could not conclude from capital scarcity compared with other nations, for example, that too much capital is used in a given process or industry. The pertinent criterion is whether labor is released and capital absorbed at a ratio greater than the reciprocal of their marginal productivities. In many industries, if mechanization with rising volume were avoided, more labor *and* capital, though perhaps in a simpler form, would have to be used. In the United States compared with Latin America, Asia, and Africa, mechanized and automated processes reflect not only opportunities to use capital more economically because of a high volume of production for mass markets but also opportunities to use capital more lavishly because of its greater abundance and lower price.

The problem of appraising any change in technique is complicated theoretically by the difficulty of knowing the ultimate capital-saving effect. If cheaper machines release funds for use elsewhere, capital costs in the economy should fall and wages should rise. If the wage-capital cost ratio rises noticeably, all the original decisions will have to be reconsidered, and additions may now be made profitably to the cheapened installations *perhaps* to such an extent that the capital-labor ratio in that industry will not have changed after all, and capital will not in fact have been "released." Instead, the economy as a whole is using capital at lower marginal productivity compared with labor; and it is this effect with its implication of lower interest rates and therefore a lower share of total income for capital that has come to be the criterion of capital saving in pure theory. Conversely, a labor-saving change lowers the marginal productivity of labor compared with capital; hence wages and the income share of labor are also lowered.[1]

Although capital-saving changes in technique may have no set effect of lowering capital-labor ratios in production, the conditions that would let capital's share of national income fall exactly as argued are hardly commonplace. The lack in underdeveloped countries both of a truly competitive structure and of managers erudite in practical optimizing is sure to twist or break the needed chain of repercussions. Even with competition, some interesting problems need to be implausibly assumed away before the optimum technique from a given set can be identified. There are two groups of problems which will be discussed insofar as they are relevant to early industrialization.

[1] J. R. Hicks first developed this analysis in *The Theory of Wages* (London: Macmillan, 1932), pp. 117–30. For a review of elaborations and variations, see M. Blaug, "A Survey of the Theory of Process-Innovations," *Economica*, Feb. 1963, pp. 14–20.

One group arises from *lack of homogeneity* among inputs and outputs, which affects both the capital-labor elasticities of substitution and economies of scale. The other group involves *time* and raises familiar riddles of capital theory, such as the treatment of diverse rates of use and depreciation and the effects of alternate time horizons. These factors may move the marginal productivity of capital and its share of national income in opposite directions or otherwise leave the optimum capital-labor intensity unsettled.

If, in the first problem group, the diversity of materials and intermediate products is ignored, one still has the lack of homogeneity of original inputs and final outputs. Capital-intensively made final products may be different from those made labor-intensively and their demand may be more price-elastic. A capital-saving improvement in technique can then have a net effect of *raising* the relative demand for capital and its share of income, instead of the expected opposite.

The more precisely units of output are defined—not "food" or even "bakery goods" but "tortilla paste"—the more precisely or heterogeneously defined are the corresponding forms of labor and capital and the less the possibility of substitution of units. Capital will not be gradually substituted for labor as relative costs change, but more suddenly when the minimum conditions for the closest competing process are finally reached. Returns to scale are thus likely to rise and to rise discontinuously.[2]

Even where continuous substitution is possible, little can be said about associated scale effects without knowing the engineering properties of the actual mechanism of substitution, perhaps the geometry of valves, effects of higher machine speeds, ways of intensifying maintenance, and such matters.[3]

[2] Robert Haney Scott, " 'Inferior' Factors of Production," *Quarterly Journal of Economics*, Feb. 1962, pp. 86–97.

[3] Vernon L. Smith, *Investment and Production* (Cambridge: Harvard University Press, 1961), pp. 4–5, 18, 55–61, 65n.

Since these mechanisms show great diversity, their combined effect on economies of scale in the aggregate production function cannot be easily predicted. But whenever such uncertain scale effects come into play, the final effect on marginal productivities and shares of income after an improvement in technique do not depend on initial capital-labor saving tendencies alone.[4]

Although the marginal route toward picking optimum capital-labor intensities has failed to give a final and perfect answer for the characteristics of a best current choice, in recent decades it has outlasted two alternatives which raise the second group of problems that involve time. During the 1940's, minimizing the capital-output ratio in development planning grew popular because it was assumed that prompt income rises mattered more than durability and that widespread unemployment (open or disguised) nullified the opportunity costs of labor.[5] But the shortcomings of capital-output ratios were recognized within a few years,[6] and only their striking simplicity accounts for their continued use in projections and planning.

The other novelty overlooked neither labor nor investment

[4] A. A. Walters, "A Note on Economies of Scale," *Review of Economics and Statistics,* Nov. 1963, pp. 425–7; Caleb A. Smith, "Survey of the Empirical Evidence of Economies of Scale," *Business Concentration and Price Policy* (Princeton: Princeton University Press, 1955); W. E. G. Salter, *Productivity and Technical Change* (Cambridge, England: Cambridge University Press, 1960), pp. 132–46.

[5] The pioneering discussions were in N. S. Buchanan, *International Investment and Domestic Welfare* (New York: Holt, 1945), pp. 24, 72, 106–8; N. S. Buchanan and F. A. Lutz, *Rebuilding the World Economy* (New York: Twentieth Century Fund, 1947); and in J. J. Polak, "Balance of Payments Problems of Countries Reconstructing with the Help of Foreign Loans," *Quarterly Journal of Economics,* Feb. 1943, pp. 459–93.

[6] A. E. Kahn, "Investment Criteria in Development Programs," *Quarterly Journal of Economics,* Feb. 1951, pp. 38–61; Hollis B. Chenery, "The Application of Investment Criteria," *Quarterly Journal of Economics,* Feb. 1953, pp. 76–96; Francis M. Bator, "On Capital Productivity, Input Allocation and Growth," *Quarterly Journal of Economics,* Feb. 1957, pp. 101–6.

needs and possibilities during later periods but, on the contrary, stressed these to reach a paradoxical conclusion. High capital-labor and capital-output ratios would be preferable to lower alternative ratios yielding a greater output if the investible surplus were higher. Out of a smaller total, a larger amount could be saved and reinvested. Specifically, income generated labor-intensively might accrue in greater proportion to less thrifty but more tax-resistant groups, and vice versa.[7] This and related, more or less Marxist arguments based on simple industrial structures in closed economies,[8] were formally correct but of doubtful relevance to actual situations.[9]

There are other ways of circumventing the problem. If large amounts of surplus labor can be drawn from agriculture without raising agricultural wages or lowering farm output and if shifting the "center of gravity as quickly as possible from the agricultural to the industrial sector" is the essence of development, then choice of technique is simple. Among innovations that raise the average productivity of capital equally, the one with the greatest possible use of labor is best. If one technique com-

[7] Walter Galenson and Harvey Leibenstein, "Investment Criteria, Productivity, and Economic Development," *Quarterly Journal of Economics,* Aug. 1955, pp. 343–70. See discussions of this article by H. Neisser, J. Moes, H. H. Villard, A. O. Hirschman, and Gerald Sirkin, and replies by the authors in *Quarterly Journal of Economics,* Nov. 1956, Feb. 1957, Aug. 1957, Aug. 1958, and Feb. 1963.

[8] Amartya Kumar Sen, "Some Notes on the Choice of Capital-Intensity in Development Planning," *Quarterly Journal of Economics,* Nov. 1957, pp. 561–84; Amartya Kumar Sen, *The Choice of Techniques* (Oxford: Blackwell, 1960); Maurice Dobb, "A Note on the So-Called Degree of Capital Intensity of Investment in Under-developed Countries," *Economie Appliquée,* 1954, reprinted in his *Economic Theory and Socialism* (New York: International Publishers, 1955). Also his "Second Thoughts on Capital Intensity of Investment," *Review of Economic Studies,* 1956–57; and his *An Essay on Economic Growth and Planning* (London: Routledge and Kegan Paul, 1960).

[9] A. K. Bagchi, "The Choice of the Optimum Technique," *Economic Journal,* Sept. 1962, pp. 664–8.

pared with another uses both less labor and less capital, it is superior if the saved capital employs more workers in another industry than remained unhired originally. But this new technique is not better if it also means a lower profit rate for both industries combined, therefore less capital accumulation, and ultimately slower absorption of labor into industry.[10]

Ultimate canons for judging capital-labor intensities have remained beyond the reach of thought because men's attitudes toward work and the future cannot meaningfully be judged right or wrong. The result is that the economic planner is hindered without a wise clairvoyant. Until an optimum growth rate for the economy has been chosen in some fashion, the level of investment and the rate of interest cannot be determined.[11] These three must be decided simultaneously in part because the interest rate has a feedback effect on the cost of capital. The aggregate annual cost of capital is not independent of its rate of return: the higher the interest rate, the less income need be set aside yearly for depreciation. The capital-labor ratio rises because higher interest earned on invested depreciation reserves helps pay for replacements.[12] Moreover, even optimum rates of growth are not likely to be uniform. Unless every industry were to use every good, the economy need not be in rigid lockstep, from abrasives to zwieback, but can be a set of interrelated subeconomies, each with its own growth rate. Any national growth rate selected may then fit one period under a

[10] John C. H. Fei and Gustav Ranis, *Development of the Labor Surplus Economy: Theory and Policy*, a publication of the Economic Growth Center, Yale University (Homewood: R. D. Irwin, 1964), especially pp. 91–101.

[11] Otto Eckstein, "Investment Criteria for Economic Development and the Theory of Intertemporal Welfare Economics," *Quarterly Journal of Economics*, Feb. 1957, pp. 56–85.

[12] E. D. Domar, "Depreciation, Replacement and Growth," *Economic Journal*, March 1953, pp. 1–32; D. G. Champernowne and R. F. Kahn, "The Value of Invested Capital," reprinted in Joan Robinson, *The Accumulation of Capital* (Homewood: Irwin, 1956), pp. 103–6, 429–35.

given method of aggregation, but not necessarily any other period or way of computing.[13] Choosing a period or time horizon is hardly less subjective than choosing the growth rate itself.

Capital-labor intensities, therefore, do not follow mechanically from past rates of accumulation and current scarcities without bringing into play highly subjective and uncertain judgments. Nor has the list of such estimates been exhausted: How confident are investors and designers in themselves? If very confident, or, paradoxically, if correction for undermechanization mistakes is expected to be expensive, then capital intensity will be higher than otherwise. Furthermore, capital intensity will also be higher if maintenance, a substitute for durability, is inefficient and not expected to improve at a rate offsetting any growing scarcity of labor compared with capital.[14] Durability may likewise vary with more vigorous use, such as extra shifts. But a higher use rate raises complications similar to those mentioned earlier. It means earlier recovery of funds; hence, lower interest costs, a condition favorable to greater capital intensity.[15]

To sum up, a formula giving the capital-labor ratio of optimum techniques cannot be immune to conjectural humors and fleeting circumstances. Even if poor countries had perfect mobility of capital and labor among firms and industries, competition in product markets, and flexible wages and prices all around, subjective elements would still play a crucial role.

---

[13] J. von Neumann, "A Model of General Economic Equilibrium," *Review of Economic Studies*, 1945–46, pp. 1–9; J. G. Kemeny, O. Morgenstern, and G. L. Thompson, "A Generalization of the von Neumann Model of an Expanding Economy," *Econometrica*, 1956, pp. 115–35; A. K. Bagchi, *op. cit.*, pp. 669–70. It is assumed that each industry by definition produces different goods.

[14] Rudolph C. Blitz, "Capital Longevity and Economic Development," *American Economic Review*, June 1958, pp. 313–32; and "Maintenance Costs and Economic Development," *Journal of Political Economy*, Dec. 1959, pp. 560–70.

[15] Bagchi, *op. cit.*, pp. 660–64.

Still more elusive would be a formula specifying optimum techniques under conditions of market imperfections and structural disequilibria of varying complexity. If some but not all imperfections can be accounted for with corrected "shadow" prices,[16] does their use cure in proportion or compound remaining errors?[17] One cannot say for sure. But it does seem unlikely that forces tending to raise wages above opportunity costs would be just offset by factors distorting capital charges, while inadequacy of information was corrected by errors in manipulation. Dislocation, misinformation, and poor judgment stubbornly strengthen each other. Discussion of these problems, that is, market imperfections and entrepreneurial miscalculations, are the main parts of this chapter.

II. Capital Market Imperfections

In the following two sections, a few obvious obstructions to the determination of opportunity-cost wages and capital charges will be considered, particularly some deviations common in underdeveloped countries and most closely associated with technological choice. Imperfections in commodity markets will be mentioned only in passing, and no estimate of the total cost of the combined imperfections in Mexico or anywhere else will emerge. The main point is that persistently and in a variety of ways the price of capital is lowered and the price of labor is raised so that most entrepreneurs will produce too capital-intensively and, thus abandon many potential employees to unemployment or relatively unproductive jobs.

Irregularities in the pay rates of labor pose only modest problems when set against the riddles of capital cost and capital

[16] Hollis B. Chenery, "The Application of Investment Criteria," *op. cit.;* and "The Role of Industrialization in Investment Programs," *American Economic Review,* May 1955, pp. 40–57.

[17] K. Lancaster and R. G. Lipsey, "The General Theory of Second Best," *Review of Economic Studies,* 1956–57, pp. 11–32.

mobility. If capital could be treated as a fund, the twin of the labor force, it would follow that the price per unit should prompt use of both capital and labor in production at those changing ratios that in each setting foster highest voluntary growth rates. Were capital a permanent reservoir, maintained independently of the needs of industry, capital market imperfections would be mirrored in disparities of actual interest charges from the (no doubt somehow arbitrarily determined) opportunity cost of capital.

But capital is no such reservoir furnishing services in trade for interest payments. Like families of indentured servants committed for several generations, not just services but a part of the stock is committed to a firm. Survival, as well as shrewd daily use, becomes an issue. Risk premiums are added to the interest rate, and loan repayment and amortization become a business expense. Clearly personal risk may also be offset by wage differentials, but spending for perpetual renewal of the labor force is not identified as such in business accounts. The free worker does not become as merged with the business as does capital because in-plant training, strange location, and queerness of task seldom render him as unfit for employment elsewhere as are some specialized instruments and buildings.

It is therefore a misconception to hold that all the entrepreneur has to provide for out of his future income stream is a return equal to the interest rate. Most installations wear out and must be replaced so that sales of output must cover depreciation in addition to interest. Where loans run down, perhaps in three to five years, before the machines or mills give out, payments must be still higher. Ability to make these rather than interest payments alone tells the manufacturer whether or not new equipment will raise profits. Perhaps more significant, it tells the lender. As a corollary, imperfections in the equipment market (such as uneven access to wholesale prices) may compound imperfections in lending and add to capital costs.

Like the labor market in early phases of development, the capital market has more than a dual structure. Rosen's description of the Indian market fits many other countries:

For the large firms in the organized sector, capital is available in apparently abundant amounts within a range of relatively low rates of interest, but this abundance is absolutely limited to normal working capital requirements, and to expansion or construction of new plants that are not unduly expensive; for smaller firms capital is available in a smaller absolute total quantity and within a range of much higher, although not prohibitive, rates of interest (it may be entirely unavailable for individual firms); and for individuals wishing to begin or expand a small factory, and without satisfactory financial connections, the capital available from sources outside the family or community group is absolutely very small and the range of interest rates is very high. There is little overlap of these ranges.[18]

At the Industrial Programming Seminar held by United Nations agencies in São Paulo in March 1963, representatives of development banks and international lending agencies agreed almost unanimously that at least temporarily the supply of low-interest foreign capital exceeded the need for funds by acceptable investment projects. Skilled labor and reputable management were the shortage. In India rates on debentures, loans, and preferred shares of large firms varied between 4 to 8 per cent in the period of the early 1950's to the early 1960's,[19]

---

[18] George Rosen, *Industrial Change in India* (Glencoe: Free Press, 1958), pp. 159–60. See also his *Some Aspects of Industrial Finance in India* (New York: Free Press of Glencoe for M.I.T. Center for International Studies, 1962).

[19] Bills of small traders were discounted by *shroffs* at bazaars anywhere between 9 and 12 per cent. Small industrialists and contractors paid 12 to 15 per cent (S. L. N. Simha, *The Capital Market of India* [Bombay: Vora, 1960] pp. 259–76).

which compares with 9 to 15 per cent for Mexico, excluding foreign loans. These are nominal rates that must be adjusted for higher price inflation in Mexico (7 per cent annually during the 1950's) compared with India (2 per cent for all commodities and 1 per cent for manufactured goods for fiscal 1953–59).[20] Unsteady inflation, as in Mexico, complicates study of capital-labor choices because entrepreneurs necessarily adjust the interest rate, not by the actual, still unknown, but by the *expected* rate of inflation. These two often differ.

Lowest nominal interest rates in Mexico at the time of the interviews were 5½ to 6½ per cent charged by international lending agencies, such as the U.S. Export-Import Bank. Industrial first-mortgage bonds offered 10 to 12 per cent, at times with one-sixth of the yield contingent on profits. Ten years earlier, legally authorized bond rates had never been more than 8 or 9 per cent, and no initial sales below par were allowed. At these low rates, offers to sell bonds had exceeded sales by 75 per cent.[21] The later rates came closer to balancing supply and demand in that market and corresponded roughly to the average market discount rate of 11.5 per cent for commercial paper up to 180 days maturity, charged by leading Mexico City banks in 1959–61. Interest rates on loans not channeled by government regulations, the *cartera libre* of private banks, reached 14 per cent in 1962.[22] Less credit-worthy sample firms, particularly in Nuevo Leon, received medium-term loans at 15 to 18

[20] Reserve Bank of India, *Report on Currency and Finance for the Year 1958–1959* (Bombay, 1959), p. 19.

[21] Comisión Nacional de Valores, *Memoria Anual: 1958* (México, D.F., 1958), p. 47; Comisión de Valores, *Boletín Mensual,* May 1960, pp. 176–83.

[22] The use of various commissions and surcharges makes calculation of actual rates difficult. Cf. O. Ernest Moore, *Evolución de las Instituciones Financieras en México* (México, D.F.: Centro de Estudios Monetarios Latinoamericanos, 1963), p. 275. By 1964, interest rates on bonds and mortgages had fallen back to 8 to 9 per cent, largely because of capital inflows.

per cent from *financieras,* the private investment banks. A few smaller firms reported paying interest rates in excess of 24 per cent. In part, these rates covered higher risks and the greater administrative costs of smaller loans. The national development bank, *Nacional Financiera,* has had a fund for helping small and medium-sized industry since 1954, but this fund was little known in the provinces. Regional flows were further impaired by the limited lending power that large banks delegated to provincial branches.[23] A comprehensive study of rate structure and trends does not exist.

No one can say what was *the* interest rate which reflected *the* scarcity of capital, adjusted for various maturities. When no one collects, weights, adds, divides, interprets, and feeds back what is going on, the variety of rates agreed on in isolated transactions by lenders and borrowers in a great variety of circumstances does not average out to a meaningful market price. The opportunity-cost interest rate, especially, is not a phenomenon that hides under all investment and lending decisions like a pantheistic god under mossy rocks and shadowed ponds. Wherever rates cluster enough to form a single structure, that fusion is due to the interdependent bargaining and reporting of an organized capital market. With no single structure, trends also vanish, leaving visible only official rate policy and the wayward fortunes of specific enterprises. Underpricing of capital here does not lead to compensatory overpricing there in ways that make the unknown average reflect true scarcity. It could *all* be overpriced, or *all* underpriced. What is certain is that the amount of overcapitalization is by definition equal to the amount of undercapitalization. The isolated interest rates give little clue about what is wrong and where, and to what extent.

How capital has been partly allocated in Mexico by various

[23] Paul Lamartine Yates, *El Desarrollo Regional de México* (México, D.F.: Banco de México, 1961), pp. 199–201.

nonmarket devices from tax incentives to bank lending regulations is described in Appendix A. The basic similarity of the system of controls by means of tariff, price, tax, and credit policies to that of other countries stressing industrialization is probably high.[24] More unusual is the liquidity provided in Puerto Rico by government-leased plants and sites. The Puerto Rican Government Development Bank charged 6 per cent on industrial loans. Rates charged by commercial banks were not much higher and at the most only about one-fourth above mainland American rates in cities of comparable size.[25] Small enterprises paid an average of 8.5 per cent interest to small banks for small loans in 1958.

An incidental and officially unwanted effect of most nonmarket allocations is their encouragement to substitute machines for labor. Low interest foreign loans, for example, seldom are, and sometimes cannot be, allocated in terms of the domestic scarcity of capital. Use of the international rate makes sense for branches of foreign corporations with ample borrowing and investment opportunities abroad. But when foreign capital is reallocated to wholly domestic enterprises, higher rates should be used. A Mexican paper-products maker bought new, higher-priced, automatic American equipment rather than cheaper, rebuilt or less automatic Mexican equipment because credit was available on easier terms for the American equipment.

The issue might be restated as follows: The higher price that

[24] Rosen summarizes the Indian pattern, *Industrial Change in India,* pp. 16–18. For small industry see P. N. Dhar and H. F. Lydall, *op. cit.,* pp. 69–84; Society for Social and Economic Studies, *Capital for Medium and Small-Scale Industries* (Bombay: Asia Publishing House, 1959); K. T. Ramakrishna, *Finances for Small-Scale Industry in India* (New York: Asia Publishing House, 1962). For a critical account, see P. T. Bauer, *Indian Economic Policy and Development* (New York: Praeger, 1961), pp. 85–96.
[25] See Chapter 2, and John S. deBeers, *A Study of Puerto Rico's Banking System* (San Juan: Finance Council of Puerto Rico, 1960), pp. 66–70.

firms are willing to pay at the margin is equal to the amounts that higher local interest rates, compared with foreign charges, raise the cost of local equipment. Assume A is the highest price for foreign equipment a firm will pay considering that B is the price of local or second hand equipment. The foreign interest rate is r_1, the local rate is r_2, and n is the number of years in which loans for both purchases must be repaid. Then:

$$A - B = \frac{B(r_2 - r_1)}{1 + r_2} + \frac{B(n-1)(r_2 - r_1)}{n(1 + r_2)^2} + \cdots \frac{B(r_2 - r_1)}{n(1 + r_2)^n}$$

$$A - B = B(r_2 - r_1)\left(\frac{1}{1 + r_2} + \frac{n-1}{n(1 + r_2)^2} + \cdots \frac{1}{n(1 + r_2)^n}\right)$$

Assume local interest rates are 15 per cent and foreign rates $5\frac{1}{2}$ per cent, and there is no danger of currency devaluation. Loans from either source must be repaid in three years. It will then be rational to pay any price for equivalent foreign equipment up to 14 per cent above that of local equipment. If the new foreign equipment has labor-displacing features, these will raise the allowable price further, depending upon local labor costs. Although any support is better than none, foreign loans will contribute more to an economy if use of investment funds is not limited to one kind of purchase.

Another bias toward greater capital intensity comes from tax incentives to reinvest profits. Benefits are obtained if machines are bought, but not if workers are hired. Until 1963 Mexican net profits after income and excess profits taxes, and after allowing for 35 per cent legal and reinvestment reserves, were subject to a 15 per cent dividends tax. This tax was collected from the paying firm. Insofar as profits were reinvested, the tax could be forgiven. Savings to business are not a pure gift in a case where to deduct investment costs from income this year prohibits the subtraction of depreciation from income in later years. Lower taxes now mean higher taxes later, and the benefit is no more than an interest-free loan. If straight-line depreciation in ten years is allowed and future tax payments are discounted at 12 per cent, then the present value of interest payments foregone on the quasi loan is 6.6 per cent of the investment.

To correct the bias, an increase in the payroll should be as privileged as the accumulation of equipment. If a manufacturer, instead of spending more on machinery alone, chooses to add $10,000 for labor over a period of ten years, he should be entitled to the same $660 incentive (6.6 per cent) on the payroll. Perhaps the equivalent of the interest that would otherwise have been forgiven (present value) could be paid if employment is maintained for five years. In the example used: $660 $\times 1.12^5 = \$1,160$.

What if the equipment bought with forgiven taxes can later be depreciated, once more lowering taxes? Clearly, the capital-using bias would be much greater. Instead of being financed by a quasi loan at zero interest, the equipment becomes a gift to the entrepreneur. But it is not a free good to the economy. The resources are given to industry at the expense of the public sector which might not operate with the same bias against using labor to a more rational extent. If industry is to keep the incentive to expand, but without the bias against labor, higher payrolls must give benefits equivalent to higher investment. In practice, however, the Mexican government did the reverse by enacting a two per cent wage bill tax, earmarked for education.

The bias toward increasing capital-intensity created by reinvestment allowances further widens the gap in production methods chosen by large and small firms. The larger the firm, the greater is its access to capital markets at low interest rates, but the less its need to borrow. More will be spent on plant and equipment, less on labor. Table 6 illustrates the pattern for Mexico.

Table 6. Profits and reserves as a percentage of real assets, and labor payments as a percentage of annual expenditures, by size of firm (sample of 9,000 firms, Mexico, 1951*)

Size of firm by income (thousands of pesos)	Profits and reserves as a percentage of real assets	Wages, salaries, and emoluments, as a percentage of total annual expenditures†
100– 999	17.3	21.9
1,000– 4,999	18.1	19.9
5,000–24,999	21.2	15.2
25,000–49,999	31.6	13.3
50,000 and above	43.9	9.0
Average, all manufacturing	28.1	13.9

Source: Secretaría de Hacienda y Crédito Público, *Estados Consolidados de Balance General y de Ingresos y Gastos, Por Actividades Económicas* (9,000 Empresas con un Ingreso Total de $25,654,503,000), 1951.

* Information was obtained by the Ministry of Finance in reply to a questionnaire that was answered by firms accounting for 93 per cent of the income tax collected that year. The figures broken down by income size probably include about one-eighth of firms outside of manufacturing. Insofar as small firms distorted their earnings or failed to reply, they are also not influenced by the bias of tax incentives.

† Profitable firms only. Unprofitable firms were a small fraction of the smaller four categories. Their labor payments were 29.7, 24.8, 19.3, and 15.2 per cent respectively.

Of the many other capital market imperfections, only one more will be mentioned: asymmetry of promotion. Minneapolis-Honeywell has a large sales force abroad armed with ingenious literature to coax entrepreneurs to add instrumentation to their plants. In Mexico the company conducts training courses in the use of instruments it has sold.[26] That kind of salesmanship is laudable—but who provides it for the unhired worker? More often than not, labor-saving ideas are embodied in a saleable piece of capital equipment. Replacing capital with

[26] Simon Rottenberg, *Technical Cooperation in Latin America: How United States Business Firms Promote Technological Progress* (Washington: National Planning Association, 1957), p. 65.

labor, however, may take more than a purchase: the manager might have to be converted to the subtleties of efficient organization, a far more taxing teaching assignment.[27]

III. Labor Market Imperfections

A perfect labor market might be defined as one that lets wages rise to permit and compel those capital-intensity changes that foster the desired growth rates. Subsumed are the conditions of capital accumulation and evaded are all the other problems raised in the first part of this chapter. If some inflexibility keeps wages too low in one sector of the economy, will they be too high proportionately in all other sectors? In weighing the great regional, industrial, and occupational diversity of pay rates as signs of possible market imperfection, one must account for the role of immobility and its repercussions as well as for differences in training, hence productivity, with given amounts of capital. Since there is no obvious bench mark for the opportunity cost of labor (mere numbers of people in a certain age bracket are not a labor force), one cannot know how great the deviations from the unknown norm are.

Mexico, Brazil, India, Turkey, and most other developing countries have their labor market imperfections interlaced in complex patterns, rather than in the form of only two markets —one for small, low-paying traditional workshops, the other for modern, high-wage factories. There is, instead of this simple duality, a whole rainbow of gradations, each hue distinct and yet merging with others. The constraints of paternalism, for example, vary in strength with the size of the firm, the kind of community, and the ethnic origin and idiosyncrasies of the owners. The cut-rate food deliveries and free movies of the large publisher are hard to compare with the help in emergencies offered by a small ink maker to his half-dozen workers.

Labor laws that discriminate in favor of small employers can

[27] Habakkuk, *op. cit.*, pp. 164–5.

be a market imperfection. In Mexico small firms (one to ten workers with power-driven machinery; one to twenty workers without) have little obligation to provide vacations and to indemnify injuries, and firms using only family labor are exempt from almost all responsibilities except health and hygiene rulings.[28] Even these requirements may be avoided by "clandestine industries," which allegedly defraud the Treasury and pay unjustly low wages to homeworkers, according to outraged writers in *Vestir*, the trade journal of the Mexican clothing industry.

Labor laws in underdeveloped countries are often advanced, specified in detail, and fairly well enforced around the capital, particularly among foreign-owned firms. In the provinces, degree of enforcement varies. In Mexico, even legal minimum wages varied between municipalities from a low level in rural Chiapas to five times higher along the California border, where an equivalent of $2.32 U.S. dollars daily was paid in 1962–63.[29] Until 1964, these minimum wages were set by local boards representing employers, workers, and government, ostensibly at a level which, "under the conditions prevailing in each region, is sufficient to fulfill the normal requirements of life of the workman, his education and honest pleasures, considering him the head of the family, and taking into account that he should have sufficient resources for his maintenance during the weekly days of rest when he receives no wages."[30] In 1964, a sample survey by the National Commission on Minimum Wages found that 23 per cent of manufacturing workers,

[28] *Federal Labor Law* (Eng. trans. by Traducciones, Plaza de la República 49), ch. 18, pp. 206–16.

[29] Secretaría del Trabajo y Previsión Social, *Salarios Mínimos, 1962–63* (México, D.F., 1962), p. 6. The wage was paid seven times for a six-day workweek.

[30] *Federal Labor Law*, ch. 5, art. 95. Beginning in 1964, tripartite Regional Commissions, under a National Commission, set regional minima and had the right to differentiate among occupations.

most of them in small and medium-sized cities and rural areas, were paid less than the legal minimum.[31]

Variations in labor relations must also be expected. At one end of the scale in Mexico was the nonunionized provincial boot factory which paid piece rates and had a policy of limiting its one hundred or so jobs to pliant young men, no more than twenty-five years old. Many workers had their younger brothers along as helpers and as future replacements. Older men were found in a mere half-dozen key posts. At the other end of this scale, in another industry, was a government-affiliated cooperative with a membership expanding rather independently of staffing needs but paying wages a sixth higher than private competitors. Yet other public-sector firms paid below-average wages. In the private sector, trade union policies ranged from gentle to bellicose. From 1936 through the early 1960's, none of the "independent" unions around Monterrey, claiming over 25,000 members, struck.[32] But in some old factories elsewhere, pride in the uprisings of fathers and grandfathers prevents almost any compromise on modernization. "Did we make a Revolution to trade stop watches for sticks?" When obsolete methods raise costs too high, such plants are abandoned, and a new enterprise is organized in another province. Yet aggressive pushing for higher wages is found among few Mexican unions. Because it is an integral part of the labor sector of the government party, union leadership is under pressure to keep demands in line with the government policy of stable prices and high, reinvestible profits.[33] In fact, even a rising price level does not

[31] *Excelsior,* July 30, 1964.

[32] Arthur Neef, *Labor in Mexico,* Bureau of Labor Statistics Report No. 251 (Washington, 1963), p. 93. These "white" unions are independent of the "red" national federations and of the ruling, sectorially organized, political party, the P.R.I., and they cooperate closely with local employers' groups, particularly the *Centro Patronal* which maintains a card file on "undesirables" and their relatives.

[33] Robert E. Scott, *Mexican Government in Transition* (Urbana: University of Illinois Press, 1959) cites a number of Mexican sources on labor

legally justify strikes. Higher wages may not be sought through strikes if, in the opinion of a public tripartite Board of Conciliation and Arbitration, current wages are in "equilibrium" with wages of similar plants in the area. But enforcement of this and other provisions can be very selective. Partly as a result, at a foreign automobile assembly plant newly-hired unskilled workers (sweepers and gardeners) earned 37.00 pesos (U.S. $2.96) daily in 1961, which was low for the plant but not low compared with the *average* wages of 35.00 pesos (U.S. $2.80) paid in cement making or 27.00 pesos (U.S. $2.16) in cotton spinning and weaving.[34]

In general, Mexican wage data are meager. During 1961, when most of my original information was collected, government statistics showed a range of average wages for manual workers in manufacturing from 9 pesos daily in low-paying industries to 50 pesos in high ones.[35] Since the peso exchanged for U.S. $.08 and eight-hour working days prevailed, daily wages in pesos equaled hourly wages in U.S. cents. A 48-hour work week prevailed, but workers were paid for 56 hours,

---

in politics, especially on pp. 155, 163. In 1964 a profit-sharing law went into effect with much fanfare. The fraction of profits shared with workers ranges from 2½ to 12½ per cent legal limits, depending on the ratio of net worth to payroll. To a great extent profit sharing firms stopped paying the once customary voluntary bonuses. Profit sharing was opposed by many unions who wanted compulsory bonuses. The 5 to 7 per cent of profits that were typically shared often meant a net saving to employers.

[34] *Memoria de Labores* (Secretaria del Trabajo y Previsión Social, Mexico, D.F., 1962) cited by Neef, *op. cit.*, p. 71; "Collective Labor Contract, General Motors de México, S.A. de C.V. and Workmen's and Employees' Union of the Assembly Plant, of General Motors de México, S.A. de C.V.," Jan. 20, 1961. Most workers of G.M. being in the Second through Fourth Categories, earned between 44.00 and 67.00 pesos daily (U.S. $3.52–$5.36). At the top of the scale was the Assistant Foreman with 88.00 pesos (U.S. $7.04). This plant had a 40-hour workweek. Average wages in twelve assembly plants were 46.61 pesos (U.S. $3.23) in 1961 (Dirección General de Estadística, *Revista de Estadística*, March 1962).

[35] *Révista de Estadística*, March 1962, pp. 277–310.

which meant a day of paid rest a week. In the sample of 51 Mexican firms studied, the lowest average daily wage paid by any firm was 16 pesos and the highest was 51 pesos. The majority paid between 20 and 30 pesos; only a few large firms and foreign subsidiaries paid over 40 pesos. A few foreign subsidiaries, however, paid below-average wages. Sample and official data suggest that wage levels in Mexico City were about one-fifth higher than in industrial Monterrey, and a higher differential existed in relatively skilled industries. The typical minimum wage per plant was 18 or 19 pesos daily for temporary workers, but some received as little as 10 pesos. The sample was, of course, not designed to be representative but to consist of new and sharply expanding firms. To the paid wage must be added a percentage for *prestaciones*—bonuses, allowances, social insurance, and a wide variety of payments in kind. Mexican statistics on these supplements are scanty and sometimes inconsistent, but according to most estimates the supplements range from 10 to 30 per cent of wages and salaries. In the sample, Mexican-owned firms tended to give *prestaciones* below 15 per cent while foreign subsidiaries gave above 25 per cent, discrepancies which may reflect variations in accounting practice as well as different government, management, and union policies.

These differences in pay rates, which are typical of many countries,[36] become variations in labor cost only after allowing for differentials in training costs per man, hourly productivity, absenteeism, turnover, and other uncertainties. Note also that,

[36] Factories employing 20 to 49 workers in India (1955) and Japan (1952) paid wages and salaries only 51 and 53 per cent as high as those paid by factories employing 1,000 and more. For Britain (1949) and the United States (1947) the comparable percentages were 83 and 84 (P. N. Dhar and H. F. Lydall, *The Role of Small Enterprises in Indian Economic Development* [New York: Asia Publishing House, 1962], p. 26; Gustav Ranis, *Industrial Efficiency and Economic Growth: A Case Study of Karachi* [Karachi: Institute of Development Economics, 1961] pp. 33–4).

with all else equal, lower managerial and labor efficiency in unseasoned firms of untried areas can mean a higher rate of substitution of capital for labor than in long-industrialized areas. A small rise in capital from any given total in these cases can remove baffling problems of organization, as already described in Chapter 3, and will therefore release more workers than would be the case at the same wage-capital-cost ratio in a more developed region or accomplished firm. Whatever the ratio, more capital will be used per unit of output than would otherwise be expected.[37]

But in Mexico capital-intensity in this sense (the capital-output ratio) is also raised by another factor which decreases flexibility: Article 128 of the Federal Labor Law. According to this article:

Whenever, due to the installation of machinery or new working processes, the employer must reduce the personnel, the labor contract may be terminated with the surplus workers, to whom he shall pay compensation at the rate of three months' salary plus twenty days' salary for each year's service or the sum stipulated in the labor contract if the latter should be higher.

This indemnity of one-fourth of a year's pay plus one-eighteenth for each year of service is somewhat higher than that due to retrenched workers in India, who are entitled to half a month's earnings (average of the preceding 12 months) for each year (up to 15 years) of continuous service.[38] Adopting

[37] For a diagrammatic analysis, see A. O. Hirschman, *The Strategy of Economic Development* (New Haven: Yale University Press, 1958), pp. 150–51. For an extreme case, see Robert E. Baldwin, "Wage Policy in a Dual Economy—The Case of Northern Rhodesia," *Race*, Nov. 1962, pp. 73–87. Werner Baer and Michel E. A. Hervé have made international comparisons of this effect in terms of installed power capacity per employee in their article, "Employment and Industrialization in Developing Countries," *Quarterly Journal of Economics*, Feb. 1966, pp. 88–107.

[38] Industrial Disputes (Amendment) Act, 1953, cited by Charles A. Myers, "Labor Problems of Rationalization: The Experience of India," *International Labor Review*, May 1956, p. 13.

a different production method, therefore, means not only purchase and installation costs of new equipment, which must be
compared with the maintenance and replacement expenditures
of the old method; it also means a large payment to workers
laid off. In effect, this payment is part of the capital cost of
the proposed change.

The general manager of one foreign subsidiary had a policy
of spending no more than U.S. $5,000 on equipment to replace
an average worker earning U.S. $900 annually including fringe
benefits. If combined amortization and maintenance expenditures are set at rates approximating actual replacement policy,
for example, 5 per cent a year or U.S. $250 in this case, the
return on the investment is U.S. $650 or 13 per cent. This rate
corresponds roughly to the parent company's record in the
United States. But a worker already employed for one year
would be entitled to a U.S. $275 indemnity which would mean
that no more than U.S. $4,725 should then be paid to obtain his
output in the alternative fashion, implying a yield of 13.7 per
cent. The indemnity to a worker employed ten years becomes
U.S. $650. To replace him, no more than U.S. $4,350 will be
left of $5,000 to pay for any installation still assumed to yield
an annual U.S. $650. A 15 per cent rate of return is marginal.

If wages rise at a rate α per year, and the wage bill is W,
after one year, $\dfrac{11 \, x \, W(1+\alpha)}{36}$ must be added to the capital
cost if x is the fraction by which the wage bill will be reduced.
$\left(\dfrac{1}{4}+\dfrac{1}{18}=\dfrac{11}{36}\right)$ After n years, the additional cost becomes
$\dfrac{(9+2n)}{36}$. $[xW(1+\alpha)^n]$. Discounting the future at r, the
present value of the indemnity is $\dfrac{(9+2n)}{36} \cdot \dfrac{xW(1+\alpha)^n}{(1+r)^n}$. To
the extent that it is probable that the investment will be made
in year n and the workers laid off, this term lowers the present

value of the income stream from postponed modernization. Indeed, postponed modernization may never be undertaken unless the market grows enough to allow employment expansion to offset labor-displacing effects of new technology. If the market does not grow, new entrants would have an advantage over established firms. Uncertainty rises, lowering expected returns by some risk factor, and investment will tend to shift away from that industry. The analysis could be refined in various ways to compare time of adoption and yields of alternate methods under conditions of growing markets, various returns to scale, uncertainty, etc. But the main effect of Article 128 is clear. A labor-saving change is likely to be adopted too soon, preferably at once, or too late, perhaps never. Wherever veteran workers cannot be adapted to a feasible electronic installation, an expanding firm is likely to keep museum pieces going in old Plant *Numero Uno*, creaking, clanking, and dripping along with forced philanthropic inefficiency. Such plants exist and so does evasion of Article 128. Executives of sample firms were generally aware of the advantage of hiring as many temporary workers (*eventuales*) as local inspectors and labor leaders would tolerate, dismissing these workers near the end of their 30-day probationary period and then usually rehiring them. But in 1964 a new law gave *eventuales,* if rehired, the same rights as regular workers.

In Puerto Rico, by contrast, labor market imperfections are less varied than in Mexico and most other underdeveloped countries. The island is too small to have much regionalism; all labor relations are marked by the political, social, and economic transformation of the 1940's. Most factories are themselves part of the results of that transformation. Regional and chronological homogeneity, however, merely encourage but do not guarantee wage rates equal to the opportunity costs of labor. Estimating opportunity cost wage rates for Puerto Rico is no easier than figuring out whether or not the labor market extends to the other Antilles and the mainland United States, properly weighted for the elasticity of migration. But what does the persistence of at least 11 per cent known unemployment since 1950 imply? Emigration and manufacturing expansion during 1950–60 were not high enough to reduce unemployment in stagnant agriculture, sugar milling, and home needlework by more than 9,500; that is, from 39,200 to 29,700, or from 45 to 36 per cent of known unemployment.[39] Lower wages in manufacturing might have encouraged both a greater net inflow of capital to, and net outflow of labor from, Puerto Rico.

A quick look at employment and earnings data shows manufacturing wages and salaries rising from 1954 to 1960 in proportion to those of all Commonwealth of Puerto Rico industries: 27 per cent in real terms.[40] But gross hourly earnings of manufacturing production workers are most relevant to rates of capital-labor substitution. In real terms, these rose at more than double the rate of all employee compensation: 58 per cent from 1954 to 1960.[41] Compared with the United States, the absolute differential in hourly earnings of about $1.32 remained stable. But *relatively* during 1954–1959 rates in Fomento-assisted plants rose from 27 to 40 per cent of U.S. levels, yet per capita income had risen to only 23 per cent of the U.S. average.[42] By the time of my original plant studies in July and

[39] Puerto Rico Planning Board, *Economic Report to the Governor: 1960* (San Juan, 1961), pp. A-22, A-23. In mid-1966, 24.3 per cent of the 87,000 unemployed had completed 12 years of schooling or more.

[40] *Ibid.*, pp. A-6, A-9, A-22.

[41] *Ibid.*, p. A-24. A small part of the rise is due to a shift to higher-paying industries.

[42] H. C. Barton and Robert A. Solo, "The Effect of Minimum Wage Laws on the Economic Growth of Puerto Rico" (mimeographed, San Juan, 1959), pp. 36, 41. Fomento is the Economic Development Administration. The Fair Labor Standards Amendments of 1966 did not affect Puerto Rican wage levels as much as had been expected. By April 1968 minimum wages had to be raised by 28 per cent unless the Secretary of Labor accepted lower recommendations by special review committees.

August 1961, hourly earnings in all manufacturing were \$0.980 and in Fomento-promoted or -assisted establishments, \$0.995. This figure matches the average of the sample: exactly \$1.00. By industry, the official averages ranged from \$0.72 hourly in tobacco manufactures to \$1.46 in the combined petroleum, rubber, and miscellaneous plastics industries.[43] Average wage rates of sample firms ranged from \$0.70 to \$1.42. By June 1967, average hourly earnings had risen to \$1.41.[44]

Even with a net 5 per cent of the labor force emigrating every year during the 1950's, rising wages were not due to militant union action. Unions appeared strong primarily in old industries such as sugar where mechanization threatened large cuts in employment. Elsewhere they seemed weak, content to let pressure for higher wages come from Commonwealth and Federal Minimum Wage Boards.

Since 1940 statutory minimum wages in Puerto Rico have varied from industry to industry. In that year the U.S. Fair Labor Standards Act of 1938 was amended with respect to Puerto Rico, the Virgin Islands, and American Samoa. Henceforth tripartite employer-labor-government committees with mainland representation would set minimum wages for each rather narrowly defined industry. Wages were to reach the

---

[43] Commonwealth of Puerto Rico, Bureau of Labor Statistics, *Employment, Hours and Earnings in the Manufacturing Industries of Puerto Rico,* Aug. 1961, p. 7; and "Employment, Hours and Earnings in the Manufacturing Establishments Promoted or Assisted by the Economic Development Administration or the Puerto Rico Industrial Development Company," Aug. 1961, Release E.D.A. 52, p. 3. As defined, hourly earnings partly reflect premium pay for overtime and late-shift work and changes in output of workers paid on an incentive basis. They do not include irregular bonuses, welfare benefits, and certain payroll taxes paid by employers.

[44] *Employment, Hours and Earnings in the Manufacturing Industries of Puerto Rico* (Bureau of Labor Statistics, Commonwealth Department of Labor, Aug. 1967). Meanwhile the consumer price index rose about 18 per cent.

Federal minimum as rapidly as feasible without either "substantially curtailing employment" or giving any Puerto Rican industry "a competitive advantage over any industry in the continental United States." When some mainland industries, particularly apparel, began to be noticeably affected by Puerto Rican competition during the mid-1950's, the industry committees were forced into greater activity that included annual and biennial wage reviews. Few Puerto Rican industries had average wages much above the applicable statutory minimum, and it may be that rising wage levels have turned some mainland companies against investing in Puerto Rico altogether and others toward greater capital intensity.[45]

IV. The Entrepreneur's Response to Factor Prices

The preceding two sections have suggested that market imperfections in underdeveloped countries in practice raise the price of labor and lower the price of capital from levels closely reflecting their scarcity. In new factories it therefore pays to use labor more sparingly and capital more lavishly than is most likely to achieve highest output. In this section we shall see how further distortion comes from the manner in which entrepreneurs respond to the prospect of owning more plant or supervising more workers—a response that can only partly be explained by analysis of payments and yields. Techniques of production will be shown to be still more capital-intensive, but the distortion should not be overstated for, in many plants, technique shows some adjustment to scarce capital and abundant labor.

If the entrepreneur were asked bluntly, "What have you done

[45] Barton and Solo, *op. cit.*, pp. 36–42, estimate that if wage increases had not accelerated, 35,000 to 55,000 additional jobs might have been created in Fomento-promoted plants during 1955–59, and that private investment per worker (stable from 1950–54) might not have doubled as it did.

to substitute labor for capital?" he would probably see little sense in the question and wrongly confess, "nothing." Or he might even demonstrate the contrary with some recently mechanized step in his production line. After all, why should he take United States or European practice as a base from which any departure constitutes "substitution"? He may even be ignorant of practice abroad, except what filters down to him through engineers and machinery sellers. As he might put it, the main question is, "How much volume do I need to amortize the machine?" If volume allows, he will mechanize. Obviously different wages and capital charges would raise or lower the break-even mechanization volume, but to him the local factor-price ratio seems fairly stable. Volume is the unpredictable yet crucial matter.

More serious is that the same approach is used by consulting engineers, including large international firms for whom the factor-price ratio in different countries should be a basic variable. In the usual "feasibility study," markets, material supplies, and transportation costs are thoroughly studied to determine the kind and size of plant needed. Once the general layout is set, its yield is estimated in terms of local capital and labor prices. But these prices do not influence choice of basic design, nor is it customary to allow for effects on costs and output of possible marginal changes. If such changes are introduced, it will usually be after the project has been approved, either in the nature of second thoughts in detail design or of improvisations after startup.

Failure by entrepreneurs to think explicitly in terms of labor-capital costs, however, does open choice to sentiment. Oddly, both entrepreneurial hostility and benevolence toward labor yield the same reaction: mechanization. The hostile entrepreneur sees each worker as a potential troublemaker and wants fewer of them. The benevolent manager does not like to run a sweatshop, exploiting his men's poverty with back-breaking, antiquated methods. The corresponding attitude toward capital is delight in neatly functioning devices and an urge to avoid discouraging and unsettling thoughts about credit, interest, and inflation. A few quotations may illustrate these views.

At a glass bottle factory:

No, I'm a partisan of the most modern machinery. Continued low wages would not make me favor more antiquated equipment.

At a paternalistic cement plant:

What can you do with these people? They cannot plan or make a budget. They wouldn't be unskilled *obreros* if they could. For the same amount of money I would at once replace several of these with one skilled man. Believe me, each unskilled, uneducated worker is a problem.

In the Mexico City offices of a large chemical enterprise:

Any preoccupation about the value of money leads to unrealities because the value of money is itself unstable and unreal. One thing we have learned, and I cannot emphasize it too much. No economies can ever be realized by using *peon* labor.

At a provincial metal-working and assembly plant:

If more money were available, I would not change my recommendations. What counts is our market and the need to amortize equipment. Good projects are proposed regardless of the availability of money. Bad ones don't become good just because money is available.

Yet the byword among entrepreneurs was: "*Menos obreros; menos problemas*" ("Fewer workers; fewer problems").

The stronger the monopolistic or credit position of an enterprise, and the fewer alternatives permitted by technology anyway, the more extravagant were these statements. The extent to which they were sometimes carried out may be suggested by the decision of a steel mill. In order to replace 200 men earning 20 pesos daily (including fringe benefits) for moving material to furnaces, the company spent 15,000,000 pesos on a German

12.5 ton portable crane and on American automatic batchers, dumping cars, and auxiliary equipment. With simultaneous expansion elsewhere, no retrenchment indemnity needed to be paid. In the first year labor costs saved would come to almost 2,000,000 pesos. If money wages should rise at a yearly 5 per cent, an improbably high rate, and if the future were discounted at 15 per cent, then the present value of wages saved in ten years alone would be about 13,000,000 pesos. This amount would still be 2,000,000 pesos less than the proposed capital expenditures. It would be incorrect to add to this 2,000,000 pesos the interest due on the capital. Money could be borrowed to pay now the present value of all the wages that would have to be paid if the workers were not laid off. Only if interest is added to that, cancelling the discounting, can interest also be added to the investment. If the machinery can be bought with lower-interest foreign capital, that is in effect a subsidy which, after allowing for devaluation risks, would lower the handicap of mechanizing. The executive director of the firm thought a 5 per cent increase in output might also make up the difference. Besides, "This was also our greatest source of accidents, which are very expensive. *Menos obreros son menos problemas.* And the jobs we eliminated were, accidents apart, not really fit for human beings, were they?"

Such attitudes are not only widespread but widely encouraged, sometimes by the official publication of the Center of Industrial Productivity:

A sign of progress in our times is the automation of machines, but never can it be the automatization of the worker. To wish to relegate the worker to the inferior condition of supplement to a machine, which makes him like one of its component parts, is to minimize his personality as if one tried to subject him forever to the rhythm and blind force of the machine. . . . Automation of our factories is good. . . . Never should one try to enslave man, subjecting him to an unconscious machine.[46]

[46] *Productividad,* May 1, 1958, p. 9.

Labor intensity can replace cracked gears with broken toes, and short circuits with blindness. Can the choice between these be adequately computed on paper? Can the manager be blamed if he shifts to gears and electromagnets a little too soon and unimaginatively? Who wants to be implicated in bringing tragedy to those already in rags? The rich in poor countries do not enjoy the poverty of the poor. They try to insulate themselves from it both psychologically and physically. They do it with gleaming automatic machines in their factories and with dense walled gardens in their residential districts beyond strolling distance from slums. One cannot easily teach the rich that overmechanization does social damage.

An extreme case of zeal to modernize was the installation of a sizeable computer in the offices of a large beverage maker without any detailed previous estimate having been made of the value of increased services nor of the number of manhours to be saved. The company wished to be the first in Mexico to have one. In spite of extensive complaints about maintenance problems and breakdowns in the sample firms, only one man stressed that fewer machines also meant fewer problems. This man, an immigrant East European engineer, insisted that man was still the cheapest servomechanism.

Suiting techniques to factor prices means not only sacrificing caprice to calculation. If formulas are poor, one may merely replace one kind of distortion with other, perhaps greater, errors. Suppose a commodity has properties of small size or odd shape that physically limit to three the number of men that can work on a unit at a time. Each man performs one or more of twelve operations. If volume justifies specialization, the product moves through four stations, each with three men, and in a larger room. A substitute machine performs all twelve operations in the space of one station. If a new plant is at stake, capital-labor substitution involves a subproblem of equipment-building substitution. Formulas used must give proper weight to the greater durability of buildings, or the only difference the substitution of a dollar of building for a dollar of machine might make could be an increase in labor costs. Investments are commonly judged by the length of the "payoff" period in which outlay will be recovered—usually net of current cost, so that depreciation is lumped with profits as the "net cash flow." This method seriously understates the yield of buildings. Indeed, "net cash flow" ignores durability altogether because higher amortization payments for machines fully compensate for lower profits. Expressed differently, the concept ignores yields after the pay-off period. Unjustified space- and labor-saving automatic equipment can be found in any country, but it is least warranted in underdeveloped ones since buildings can themselves be produced labor-intensively. In both Mexico and Puerto Rico, the rule of thumb for estimates of the price of construction is three-quarters of American costs. The cost of machinery is about double American costs because of transportation and other expenses.

Nevertheless, pay-off period criteria can be modified to make decisions rational.[47] A subsidiary of a foreign chemical manufacturer had taken a step in that direction by using a one-year net cash flow period for traditional items with which the Mexican market was familiar and a five-year period for novel, "growth" products. This firm, one of the largest in the country, was also in the minority in its application of an interest rate to the internal use of its own funds and in its use of the highest rate used by any firm, 12 per cent.

In Puerto Rico, entrepreneurs and managers of only four plants studied said choice of equipment had been influenced by limitations in the absolute availability of capital, regardless of interest rates. Each of these was small and produced for the island market. Only one was a subsidiary of a mainland corporation. Two-thirds of the Mexican entrepreneurs responding

[47] Vernon L Smith, *Investment and Production*, pp. 219–41.

thought different equipment would *not* have been bought if more money could have been borrowed. Of course, lack of funds often led the remaining one-third to do no more than substitute either cheaper European for almost equivalent American equipment or second-hand for new. As Table 7 shows, small and native-owned firms were more affected by interest rates than large or foreign-owned firms.

Thus, in Puerto Rico interest rates were almost universally considered unimportant in the choice of technique. In Mexico, one-third believed interest rates had influenced equipment selection and had in fact incorporated them in preliminary calculations. This one-third was not the same as that influenced by absolute availability. Large firms considerably more often than small ones showed how a substantial rise or fall in the rate of interest might affect calculations in plant design. Table 7

Table 7. Importance of limitations in the absolute availability of capital on the choice of technique as seen by entrepreneurs

Type of firm	Influenced	Did not influence	Undecided or no reply
Small	8	7	2
Medium	6	17	3
Large	5	19	3
U.S. subsidiaries	7	17	4
European subsidiaries	—	2	—
Immigrant	2	6	1
Private national	8	15	3
Public national	2	3	—
Nondurable producers	11	21	3
Durable producers	8	22	5
Nuevo Leon	9	12	4
Central Plateau	6	17	3
Mexico (total)	15	29	7
Puerto Rico	4	14	1
Total	19	43	8

shows, moreover, that interest rates were more important for privately-owned Mexican and immigrant enterprises than for foreign or government-owned firms which had easier access to cheap capital. Apparently the rate of interest plays its small part when access to funds is neither too easy nor impossible.

Only one executive thought he could possibly have reduced costs by using less mechanization and more labor than was the case. On the other hand, 29 per cent thought they could profitably install additional equipment to facilitate the current volume of production. Sixty-two per cent of firms contemplating higher capital intensity in existing product lines thought this might be more economical because of a rising volume of output. Some were seeking improvements in quality, and five thought the investment would have been profitable all along if only capital had been available.

Table 8. The influence of interest rates on the choice of technique of fifty-one Mexican firms as seen by entrepreneurs

Type of firm	Interest rate influenced	Interest rate did not influence	Undecided or no response
Small	2	6	1
Medium	5	12	1
Large	8	13	3
U.S. subsidiaries	3	10	1
European subsidiaries	—	2	—
Immigrant	4	2	2
Private national	8	13	1
Public national	—	4	1
Nondurable producers	6	17	2
Durable producers	9	14	3
Nuevo Leon	9	14	2
Central Plateau	6	17	3
Total	15	31	5

V. Summary

This has been a largely negative chapter. Conditions for an optimum capital-labor intensity could not be stated without straying into a dreamworld of expectations. Yet the motes flawing theory were less than the beams darkening practice. In Mexico and Puerto Rico, capital and labor are used in proportions reflecting imperfect signals, imperfectly applied. Error is in the direction of using capital and labor too little with one another. The sectors with too much of one factor cannot get, or do not seek, enough of the other. But imperfections are not total and perfection is not crucial. Hence, the next chapter can be more positive in its exploration of another capital-labor issue —when can machines best do the work of men?

5

Forms of Labor-Capital
Substitution

Capital-labor substitution follows the spurs of relative scarcity, as felt and understood by entrepreneurs, into grooves made by technology. This chapter is about the grooves available to underdeveloped countries. Not all technological change is taken in: not that aimed at sharply novel products nor at uncommon use of possibly odd materials. Stress is on the employment or dismissal of human beings in production, on the work they can or cannot do—where they alone can serve, where they are powerless, and the range in between. When are factor proportions fixed or variable? And what prevents or allows the variation?

If underdeveloped countries had access to competing manual and machine processes with cost and quality identical at all volumes, little could be said about these alternatives. Section II discusses the case most like it: where quality varies somewhat at given volumes with more or less negligible cost differences. In Section III, the emphasis is reversed and probable economic efficiency of man and machine is compared at given levels of quality. We are not concerned with physical efficiency, the rate of converting material input units into output units.[1] Capital-

---

[1] If half of the input units are wasted in the course of production and if half of the output units are defective, with no use as scrap, then physi-

scarcity makes economic efficiency, reflecting wider social conditions, run counter to physical efficiency in some operations, a contrariety that helps explain the Mexican and Puerto Rican entrepreneurial misconceptions discussed in Chapter 4. But at very low volumes, often neither machines nor workers can be used with either physical or economic efficiency, no matter how high or low a country's degree of development. Section III shows why volume generally favors machines even with high capital-cost-wage ratios; Section IV suggests that modern, labor-intensive, small-scale manufacturing can have only a limited, partly temporary, and relatively late role in economic development.

Much of this chapter is, therefore, concerned with substitutes for high volume—that is, with remedies for low volume as ways of economizing. General remedies such as improving a transportation system to widen markets are helpful, but not within the scope of this book. Instead, Section V recalls that poor countries can effect economies of scale with no change of volume either through less diverse output (standardization) or through more diversely used machine input (multiple purpose machines). Section VI deals with multiple shift working and intensive staffing as ways of raising labor-intensity. Section VII considers the possibility of producing machines in underdeveloped countries. Where metalworking has progressed, machinery production may economize on capital because some machines cannot be mass-produced and could perhaps be redesigned for more labor-intensive use. The summary of the chapter includes findings from the Mexican sample suggesting that only half of the firms (particularly small durable-goods makers) had adjusted noticeably to the lower wage-capital-cost ratio.

------

cal efficiency is one-quarter. A time rate should be added to the concept. Aggregation difficulties limit the usefulness of physical efficiency concepts for economists.

I. Men or Machines?

History moves in the direction of enlarging the power of men with ideas and the physical embodiments of ideas, among them, machines. But when one man's power is enlarged, another is often set adrift until given a new task or machine of his own.

The machine not only supports men's aims and substitutes for unwanted exertion but for a while may run in place of some men who do not wish to be replaced. Their wish may at times be socially justified for, in some cases, machines can mean less total output as well as no tools and no work for many workers. The twentieth-century spread of technology from rich countries with fancy machines to regions of squalor and poverty thus gives rise to some eddies against the main current of history: one may seek to avoid improved machines in order to employ more people.

Where can men hold their own against the historical trend? Where do technical coefficients of production stay nicely variable? It depends mainly on the kind of task and the scale of execution. Moving from the simple to the complex, people can be compared with machines as follows in transport, fabrication, control, transfer of information, analysis, and various other services:

People can move light objects a short distance—a hundred pounds a few hundred yards. People cannot move indivisible tons at high speeds for continental lengths.

With simple hand tools, people can shape and combine materials by striking, cutting, rubbing, squeezing, twisting, and stirring. People cannot attain high precision or uniformity, nor great speed or pressure. They cannot attain anything at all in the presence of boiling temperatures, radiation, or poisonous fumes.

Men can look, feel, listen, smell, and taste in order to inspect, accept, reject, measure, and record. Their speed and accuracy is once more limited. Direct response to changes in voltage, humidity, chemical states, and the like is impossible.

To transfer information, people can file, remember, retrieve, and report. Where simple classification is possible, machines excel in speed and accuracy.

Men still surpass machines in breaking information into components for selective recombination with other data. But machines can assist. If items of data are very numerous yet involve a limited number of clearly defined factors, then programming on a computer may reveal patterns beyond the reach of searchers with desk calculators.

Jumping over a large number of activities where comparisons of man and machine are possible, one comes to the area in which people are hardest to replace, that is, where the impact of one human being on another is the very service wanted. Psychoanalysts, conjurers, athletes, dancers, Geisha girls, masseurs, priests, and legal guardians all play such roles. At this most human level it is doubtful that there have been gains in speed or subtlety since Pericles' Athens, perhaps precisely because improvable machines are least involved. Old poetry compares better with new than do old with new ways of smelting or weaving. Machines serve here only when impersonating the human being for an emotional impact—duplicating his speech or image on printed page, disk, or screen. But just as people cannot personally oxidize metal, create vacuums, or generate electromagnetism, machines cannot give a direct sense of participation in a live performance. In a few centuries most human employment may be here for, like gardenias and roses, workers will be sought not for their tensile strength and caloric potential but for the perfume of their personalities.

Of the six types of activities—clearly an incomplete list—fabrication is at the heart of manufacturing and always connected with transport and control in the plant. Men have performed well as craftsmen, porters, and testers, but only below critical levels of speed, scale, and accuracy. High-speed machines may demand superhuman precision of components and delicacy of control, and the cost of these will often be justified only by that same high speed volume and implied price-elastic demand. Human accuracy falls with speed; machine speed and accuracy are often complementary. Employment of men therefore loses quantitative importance as volume rises, and the capital-labor ratio in production loses responsiveness to relative factor prices. In addition, application of science to a process is more likely to add than to remove conditions of heat, pressure, electromagnetism, or chemical change that are beyond men's direct faculties, thus further limiting capital-labor substitutability.

If there were substitutability, it would help underdeveloped countries mobilize their resources for a better attack on backwardness. But how far can one go in giving up gains from science and possible mass production economies for substitutability? Variability in the possible combinations of capital and labor, though desirable in itself, is usually a sign of backwardness in an industry, of modern science being undigested—of a country that cannot bring the volume of an industry up to the level of applied science, nor science down to the low volume. Such variability is then not good fortune, but merely some balm for a hard lot. Raising output comes ahead of keeping factor variability. Moreover, to increase variability deliberately is probably a less efficient road toward higher output than is research that ignores factor variability. Wherever governments can offset clear maldistributions of income, they should welcome the competition of ever cheaper, perhaps fixed-coefficient, labor-displacing electronic devices that raise net income.

Even textile technology has advanced at a rate that can make methods which are five years old and more labor-intensive (with new machines) relatively unprofitable in spite of low Latin American wages. The Economic Commission for Latin America has compared the performance of mills spinning and weaving a basic cotton fabric (90 cm. wire, 18 count yarn, 20 threads per square cm., warp and weft). Most assumed interest rates were 12 per cent, and hourly wage rates were U.S. $.25 for unskilled workers, $.35 for semiskilled, and $.50 for skilled workers. Levels of technology conforming to 1950, 1960, and 1965 were worked out in detail for plants of optimum size. Table 9 shows what costs and yields would have been if the new machines were depreciated in fifteen years.

Table 9. Relative performance of optimal cotton textile plants with levels of technology corresponding to 1950, 1960, and 1965

Textile plants	Level of technology		
	1950	1960	1965
Annual output of fabric (thousands of meters)	16,833	19,626	21,495
Labor force (three shifts)	668	446	315
Total investment (thousands of dollars)	4,453	5,698	6,508
Investment per employed person (dollars)	6,666	12,687	20,659
Value added annually per unit of investment (dollars)	0.374	0.285	0.254
Profits before taxes @ $.25/meter (thousands of dollars)	716	1,165	1,388
Rate of profit (per cent)	16.1	20.4	21.3
Cost/meter at 12 per cent interest rate (dollars)	.207	.191	.185
Cost/meter at 16 per cent interest rate (dollars)	.218	.202	.198

Source: "Choice of Technologies in the Latin American Textile Industry," Report prepared for the Latin American Symposium of Industrial Development, Santiago, Chile, March 14–25, 1966 (E/CN.12/746), pp. 9, 31, 39, 44.

II. Mechanization and Quality

The possibilities for science and innovation in general are dealt with in Chapter 7. Here we are more concerned with standardization, flexibility, shifts, and other relatively mechanical adaptations that are usually related to questions of volume. But it should be noted in passing that minor capital-labor substitutions for better quality alone, rather than for lower cost, do occur. A more capital-intensive and costly process may be adopted for the sake of slight but profitable improvements in quality and with *no* dramatic change in volume. Experts on steel making, after citing various cases, concluded that: "It therefore appears clear that, in addition to excess capacity due to the need to provide for future expansion, quality considerations may lead to the temporary installation of units which are larger than necessary for the supply of a Latin American market."[2]

A Mexican television tube maker tried using a hand-operated flotation process for covering the phosphorescent screens with lacquer. Impurities and blemishes caused a scrappage rate of 30 per cent, double that found in the company's United States plant. A lacquer sprayer, still labor-intensive but wasteful of lacquer, was then installed, and the scrappage rate fell to 20 per cent. Further lowering of waste by the adoption of an automatic flotation process was thought worthwhile. It is, of course, always necessary to adjust labor incentives to quality, as well as to volume, where defects are important and can easily occur. One must at least be careful about piece rates. Where defects are correctable, as in mechanical assemblies, low-cost labor intensive inspection may, however, offset the unreliability of less automatic processes. In one Mexican plant consulting engineers

[2] *Problems of the Steel Making and Transforming Industries of Latin America* (New York: United Nations, 1958), Vol. I, p. 14.

found the loss from scrapping rejects plus inspection costs less than that of the more reliable machine that management wanted.

Needless to say, there are exceptions to the general problem of inadequate quality arising from inadequate volume. Sometimes high-volume methods make reaching minimum quality harder. Sometimes efficiency is blocked by needless stress on quality. A paper mill near Mexico City used batch instead of higher-volume continuous digestors for pulping bagasse because it allowed easier control of all variables.[3]

Excessive concern for quality may, however, be a habit of rigid management or of workers with a tradition of artistic craftsmanship, which might be needless in, say, a farm implement plant. At other times customers may insist on thin, ringing glass tumblers or producers on conventional appearance of intermediate products. The ragged but adequate "false selvage" (edge) of cloth made with newly-installed shuttleless looms forced one Mexican textile mill to go into shirt production because other shirt makers would not buy the cloth. The problem is not unique with underdeveloped countries. In the early 1950's British machine tool makers had to be urged "to educate customers in general to judge machine tools on performance, not on appearance." There was too much inspection, too much finish, too little use of easily-machined cast iron, and tolerances were not the broadest possible "commensurate with correct functioning."[4] Quality standards tend to be lower for commodities novel to an economy and higher for those that are well-known.

[3] Dante Sandro Cusi, "New Bagasse Process," *Pulp and Paper International,* March 1959, pp. 46–7.

[4] Anglo-American Council on Productivity, "Simplification in British Industry," Productivity Report No. 21 (London, 1953), cited by Seymour Melman, "Aspects of the Design of Machinery Production during Economic Development," Background Paper No. 14, U.N. Seminar on Industrial Programming, São Paulo, Feb. 1963, p. 6.

The interrelation between quality standards, novelty, labor scarcity, and volume can even be found in the early Middle Ages. As summarized by A. Rupert Hall:

The close of the so-called Dark Ages found them already master of such simple but crucial inventions as the horse-collar, the flail, and the crank. . . . In a sense the very crudity of European manufacture created the opportunity for technological innovation, the same opportunity for the multiplication of serviceable, unpretentious articles that this country enjoyed in the eighteenth and early nineteenth centuries. While Europe was so long inferior to the East in the more subtle handicrafts—sericulture and figured weaving, the blending of steel, the glazing of faience, . . . nevertheless it was running ahead in methods of basic production. The East continued to excel and even to advance further in those difficult manufactures which of necessity could only be produced by a few rare craftsmen; the West was pushing ahead with manufactures that lent themselves to quantity production. . . . As a consequence when the more artistic crafts did begin to flourish in Europe from the fourteenth century onwards, these were too practiced on a relatively large scale . . . tinged by the notion of quantity production.[5]

III. Volume

That volume and economies of scale bring about substitution of capital for labor is highly significant for capital-poor countries. But why should economies of scale be more closely associated with capital? The answer involves some engineering technicalities that apply to rich and poor countries alike and that must be spelled out at some length. To say that capital is a fixed and labor a variable factor of production—that is, as output rises, one remains a constant and the other a growing expenditure—both begs the question and says nothing about the long run when fixed costs become variable. Even in the

[5] A. Rupert Hall, "The Changing Technical Act," *Technology and Culture,* Fall 1962, pp. 505–6.

short run, only the physical stocks of capital are fixed, while intensity of use is, in terms of machine hours and speed, often variable. For those capital goods that are practically indestructible, measurement of intensity of use or volume of input can seldom be made other than in terms of units of output, which obviously leaves input-output production functions rather denuded of meaning. Hence:

The distinguishing characteristic of capital goods is simply that their *presence*, in the form of physical stocks, is required if production is to take place. . . . Furthermore, the level of output that can be produced varies directly with the physical quantities of such inputs that are present when production takes place. Such inputs are not 'consumed' in any sense similar to the consumption of raw materials or energy.[6]

Why then does the physical presence of capital goods tend to rise with the volume of output, but usually less than proportionately, though more than any rise in the number of workers? Why do the labor-capital and capital-output ratios both tend to fall with volume? The incompatibility of speed and accuracy in human workers by contrast with machines has already been noted. But volume does not depend on speed. One can buy either faster equipment or duplicate slow facilities. Why should duplicate facilities for a given volume both cost more and employ more (hence be less economical) than a single larger unit?

For homogeneous materials flowing through tubes or cooking in spheres or cylinders, much can be explained with geometry. Volume of output may literally depend on the geometric volume of equipment, but cost of equipment depends more on the surface area in terms of the materials needed to enclose the

[6] Vernon L. Smith, *Investment and Production* (Cambridge: Harvard University Press, 1961), pp. 64–5. If workers could be bought like machines, instead of being hired by time periods, the same analysis would apply, as Smith notes.

volume. The area of a sphere varies with volume to the 2/3 power, and so does the area of a cylinder if volume is changed by varying the diameter only. If the length of a cylinder alone is changed, area varies as volume to the .5 power. Hence the engineers' average ".6 rule" that the ratio of capital costs, K_1 and K_2, varies with the ratio of capacities, V_1 and V_2, raised to the .6 power.[7]

$$\frac{K_1}{K_2} = \left(\frac{V_1}{V_2}\right)^{.6}$$

The principle of the case may be applied in other areas if there is something about raising the volume of non-chemical processes—metalworking, electronic assembly, printing, etc.— that makes similar geometry applicable. A common feature of the mixing, flowing, cooking, filtering, chemical-type process is that the material treated is at all times in touch with treating equipment. Likewise major units of equipment are not left idle for long, nor are they used intermittently. Machine and material are joined until the chosen transformation is complete. By contrast, chemical workers may only intermittently take part in production; the rest of the time they check schedules, inspect control equipment, replace worn parts, and wait.

Only at extremely low volumes are these roles turned about. The pharmacist filling an unusual prescription may in turn select, grind, weigh, mix, heat, and stir, each time briefly using a different implement until the bottle is labeled. The worker is busy all the time and involved with the goods-in-process; tools are used intermittently. If he had to fill several like prescrip-

---

[7] For an extended analysis, see Hollis B. Chenery, "Process and Production Functions from Engineering Data," in Wassily Leontief *et al., Studies in the Structure of the American Economy* (New York: Oxford University Press, 1953); Leontief, "Engineering Production Functions," *Quarterly Journal of Economics,* Nov. 1949, pp. 507–31; Frederick T. Moore, "Economies of Scale: Some Statistical Evidence," *Quarterly Journal of Economics,* May 1959, pp. 232–45; and V. L. Smith, *op. cit.,* pp. 17–61.

tions at a time, the pharmacist might specialize sequentially by doing all the grinding at once, then all the weighing, etc. He would thus use a batch-type operation that would provide economies of scale in the use of labor. To the extent that the tools are seldom used, their elaboration is also less urgent. If they can easily be used a few minutes longer, doubling total time, why strain to double yield of any one tool per minute? Not that improvements are to be avoided, but, rather, that little is gained from them. No severe bottlenecks are likely to develop as targets for innovation. No change in one stage will put much pressure on others.[8]

It is important to note that at extremely low volumes even chemical processes lose their material-machine contact, the prerequisite to scale economies of the geometric ".6 rule" family. If chemicals can lose them at low volumes, do other products gain them at high volumes? Of course, "volume" must in this context be thought of as neither value nor tonnage but as the number of discrete units. This number is virtually infinite for liquids and fine powders: each physical unit is infinitesimal. Comparatively low weights can be made to stream through equipment without pause. The same flowing, unbroken machine-material contiguity is reached in other industries when the discrete unit becomes a minute fraction of daily output. In this case, all operations can go on continually, with slow and fast branches suitably balanced, with no variable breaks for handling and setting

---

[8] Edward Ames and Nathan Rosenberg define a skillful machine or worker as one that carries out many different activities and a specialized unit as one that carries out few, perhaps only one. They suggest that "technological change has made men more specialized and machines more skillful." Yet technological change may itself be induced by any growth in volume that encourages use of more integrated but already known methods (*The Progressive Division and Specialization of Industries* [Purdue University, Institute for Quantitative Research in Economics and Management, Paper No. 39, 1963], pp. 4–7, 27, reprinted in *Journal of Development Studies,* July 1965, pp. 363–83).

up, but with handling a built-in drift or quick indexing, and with setups changed by automatic valve-like controls, and with the main tasks run off in rotary form. After liquids and powders, strands and sheets are most simple and homogeneous. Hence thread, wire, cloth, paper, and galvanized steel sheets were early objects of continuous flow, rotary, winding treatment. A host of tiny, spiraled screws were the product of the first automatic, multiple-spindle lathes. City-block-long automated transfer machines for shaping engines were developed half a century later. Writing moved from hand lettering to stamping to whirling rolls of print photographically engraved, a method transferrable to decorating cloth and to electronic circuitry.

Exponential scale-rules will not apply to every phase of every continuous-flow process, but they do fit piston cylinders, pneumatic air hoses, paint and oil dispensers, drums of parts-in-process, cooling pipes, and other components including the factory building itself. The cost-capacity ratio need not fall without discontinuities, however. There will be kinks whenever capacity grows beyond the availability of standard sizes and beyond the stress limits of cheaper materials and construction methods.[9]

[9] Moore, *op. cit.*, p. 235. The study of production functions fitting the manufacture of complex products in multiphase processes has not gone as far as that of petroleum and gas transmission, aluminum reduction, cement making, and a variety of chemical processes. Studies of metalworking have been supported by the RAND Corporation and the Stanford Project for Quantitative Research in Economic Development. See H. Markowitz and A. Rowe, "An Analysis of Machine Tool Substitution Possibilities," RM-1412 RAND Santa Monica 1955, revised in A. S. Manne and H. A. Markowitz, eds., *Studies in Process Analysis* (New York: Wiley, 1963). Other studies in this book concern petroleum, chemicals, agriculture, and steels. Also see H. B. Chenery, "Capital-Labor Substitution in Metalworking Processes," Memorandum No. C-3, Stanford Project for Quantitative Research in Economic Development, Feb. 1957, mimeographed; and Mordecai Kurz and A. S. Manne, "Engineering Estimates of Capital-Labor Substitution in Metal Machining," *American Economic Review*, Sept. 1963, pp. 662–81. It is by no means certain that engineering data will

Capital-labor substitution is also encouraged by volume because volume solves machine coordination problems but labor coordination becomes more snarled as workers proliferate. The manager who can see all his workers from a desk on the production floor and who can readily crack a joke or give a command at least does not have to hire a management consultant to coordinate his coordinators. On the other hand, machines are perfectly coordinated only when output reaches the least common multiple of the lowest cost volumes of the component processes. At any lower volume one or a few components would run at more than minimum cost, most likely with overcapacity.[10]

These interrelations among machines are like "pecuniary" (appropriable) external economies among plants.[11] Lack of volume indeed prevented gains from external economies in Mexico by checking internal economies. Metal fabricators complained about the large volumes (a year's supply) they had to buy at one time from local steel mills, but the steel mills still found production runs too short and demand too unpredictable. Metal fabricators claimed that the crystalline structure of local steel was poor and often one-eighth of an inch off tol-

---

ultimately be more convenient and reliable in synthesizing production functions with predictive power than more aggregative models that boldly assume competitive equilibrium wages.

[10] The higher the wage level, the more excess capacity will be preferred to the substitution of labor for capital. According to a British productivity team, load factors as low as 15 per cent were sometimes thought high enough to keep a specialized line of machine tools set up in the United States (Anglo-American Council on Productivity, *Metalworking Machine Tools* [report of a visit to the United States during 1951], p. 24, cited by David Granick, "Economic Development and Productivity Analysis: The Case of Soviet Metalworking," *Quarterly Journal of Economics*, May 1957, p. 219).

[11] Tibor Scitovsky, "Two Concepts of External Economies," *Journal of Political Economy*, April 1954, pp. 143–51. For comments by J. A. Stockfisch and a reply by Scitovsky, see *Journal of Political Economy*, Oct. 1955. Also see H. W. Arndt, "External Economies in Economic Growth," *The Economic Record*, 1955, pp. 192–214.

erance. They needed hydraulic straightening presses and planers for correcting these deviations. Moreover, they had annoying problems selling shavings back to steel mills as scrap. High-grade alloy shavings were the least valuable. Steel mill officials countered that, even without sorting out shavings, the fact that they had to buy scrap of tin cans mixed in with auto parts was an irritating handicap. Demand for special steels was too low to make their production and prior sorting of scrap worthwhile.

Geometric scale economies, coordination problems and opportunities, and a high capital-labor cost ratio would therefore tend to make very capital-intensive and very labor-intensive techniques run side by side in underdeveloped countries even if science did not bar labor-capital substitution in some, but not all, operations, and even if there were no capital and labor market imperfections. The bent toward technological diversity may also be strengthened by demand patterns that encourage independent small-scale production of both luxury models and inferior substitutes for "standard products," demand patterns that even in advanced countries allow great dispersion of viable plant sizes.[12]

The bearing on technological choice of factor costs *and* volume clears up a number of paradoxes within plants and between large and small firms. Within plants it is not only men's better physical capacity for competing with auxiliary processes but the lower volume of discrete units that keeps these steps less mechanized. Packaging is an example. Millions of chemical grains are stamped into thousands of pills for dozens of bottles to fill a couple of cartons. The high-volume stamping is

[12] Stanislaw H. Wellisz, "The Coexistence of Large and Small Firms: A Study of the Italian Mechanical Industries," *Quarterly Journal of Economics*, Feb. 1957, pp. 116–31. Wellisz defines inferior substitutes "as goods which have a lower initial price than the 'standard' products, but which over their lifetime have a higher cost per unit service." See also T. R. Saving, "Estimation of Optimum Size of Plant by the Survivor Technique," *Quarterly Journal of Economics*, Nov. 1961, pp. 569–607.

apt to be wholly automatic; the final carton packing a hand operation; and the bottle filling in between semiautomatic, with the right number of pills going in through a weighing device, the cotton with human fingers, and the top laid on by hand and tightened by machine.

In both Mexican and Puerto Rican glass factories visited, the mechanism for stacking hot, newly-molded bottles onto a conveyor going into a cooling oven was often out of order. In Mexico, two men with tongs were always on hand to supplement the machine. In Puerto Rico, where wages were about four times as high, such stand-bys were uneconomical and the glowing bottles went down a reject chute until the mechanism was replaced or repaired. By contrast, the volume of a Mexico City bakery was large enough to allow continuous cooling of bread on a conveyor belt leading to packing machines, but a much smaller San Juan bakery used stationary hand-loaded and -unloaded cooling racks. Compared with American practice, auxiliary processes (conveying, inspecting, packaging, and handling in storage) were modified in 53 per cent of the Puerto Rican plants studied and in 70 per cent of the Mexican plants. In about half of the remaining Mexican plants, technical considerations ruled out less capital-intensive alternatives. But as one manager put it, "We have no fear of installing the most modern instrumented equipment that has been fully proven abroad—by that I mean operating there for four years in a size of interest to us." The eleven Puerto Rican firms producing for export, mainly to the United States, were set up on a scale comparable to their mainland counterparts. Hence volume would not cause a relative change in the technology of basic or auxiliary processes.[13]

Volume can explain contrasting levels of modernity, not only

[13] Granick, "Economic Development and Productivity Analysis: The Case of Soviet Metalworking," *op. cit.*, pp. 220–25, wrote the pioneering analysis that turned the attention of economists in this direction.

for different processes within plants, but also for the same process among large and small firms, and firms in different industries. Included in the pioneering studies of *Alternative Techniques of Production* made by G. K. Boon and others at the Netherlands Economic Institute are three which compare (1) hand files with small electric grinders; (2) center, turret, and automatic lathes; and (3) production of wooden window frames with planing and moulding or tenoning processes.[14] The relation between cost and volume is determined for a hypothetical "developed country" (interest rate 4 per cent, wages 0.50 to 2.00 guilders) and an "underdeveloped country" (interest rates 8 to 15 per cent, wages 0.20 to 0.50 guilders). Where the most contrasting factor-price ratios were used, it nevertheless paid the developed country to use the most labor-intensive methods for low production runs. The underdeveloped country would use these roughly five times as long. It would adopt the most capital-intensive automatic lathes at 1.7 times the volume of the developed country and the most automatic window-making equipment at 9.4 times the volume for tenoning processes and 14.8 times for planing and moulding.

Thus, scale effects offset the seesaw inversion of wage levels and capital scarcity. Short production runs may also keep workers low on the learning curve. At one-tenth the wage level and one-hundredth the volume, an American subsidiary making electric products in Mexico found that labor costs were the

[14] *Alternative Techniques of Production*, Progress Reports 1, 2, and 4 (Rotterdam and Delft: Netherlands Economic Institute and Research Institute for Management Science, 1957 and 1959). Some of the findings are reported in G. K. Boon, "Choice of Industrial Technology: The Case of Wood-working," *Industrialization and Productivity*, March 1960, pp. 25–31. Further interesting calculations by Boon based on detailed estimates of effects of lot size on setup time, hand time, and machine time for various processes, appear in his *Economic Choice of Human and Physical Factors in Production* (Amsterdam: North Holland Publishing Co., 1964).

same fraction in both countries, about 13 per cent. A plastic products maker figured that much lower interest rates would not affect his capital intensity directly. But he thought it could lower costs of warehousing and permit him to extend more credit, perhaps greatly increasing volume and, therefore, allowing more mechanization. Most astonishing was the sight of three massive tape-controlled embroidery machines, lonesome and overpowering like generators in an electric power station, each with thousands of marching needles stitching out designs in a cold and implacable way, hurried by a complexity of clicking levers and hydraulic devices. The $70,000 machines and 65 attendants in effect replaced 6,300 women working ten-hour shifts, straining their eyes, discussing family affairs, their pittance wages owed for last week's *tortilla* dough.

IV. Small-Scale Industry

Of special interest are the techniques used by small factories employing, perhaps, 20 to 49 workers, that manage to coexist in many countries with firms twenty times as large but, due to stronger unions and discriminatory government policies, often paying wages twice as high. Inspired by Japanese practice, some economists have wondered if small firms do not hold the key to industrialization for poor, densely populated countries. In Japan the share of the manufacturing labor force employed by firms with 6 to 49 workers rose more or less steadily from 14.5 per cent in 1920 to 40.6 per cent in 1955.[15] If small firms did not exactly flourish, except those few that grew out of the

[15] Teijiro Uyeda, *The Small Industries of Japan* (Shanghai: Kelley and Walsh, 1939), p. 8; Economic Planning Board, "Statistical Analysis of Medium and Small Enterprises in Japan," *Asian Affairs*, June 1957, p. 207, both cited by Bert F. Hoselitz, "Small Industry in Underdeveloped Countries," *Journal of Economic History*, Dec. 1959, p. 602. The 1955 figures include firms with four and five workers.

category, at least they met various needs well enough to proliferate. In 1954 they made all toys and sewing needles, 96 per cent of knitted underwear, 87 per cent of household utensils, 74 per cent of bicycle parts, and 55 per cent of optical glass.[16] Dozens of other industries were also in this 50 to 100 per cent range. Wages lower by half[17] and organizational advantages for supervising labor-intensive production allowed small plants to complement and to keep pace with some large factories and even to outcompete others elsewhere, though of course not in continuous-process industries such as cement, steel, caustic soda, and automobile assembly. But trends in the last decade have favored larger-scale production to the point of inspiring protective legislation for small enterprises.[18] A group of small-scale industry experts from thirteen nations visited Japan under United Nations sponsorship in 1954 and found the following pattern in choice of technique:

In cases where there is little or no competition with large-scale industry and where items are either not within the province of this industry or are manufactured in inadequate quantities for domestic or foreign markets, the manufacturing methods adopted are mostly manual, with some exceptions where mechanization has a direct bearing on the quality of the product or on any of its stages of production. Pottery articles, such as decorated art-wear, are manufactured by hand with simple appliances and tools. For bicycle parts, on the other hand, every labor-saving device is employed, first because this yields better and larger production and helps to keep

[16] Ministry of International Trade and Industry, *Vital Statistics of Production, 1955,* cited by Toyoroku Ando, "Interrelations between Large and Small Enterprises in Japan," *Industrialization and Productivity,* March 1959, p. 29.

[17] See note 36, preceding chapter.

[18] Ando, *op. cit.,* p. 31. A Smaller Enterprise Organization Law was passed as early as 1957 restricting entry into industries and encouraging cartelization within them.

costs down, and also because the operations involved are such that they have to be mechanized.[19]

As important as the choice of technique, however, is the modern setting in which small-scale Japanese industry moves. Electric power is cheap; the transportation network is good; and access to auxiliary services, such as sizing, dyeing, mercerizing, electroplating, and case hardening, is convenient. Efficient, above all, are the dependable interrelations among contracting, subcontracting, and sub-subcontracting firms and the meeting of quality standards and of delivery schedules. Perhaps this disciplined coordination is a unique survival of a preindustrial hierarchical social pattern, the *oyabun-kibun,* or "boss-henchman," system with its deeply conditioned feelings of mutual obligation.[20] It is worth noting, too, that modern subcontracting and the great rise of Japanese small enterprises (in contrast with dwarfs employing five or less) came *after* the mid-1920's. Perhaps that crucial dependability was in part a *product* of industrialization, of what Veblen called "the cultural incidence of the machine process."

Premature copying of labor-intensive, small-scale subcontracting may therefore not be as efficient around the Caribbean Sea and the Indian Ocean as in Japan. Backward economies lack managerial skill and reliability more than capital. In India the productivity of labor *and* capital rises with size in almost all industrial branches.[21] Dhar and Lydall found that the common

[19] Economic Commission for Asia and the Far East, Committee on Industry and Trade, "Report of the Study Group of Small-Scale Industry Experts on their Visit to Japan" (E/CN.11/I & T/108), Feb. 1955; mimeographed); quotation from excerpt reprinted in *Industrialization and Productivity,* March 1959, p. 39.

[20] Hoselitz, *op. cit.,* pp. 606–7, and sources cited there.

[21] P. N. Dhar and H. F. Lydall, *The Role of Small Enterprises in Indian Economic Development* (New York: Asia Publishing House, 1962), pp. 14–16. See also George Rosen, *Industrial Change in India* (Glencoe: Free Press, 1958), pp. 184–202.

facility workshops for electroplating, casting, forging, etc., which had been set up by the Central Small Industries Organization, were working far below capacity. Indeed they were shifting away from subcontracting to other kinds of production and training—also with limited success. The surgical instruments center planned for Bombay was thought "especially dubious." This center was to punch the blanks for small firms to shape. The pieces would then return to the center for hardening and tempering, and go back again to small workshops for finishing touches.[22] Even in Japan, efficiency approaches American standards only in capital-intensive, continuous-process industries such as steel and petroleum.[23]

Nowhere should one plan for much of a role for dwarf-sized manufacturing shops employing six or fewer workers, usually handicraft and cottage industries. In contrast with the share of other small firms in Japan, their share of the labor force fell

[22] *Ibid.*, pp. 68–9. However, the Dutch introduced common facility workshops, *Centraals*, with considerable success in what later became Indonesia. Inexorable targets made reliance on subcontractors too risky in the Soviet Union. Industrial employment in small-scale plants fell from 45 per cent in 1927–28 to 8 per cent in 1933, an absolute decline to one-third. (David Granick, "Organization and Technology in Soviet Metalworking: Some Conditioning Factors," *American Economic Review*, May 1957, pp. 631–42; Adam Kaufman, *Small-scale Industry in the Soviet Union*, N.B.E.R. Occasional Paper No. 80 [New York: National Bureau of Economic Research, 1962]).

[23] On the whole Japanese manufacturing efficiency appears to be around one-third that of the United States (Kenneth Arrow, Hollis Chenery, B. S. Minhas, and Robert Solow, "Capital-Labor Substitution and Economic Efficiency," *Review of Economics and Statistics*, Aug. 1961, pp. 242–3). The authors present evidence of internationally constant elasticities of substitution of capital for labor in a substantial number of industries. The capital-labor ratios at which two countries produce may be different but nevertheless on similarly shaped equal-product curves. One can then measure how far the two curves are apart as an estimate of what yields would be if capital-labor ratios in both countries were the same. The authors suggest that differences in raw material endowment may explain much of the gap in capital-labor productivity.

from 55.6 per cent in 1920 to 23.5 per cent by 1939. Labor productivity in 1950 (one to three workers) was half that of other small firms (four to forty-nine workers) and one-third that of the industrial average.[24] The dwarf shops appear too small, with products too traditional or horizons too limited, to apply many conveniences as simple as hand-spun turntables for quickly painting round objects with a steadily held brush, stencils for painting others, and innumerable similar tricks.

V. Standardization and Machine Flexibility

The restraining effects of low volume can sometimes be attacked directly. Economies of scale can be had with output unchanged per plant if there is either less diversity in products made (standardization) or more diversity in machine use so that each machine serves more than one purpose and is, therefore, more fully employed at low volumes. One may redesign products or processes, or both; the aim is to move toward simple-component objects made in well-defined phases. In a particular industry can components be simplified, perhaps along modular principles, for easy rearrangement to make a variety of products? Complex, many-phase processes may be simplified so that some machines are eliminated and others serve in a multiple capacity. Carving chessmen out of wood is to make six types of units with dozens of different cutting operations. Molding them in plastic, however, lets a single pressing machine treat the pieces alike in one process, interrupted by an occasional mold change.[25]

[24] Hoselitz, *op. cit.*, pp. 602, 604, 611–12. See also P. N. Dhar, *Small-Scale Industries in Delhi* (Bombay: Asia Publishing House, 1958) and K. Prasad, *Technological Choice under Developmental Planning—a Case Study of the Small Industries of India* (Bombay: Popular Prakashan, 1963). The 1950 figure applies to firms with one to three workers only.

[25] Dies and molding machines may have to be imported. Their production like the cutting of lumber and making of plastic could be analyzed

Bold attempts at standardization are nevertheless rare. As a warning to others, a Corning-associated factory in Mexico that tried to make glass tumblers with month-long production runs failed. The plant was sold to the competing Vidriera Monterrey that could make twenty times as many designs with its novel tumbler machine.[26] The manager of an electric appliance-making subsidiary granted that product design research combined with market research was sorely needed. "We're willing to change from eighteen to five cubic foot refrigerators, all right. But not if we have to reinvent the wheel."

Considerable progress occurred, however, in the use of both components and designs of electronic circuits, due primarily to the ease with which any component maker could get "the border closed" against competition. One assembler was making loudspeakers, tuners, deflection yokes, and flybacks for the whole industry while buying tubes and motors from other firms. The first manufacturer of a component could usually count on such government cooperation as withholding licenses for production from possible competitors. Nor would import licenses for similar components, if sought by other assemblers, often be

---

as an earlier process with its own economies of scale, perhaps attained through selling to more widely dispersed and diversified customers. The implied process of "vertical disintegration" was analyzed by George Stigler in "The Division of Labor is Limited by the Extent of the Market," *Journal of Political Economy*, June 1951, pp. 185–92. For an interesting elaboration, see Harvey Leibenstein, *Economic Theory and Organizational Analysis* (New York: Harper, 1960), pp. 111–15. For a discussion of the procedures of standardization at both the national and plant levels, see *Industrial Standardization in Developing Countries* (New York: United Nations Center for Industrial Development, 1964), ST/CID/2.

[26] As in other failures, choice of technique was not the sole cause but reinforced a number of other management difficulties. At one point one of the leading Mexican stockholders was able to force Corning out but was then forced out of control himself by others who invited Corning back.

granted without the new manufacturer's approval. Price and quality disputes were settled by the Ministry of Industry and Commerce. In one extreme case, all assemblers suspended phonograph production, forcing a presumably offensive, and perhaps incompetent, maker of small motors into bankruptcy. A European firm with several Mexican branches threatened to reverse its investment plans for a new plant if circuits had to be redesigned to conform to usual American standards. It found that the government was in a position to reverse its policy on enough matters affecting the firm's other operations to make circuit redesign the lesser of evils.

A similar process of partial standardization under the import-substituting "Mexicanization" program took place in automotive assembly. One assembler was persuaded to specify only one type of battery for his production instead of three as before. But another assembler stated that local parts were incorporated only if they could be used or modified without radically changing the design. Even then, nothing could be done without approval from Detroit, usually granted with reluctance. Nationally-owned vehicle makers were under no such restriction even if largely managed by foreigners, often under private technical assistance contracts. The technical director of a plant making five hundred trucks and buses a year had previously managed an American machinery and implement subsidiary. As he put it, "You make the design fit the tools you have. When I buy new tools I never calculate labor costs and all that for one process or another. I just let experience be my guide about when to mechanize. Of course, we buy nothing but standard equipment. And we don't really have a manufacturing plant here. It's just a big shop. We do practically everything by hand."

No visitor to this plant could be concerned about excessive capital intensity. The sheet metal for truck cabs and hoods was ironed over forms, a crowd of workers around each piece, clanking, banging, and buzzing. It was like a somewhat electrified medieval armory or the workshop of Santa Claus. Die making was simplified for the kinds of labor and machine tools available. Unlike American practice, three pieces would be machined separately and then bolted to a plate to make a single die. Forging took place with several blows of a 1,200-pound hammer instead of one blow with an 8,000-pound hammer. There was not even a multiple-spindle drill. Pieces needing several identical holes were moved around by hand to get each hole drilled separately by a single spindle. But would a larger volume necessarily mean multiple-spindle drills? The next step might be a turret drill press that allows faster shifting from one size drill to another and faster manual shifting of the drilled piece by means of templates marked with grooves colored differently for each size of hole.

In many ways this truck and bus plant illustrates redesign of *process* more than redesign and standardization of *products*. As volume grows, there is often a shift from multipurpose to single-purpose equipment and then back to multipurpose. But the multiple purposes of the first and last stage are not alike. At first a machine must participate in the making of different products or in making more than one phase of a single product. If the products and phases are standardized, then the machine needs to be less adaptable and the workers less skilled at adapting it. In the last stage of machine development, multiple purpose means the integration of several processes, often their simultaneous execution, for making a single product. By contrast with the first stage, the many purposes of the last stage involve no repeated shifting and adapting. Its many functions do not change because they are subordinated to a large volume of a complex specialty.

At in-between volumes, machines have a single purpose in terms of both activity and product, and so do workers.[27] United

[27] See note 7, above.

Nations small-scale industry experts found a great contrast in this sort of operation between Japan and Southeast Asia:

The most striking feature of production techniques in Japan is, however, the use of a single-purpose machine for any specific operation. This not only saves considerable time which would be required in changing tools, dies and fixtures on multiple-purpose machines, but also ensures better and larger production. In the other countries of the region, however, the tendency is to use one machine for multiple-purpose operation; it would be to their advantage to follow instead the pattern adopted in Japan. The total capital investment for installing a large number of single-purpose machines need not be more than that for fewer multiple-purpose machines. In fact, it is less expensive to install single purpose machines for a given job. Moreover, they are easy to handle, repair and maintain locally, and their total consumption of power is considerably lower.[28]

First-stage multipurpose equipment, as the quotation implies, may be more than hand tools or general purpose standard equipment. The flexibility-giving features of the turret drill press mentioned above raises its price from $35,000 to $40,000, many times that of most ordinary single- and multiple-spindle drill presses. Multiple-purpose dies need features that allow disassembly and recombination. One Mexican metal furniture maker paid 12 per cent more for a 600-ton press to get a special table and air cushion attached. These allowed use of the press for making small items like pots, pans, and window frames when furniture sales lagged. "Universal" lightbulb-making machines that can make bulbs of various sizes and with different filaments are more complicated than single-purpose machines. In many cases the higher expense and complexity

[28] "Organization and Operation of Cottage and Small Industries," *Industrialization and Productivity*, March 1959, pp. 39–40. The same strategy was Soviet policy during the First Five Year Plan and then relaxed for greater flexibility during the Second Five Year Plan (David Granick, "On Patterns of Technological Choice in Soviet Industry," *American Economic Review*, May 1962, p. 155).

is a substitution of capital for even scarcer labor skills through mechanisms that guide the shift from one use to another. This form of substitution was approved at the São Paulo meeting on steel making and fabricating:

The meeting showed that, although at first sight the adoption of more mechanized equipment in Latin America would appear to be inconsistent, since it would involve substitution of cheap and abundant labor by capital, it appears to be necessary because of the shortage of skilled labor required for the operation of more simple machines. On the basis of this assertion, and those mentioned earlier, it may be stated that the center lathe, for instance, is an obsolete machine in so far as production operations are concerned not only in more industrialized areas, but also in Latin America and that the transformation of universal machines by the use of hydraulic tracer attachments is a most satisfactory solution. The advantages of the tracer lathe lie in the rapidity of setting up, precision, the use of simple tools of more or less standard design, and its great versatility. These comments are also applicable to other machine tools such as boring lathes, facing lathes, milling machines, special grinders and planers.[29]

One-tenth of the Mexican and Puerto Rican firms studied used multipurpose equipment that would be unusual in the equivalent American plant. Another four-tenths used standard equipment for more than one phase of production, often at the expense of continuous-flow layouts. It is not surprising that chemical plants were not among this four-tenths. In Table 10, large firms seem to be more adaptive than small, partly because the more machinery a plant has, the more likely some of it will be multiple purpose in design or use. Since workers can almost always be shifted from one use to another, the flexibility of more labor-intensive small firms appears slighted. Even one medium-sized firm had abandoned mechanical decorating of

[29] Problems of the Steel Making and Transforming Industries of Latin America (New York: United Nations, 1958), Vol. I, p. 19.

Table 10. Flexibility in equipment (seventy Mexican and
Puerto Rican manufacturing plants)

Size, ownership, and location	A Multiple use of standard equipment only	B Special multi-purpose equipment	A + B	C No special emphasis on equipment flexibility
Small	8	—	8	9
Medium	8	2	10	15
Large	11	5	16	12
U.S. subsidiaries	10	3	13	15
European subsidiaries	—	—	—	2
Immigrant	5	1	6	3
Private national	11	3	4	12
Public national	1	—	1	4
Nondurable producers	12	5	17	19
Durable producers	15	2	17	17
Nuevo Leon	10	2	12	13
Central Plateau	11	4	15	11
Mexico (total)	21	6	27	24
Puerto Rico	6	1	7	12
Total	27	7	34	36

ceramics because the flexibility of using hand stencils allowed
an increase in variety and, therefore, revenue that offset higher
cost. Six of the seven Puerto Rican firms that had greater equipment flexibility than is typical in the United States produced
for the island market.

VI. *Intensive Staffing and Multiple Shifts*

Adding workers to given machines, instead of buying more
equipment, is one of the simplest and oldest forms of labor-
capital substitution. More intensive staffing crowds additional
workers around the machines; multiple shifts add time for them

at night; and greater maintenance adds time by extending machine lives.

More intensive staffing can add time, eliminating interruptions for meals and other reasons during regular working hours. Output from hand-fed machines may rise by 30 to 60 per cent after adding 30 to 50 per cent more workers. Roughly 30 per cent seems to be the limit for raising both output and employment in semiautomatic operations.[30]

An early example of intensive staffing was reported by the Indian Factory Labor Commission in 1908. An expert compared the staff of a cotton mill in Madras using 35,000 ring spindles, and 800 looms, which worked 67.5 hours a week, with the staff of a mill in Lancashire which worked 54.5 hours. Table 11 shows the way labor was deployed in the two plants' twelve divisions.

Twenty-one per cent, or 548 workers, in the Madras mill worked half-time (weighted by .5 in the table) and were learners, spare hands, assistants, sweepers, and laborers who had no Lancashire counterparts. Without them the ratio of employment in the two mills falls to 2.2.

The decision to work extra shifts or not is an interesting one when basic investment decisions are part of the problem. Assume that two labor-intensive machines, L, might turn out a given weekly output at higher cost than one capital-intensive machine, K. But machine K might have a hard time competing with one L working two shifts. But perhaps L would wear out twice as fast. Yet if that cancels the gains from more than one shift, one might as well buy sixteen Ls and operate each only one hour a day to make them really last.

[30] G. K. Boon, *Eonomic Choice of Human and Physical Factors in Production*, ch. 2; United Nations Department of Economic and Social Affairs, "Choice of Capital Intensity in Operational Planning for Underdeveloped Countries," São Paulo Seminar on Industrial Programming, ST/ECLA/Conf. 11/L.4, March 1963, p. 7.

Table 11. Employment by department in 35,000 ring spindle, 600 power loom cotton mills in Madras and Lancashire, 1908

Division	Madras	Lancashire	Ratio of Madras to Lancashire
Engine department	64	12	5.3
Carding	419	113	3.7
Spinning	644	149	4.3
Doubling	30	9	3.3
Winding	86	50	1.7
Color winding	219	88	2.6
Color printing	160	98	1.6
Warping	19	13	1.5
Sizing	38	15	2.5
Reeling	137	51	2.7
Twisting and drawing	35	34	1.0
Weaving	971	350	2.8
Total	2,622	982	2.7

Source: (East India) Factory Labour Commission, 1908, *Indian Factory Labour Commission,* Vol. II, Evidence, 1909 (London: H.M.S.O., 1909), ed. 4519, Testimony of Mr. C. B. Simpson, pp. 313–14.

The flaws in this last choice are clear; they are the inverse of gains from working shifts: first, yields would not justify pulling that much capital from alternate uses; and, second, obsolescence, rust, and other forces of deterioration, independent of machine use, are given longer to do damage. The role of obsolescence, etc., is illustrated very simply in Table 12. Given output, fixed cost falls to one-third with three shifts. Over the life of given capital equipment, three times as many workers can be employed. To work shifts is to use capital more thriftily.

But shifts have their drawbacks, too, and the weight of the drawbacks will determine the correct marginal decision. These considerations are a possible fall in efficiency and rise in risk. If second- and third-shift workers must be paid more and work under less expert and authoritative supervision, productivity

Table 12. Effect of equipment mortality and multishift production on employment of capital and labor with constant returns

Source of mortality and number of shifts	Life of equipment (years)	Capital needed for producing output x in t days A.1 = 100	Fixed cost per hour A.1 = 100	Production labor needed with capital K A.1 = 100	
				During period P	Over life of K
Mortality dependent on equipment use: Wear and tear					
A.1 1 shift	30	100	100	100	100
A.2 2 shifts	20	50	100	200	100
A.3 3 shifts	10	33.3	100	300	100
Mortality independent of equipment use: Obsolescence, bacteria, oxidation, temperature					
B.1 1 shift	30	100	100	100	100
B.2 2 shifts	30	50	50	200	200
B.3 3 shifts	30	33.3	33.3	300	300

will sag. This has been true in Mexico and seems to apply generally in newly industrializing areas. Nightshift breakdowns, moreover, seem to have a peculiar intractability all their own. Other risks may come from having too small a plant for good times and too large a labor force for bad. A one-shift plant can work overtime more easily and has less of a labor retrenchment problem when obsolescence hits than a three-shift plant.[31]

Finally, there may be external social gains and losses associated with the higher employment of multiple shifts and inten-

[31] For an analysis under perfect competition, see K. J. W. Alexander and John Spraos, "Shift Working: An Application of the Theory of the Firm," *Quarterly Journal of Economics*, Nov. 1956, pp. 603-12.

sive staffing. Does the extra shift create or drain managerial resources? A few Mexican entrepreneurs were wary of training potential competitors; and Dhar and Lydall report that the small Indian industrialist's reluctance to delegate managerial tasks to non-relatives "is the principal reason for his unwillingness and inability to work for more than one shift." Of 206 small Indian factories, only 25 worked second shifts, usually with the owner's son or brother in charge.[32] On the other hand, Soviet planners in the early 1930's may have seen multishift operation as a drain on managerial resources since extra shifts needed not only supervision but demanded more expert planning for all production.[33] The manager of a small Monterrey cheese plant had his own version:

Why aren't we adding a second shift? Because we can't find and train more supervisors. We have one supervisor for every six workers. No Stateside plant would have that. I keep my desk right here on the production floor so I can see what goes on. [He gestured, pulling down a lower eyelid with one forefinger and aiming his other forefinger here and there like a pistol.] Otherwise there's fooling around. You know that mayonnaise jar that broke a moment ago? Without supervision things like that are never cleaned up as fast as they should. That's the main difference between these people and Americans, responsibility! My mother was Mexican, and I've lived here most of my life, so I'm hurting myself when I say that. But it's true. A Mexican with responsibility opens up a small shop for himself. That's why this town has a thousand industries.

Both working shifts and intensive staffing for a given volume raise employment in an enterprise. If capital is released for use elsewhere, again lowering unemployment, the production gen-

[32] Dhar and Lydall, *op. cit.*, p. 56.
[33] David Granick, "On Patterns of Technological Choice in Soviet Industry," *American Economic Review,* May 1963, pp. 153–6.

erated outside is an additional gain from multiple shifts—or conversely, if multiple shifts are stopped, their loss must be counted as a social opportunity cost of single shifts. On the other hand, nightshifts may take an around-the-clock expansion of an urban public transport system or, in a sparsely settled area, more housing and social overhead for workers who might have to immigrate. Such costs, whether borne privately or socially, may tip the decision back toward capital-intensive methods.

In fact, if there are alternate techniques, multiple shifts are apt to go with the more capital intensive method. In India, factory power looms are worked two shifts; cottage looms, one.[34] Large factories working two or three shifts are likely to have both higher capital-labor and output-capital ratios than smaller competitors employing less than fifty workers. Indian three-shift tire, superphosphate, and sewing machine makers had 33, 61, and 70 per cent higher average capital productivity than small one-shift plants.[35] If policy makers think they have to choose between labor-intensity *versus* multiple shifts, or employment *versus* output, they will do well to be guided by profitability; that is, the decision should generally favor shifts and output. A tax incentive for extra shifts may be worthwhile in theory, but it appears doubtful that a workable formula can be developed that does not lead to losses from improper exploitation, or, alternatively, rigid inspection that discourages the hoped-for gains.

According to the Industrial Census of 1956, the shift coefficient for Mexican manufacturing was only 1.07.[36] In the Fed-

[34] Amartya Kumar Sen, *The Choice of Techniques* (Oxford: Blackwell, 1960), Appendix C, p. 106.

[35] Dhar and Lydall, *op. cit.*, pp. 16–17.

[36] Dirección General de Estadística, *Censo Industrial 1956* (Información Censal 1955) *Resumen General* (Mexico, D.F., 1959), Vol. I, pp. 35–45. The shift-coefficient is the ratio of all workers to those in the main shift.

eral District it was 1.08 and in Neuvo Leon 1.10.[37] By contrast New York had 1.14 and Detroit 1.45.[38] Among the highest Mexican industries were basic metals (1.55), petroleum (1.46), and paper (1.22).[39]

In my sample of seventy new and progressive firms, 42 per cent operated two or more shifts in all departments. Nine firms among the rest worked extra shifts in a few departments; the rest worked one shift only. Table 13 shows that the larger the firm the more likely was multishift working. Only 18 per cent of small firms had them, compared with 65 per cent of large firms. But of the firms operating multiple shifts, 81 per cent did so for compelling technical reasons, such as the inexpediency of stopping furnaces overnight. A plant making acetylene, oxygen, and argon was operated on a three-shift basis, but only one week a month. During the other three weeks workers were used for maintenance, painting, gardening, and deliveries. With one or two exceptions, small firms avoided such techniques of production, and the products which demanded them. Fifty-one per cent of nondurable goods makers worked multishifts, compared with 29 per cent of the durable goods producers. Of the six plants operating extra shifts without technical compulsion, four were foreign subsidiaries.

One important form of labor-capital substitution in the form of adding men to given machines has not yet been mentioned: a larger staff of maintenance and repair workers. By adding more of these, machine life can be prolonged, furnishing time for adding more production workers. If machine life is doubled, it is somewhat like adding a fourth, fifth, and sixth night shift. This time may be added to secondhand machines bought from others. The opportunities and problems involved are so great, however, that they will be treated separately in Chapter 6.

[37] *Ibid.*, Vol. II, p. 177.
[38] 1953–54. Alexander and Spraos, *op. cit.*, p. 603.
[39] *Censo Industrial de 1956*, I. pp. 35–45.

Table 13. Multiple shift operations in seventy Mexican and Puerto Rican manufacturing plants

Size, ownership, and location	A One shift	B Largely one shift: two or three in departments	C Two shifts	D Largely two shifts: three in departments	E Three shifts	A + B	C + D + E	Policy not clear
Small	13	1	2	—	1	14	3	—
Medium	12	5	—	2	7	17	9	—
Large	5	3	1	2	12	8	15	4
U.S. subsidiaries	11	5	2	2	7	16	11	1
European subsidiaries	1	—	—	—	1	1	1	—
Immigrant	4	2	—	2	1	6	3	—
Private national	13	1	1	—	8	14	9	3
Public national	1	1	—	—	3	2	3	—
Nondurable producers	16	1	2	1	15	17	18	—
Durable producers	14	8	1	3	5	22	9	4
Nuevo Leon	13	1	—	1	6	14	7	4
Central Plateau	9	3	1	3	10	12	14	—
Mexico (total)	22	4	1	4	16	26	21	4
Puerto Rico	8	5	2	—	4	13	6	—
Total	30	9	3	4	20	39	27	4

VII. Local Machinery Production

Last of the products that a developing country should start manufacturing are those made abroad by technically sophisticated, capital-intensive industries with great economies of scale. Most machinery production fits this category, but in certain cases, listed below, building machines locally permits the use of less capital and more labor:

1. Throughout the world, rarely-bought machines may have to be made labor-intensively and without benefit of scale economies. Transportation costs and lower wages may offset the headstart of any industrialized country, early in the field, especially if the given machine can be made in a still more labor-intensive way in a developing country.

2. To perform a given operation, the design of a machine may be changed to allow its construction with more labor and less capital. As a result, mechanization and the use of machines may rise compared with labor while the measured capital-labor ratio remains unchanged or possibly falls.

3. The design may be changed to allow more flexible or labor-intensive operation. Thus, more labor-intensively made machines can lower the price of capital, but instead of bringing about substitution of capital for labor, they may create the reverse situation.

That machinery production in poor countries is feasible at all can be shown more readily than comparative advantage in particular cases. Argentina exported lathes, shapers, and drill presses to Britain and the United States during World War II.[40] Roller bearings, calibrating equipment, and special steels were imported, but not chucks, collets, motors, and hydraulic mechanisms. In the mid-1950's under strong import protection some 250 Argentine firms were still making over 9,000 machine tools a year. Brazil had some builders employing up to 900 workers,

[40] ST/ECLA/Conf. 4/I/D-8.

and made even more lathes than Argentina.[41] In India the Hindustan Machine Tools Company, Ltd., reported that in 1960-61 the prices of its standard and turret lathes, milling machines, and radial drills were less than the comparable landed cost of imports.[42] India was also building machinery for jute and cotton mills, cement plants, chemical industries, and other operations.

The Mexican machinery builders I visited had usually begun as repair shops and then branched out. A former railway mechanic began in 1931 making presses, mixers, and polishers for mosaic tile. Competition from North Americans was no problem because they did not use that kind of tile, and consequently made no machinery for its production. The mechanic's company made machine tools during World War II and has lately overcome some European competition in tile-making machinery.

Another larger repair shop bought extensive plans, patents, and instructions for making glass-fabricating machinery during the 1930's. The American seller thought this was a riskless way of showing the U. S. Department of Justice that it was not a monopoly by choice. "These plans came in handy during the War," said the Mexican buyer. "We started making those machines with our fingernails." By 1960 he had inquiries from machinery importers in the United States and Europe but had not yet made export sales. Nevertheless, Mexican firms using his machines sold glass products in the United States and South America.

At the subsidiary of an American pump manufacturer, workers were making the mold for casting a large impeller to replace one broken in an American mine. It was a highly skilled,

[41] *Problems of the Steel Making and Transforming Industries of Latin America* (New York: United Nations, 1958), Vol. I, pp. 23–4.

[42] Hindustan Machine Tools, Ltd., *Eighth Annual Report, 1960–61,* pp. 24–5.

labor-intensive operation that would have been far more expensive in the United States. Another manufacturer exported large welded castings.

These are four examples from Monterrey, which has a long industrial tradition. It could not yet be typical of Puerto Rico, where most precision repair was still referred to mainland plants, at times after several local failures. The prerequisites for complex production machinery making were still lacking, as they were in the original and unsuccessful attempt to make automatic looms with Japanese technical assistance during the 1950's at remote Ciudad Sahagún, Mexico. By 1964 technical assistance from an American company at Sahagún and a changed policy toward retrenchment of textile workers had produced success. Twenty-nine per cent of the Mexican sample firms (six Mexican-owned private firms, three immigrant-owned firms, and eight foreign subsidiaries) used Mexican-made machinery. Not included are the many firms buying only import-protected hand tools, pumps, small electric motors, or items like tanks and furnaces that do not lend themselves to transport.

Local machinery builders must get along with whatever finance, materials, and skilled labor happen to be available. If possible, they will redesign the machinery to economize on inputs. In Russia during the 1930's, scarcity of skilled labor and of precise grades of steel led to a preference for casting over forging. In forging, the preference where possible was for hammer forging without dies because of its adaptability to steel of varying dimensions and because it might cut out the delicate die work. Machines and engines were redesigned to suit these production methods and their associated materials and tolerances.[43] Russia has also led in the development of welding in machine building. Instead of casting or forging massive and

[43] David Granick, "Organization and Technology in Soviet Metalworking: Some Conditioning Factors," *American Economic Review,* May 1957, pp. 632–3, 638–40.

complex pieces, smaller and simpler components are welded together. Novel methods, such as electroslag and carbon dioxide shielded welding, had to be perfected for making certain machine parts, such as heavy shafts. Savings follow in both casting or forging capacity and from materials used in the process. Welded machines can also be redesigned to weigh less.[44]

Redesign of machinery is a function of the Indian Prototype Production and Training Centers and of the Machine Tool Design Institute at Bangalore. Foreign prototype machines are redesigned to fit Indian volume, skills, and materials, particularly to maximize use of standard components from screws, bolts, and lubricants, to grades of steel.[45] Mexican firms have also redesigned machinery to allow cheaper production. A foreign subsidiary making agricultural equipment systematically examined imported parts and subassemblies to see if they could be redesigned for production with machinery on hand. They had learned that in Mexico welding was cheaper than hot upsetting, and that flame cutting costs less than shearing, contrary to United States practice. Other design changes with considerable ramifications were necessary during years when Mexican steel mills made no No. 38 carbon steel bolts and instead No. 18 carbon steel bolts had to be used. Another machinery builder made savings by replacing imported stainless steel shafts in his product with shafts made of ordinary steel. The crucial part exposed to wear was filed down, chromium plated, and polished: a highly labor-intensive substitution.

Still more interesting, however, are changes in machinery design that affect operation as well as construction. Foreign machines are still the prototypes from which departures are made,

---

[44] Evgeny P. Unksov, "Use of Welding in Machine-building," *Industrialization and Productivity*, Bulletin No. 3, March 1960, pp. 32–8.

[45] A. D. Bohra, "Training for Industrial Production of Prototype Machinery," *Industrialization and Productivity*, Bulletin No. 6, 1963, pp. 39–40.

with or without patent permission. Usually the working mechanism is kept intact but control mechanisms are simplified or eliminated. Levers may be substituted for electric relays and buttons. A work clothing manufacturer had a machine shop imitate a travelling buggy for moving along tracks on his cutting table, carrying a bolt of cloth, rolling back and forth one hundred times, feeding out the material to exact marks, then doubling it over and changing direction. "Just like an expensive import," the owner said proudly. "But without hydraulic and other devices, you may not find it *bonito*." The hundred pieces of cloth were then cut at once, electrically, not with scissors. For an underwear maker, a similar, copied machine never worked properly and was in time replaced with an import.

A paper machinery maker said he had a mechanic, a prize of a man, highly talented:

After we buy one American machine of any type, we don't need to buy another. Our man knows what quality controls make no sense here. He knows where high quality parts and accessories are unneeded. You won't like it, but he even cuts out protection for moving parts and gears. What's the result? We make machines at one fourth the imported price!

It is likely, however, that omitted safety devices may reduce output far more than their omission saves in capital cost. A productivity mission to India found that putting a guard around a circular saw raised output by 12 per cent: Workers could now move around the machine without fear. The mission concluded that lack of safety was a rather common cause of low productivity.[46]

A Monterrey engineering firm specialized in designing industrial equipment and getting it built to order in local shops.

[46] *Report to the Government of India on a Productivity Mission* (Geneva: International Labor Office, 1955, mimeographed), p. 11, quoted by James J. Berna, *Industrial Entrepreneurship in Madras State* (Bombay: Asia Publishing House, 1960), p. 167.

By lowering the highgrade alloy content, labor costs, etc., they claimed they could lower prices of machines to one-quarter that of competing imports. In the case of some machines they could allow a company to buy it with only one or two positions complete at the time of installation. Remaining parts would be added as the enterprise could afford them. A partner said,

> We also save money by designing the machine only partially. There is no need to engineer and draw it down to the details for only one. It's easier to tell a shop manager what is wanted with a rough sketch and much cheaper. He knows what to do. We have very good people in such things. Our machines will have bugs for six months or so, but the labor that eliminates those problems is very cheap.

The enterprise was affiliated with a Texas engineering firm through which it drew on American technical knowledge. The Texans for their part often used the Mexican firm's draftsmen to complete blueprints, for which, to be sure, they charged their U. S. clients as if American wage rates had been paid.

Important in all the examples cited is the close contact between machine builders and users, their working together to solve technical problems standing in the way of lower capital costs. Such cooperation is nothing novel in the history of technology.[47] The increased efficiency derived from the intellectual exchanges that geographic proximity makes possible may be greater than the material savings achieved through international trade between machine buyer and seller, and thus be an added reason for encouraging simple domestic machinery

[47] Nathan Rosenberg, "Technological Change in the Machine Tool Industry, 1840–1910," *Journal of Economic History*, Dec. 1963, pp. 414–43; Rosenberg, "Capital Goods, Technology and Economic Growth," *Oxford Economic Papers*, Nov. 1963, pp. 217–27; Merton J. Peck, "Inventions in the Postwar American Aluminum Industry," in *Rate and Direction of Inventive Activity* (Princeton: N.B.E.R. and Princeton University Press, 1962), pp. 292–5; W. Paul Strassmann, "Interrelated Industries and the Rate of Technological Change," *Review of Economic Studies*, Oct. 1959, pp. 16–22; Habakkuk, *op. cit.*, pp. 96–7, 116–7, 163–9, 183–7.

production. By the same token, machinery exporters around the North Atlantic would do well to imitate these local adaptations of their own imitated prototypes.

VIII. Summary

Economic development means that more and better goods are in demand, which results in higher volume and quality of production. Science, rather than skilled handicraft, makes possible the qualities of new materials and modern devices. Science allows voltages, pressures, temperatures, speeds, and sensitivities beyond the reach of man. Volume allows and prescribes their use in production. Volume also favors use of equipment over men because of geometric scale effects and because more machines become easier, and more men harder, to coordinate. Science, quality, and volume therefore combine in the course of development to lower the substitutability of handworkers for machines. Where labor-intensive options remain, they should be welcomed, yet be recognized as silver linings that are nevertheless part of the cloud of backwardness.

The handicap of low volume can be offset through standardization or increase of machine flexibility. Fewer products and processes mean longer production runs and less excess capacity.

Instead of replacing machines altogether, men can be added to modern equipment in daylight through intensive staffing, at night in shifts, or in the future with longer maintenance. Finally, if skills are available, capital may at times be saved by building machinery locally, in a more labor-intensive way for more labor-intensive use. All of these schemes are potentially important, yet none have widespread and intensive use, with the partial exception of longer maintenance, as will be seen in Chaper 6.

No interview and no plant visit to any sample firm was terminated until I had a fairly clear idea of whether or not, compared with U.S. practice, labor had been substituted for capital and, if so, whether the substitution represented an accommodation to lower volume only or was partly a response to different factor-price ratios. The results are shown separately for Mexico and Puerto Rico in Table 14. It would, of course, be more significant if I could show not merely whether or not certain types of technological change occurred, but the cost reduction attained by the change (or foregone by the lack of it) compared with the most likely alternative. A few firms made data available for specific substitutions, such as the blast furnace mechanization reported in the last chapter, but these cases were too few and disparate to warrant aggregation and precise generalization.

Perhaps most noteworthy in Table 14 are the following points about Mexico: (1) Half the firms showed little response to different factor prices, and half of these made almost no change in technology compared with U.S. practice (except perhaps replacement policy). (2) All small firms had lowered the capital-labor ratio below the demands of shorter production runs; but two-thirds of large firms had not. Medium-sized firms were evenly divided. About one-third of large firms had made almost no change at all. (3) Least responsive to factor prices appeared to be those Mexican firms which were privately owned but not by immigrants. A larger fraction of these had also made little change of any kind compared with U.S. practice. Yet, relatively more of them made durables than nondurables. Substitutability is less in making liquids, powders, and other nondurable goods. (4) 85 per cent of durables producers had changed technique, and factor prices played a part in most. Only two-thirds of nondurables makers had made changes, of which only half reflected factor prices. In short, a small U.S. subsidiary making durables was most, and a large privately-owned Mexican firm making nondurables was least, likely to adjust.

The smaller Puerto Rican sample allows fewer observations.

Table 14. The role of volume, wages, and the availability of capital in the choice of technology (excluding replacement policy), Mexico and Puerto Rico: Part I—Mexico

Characteristic of enterprise	A Almost no change in technology compared with U.S. practice	B-C-D Change in technology compared with U.S. practice	B Changes reflecting lower volume only	C Changes in production processes reflecting B and D to a negligible extent	A-B-C Little response to factor proportions	D Increases in labor intensity partly reflecting capital scarcity and lower wage level
Small	—	9	—	—	—	9
Medium	3	15	5	1	9	9
Large	9	15	3	4	16	8
U.S. subsidiaries	2	12	2	2	6	8
European subsidiaries	1	1	—	—	1	1
Immigrant	2	6	2	—	4	4
Private national	6	16	3	3	12	10
Public national	1	4	1	—	2	3
Nondurable producers	8	16	3	3	14	10
Durable producers	4	23	5	2	11	16
Nuevo Leon	4	21	2	2	8	17
Central plateau	8	18	6	3	17	9
Total	12	39	8	5	25	26

Table 14 (continued)
Part II—Puerto Rico

Characteristic of enterprise	A Almost no change in technology compared with U.S. practice	B-C-D Change in technology compared with U.S. practice	B Changes reflecting lower volume only	C Changes in production processes reflecting B and D to a negligible extent	A-B-C Little response to factor proportions	D Increases in labor intensity partly reflecting capital scarcity and lower wage level
Small	3	5	1	1	5	3
Medium	2	6	—	2	4	4
Large	3	—	—	—	3	—
U.S. subsidiaries	6	8	—	2	8	6
European subsidiaries	—	—	—	—	1	—
Immigrant	—	1	—	1	—	—
Private national	2	2	1	—	3	1
Public national	—	—	—	—	—	—
Nondurable producers	2	8	1	2	5	5
Durable producers	6	3	—	1	7	2
Total	8	11	1	3	12	7

Two-thirds showed little response to factor prices, which, of course, were much closer to United States levels. Six of the eight firms that did reduce capital intensity on account of cost differences and volume produced for the small Commonwealth market. In these enterprises, wages tended to be lower because they alone were subject to Commonwealth Wage Boards which were less eager for raises than the Federal Wage Boards governing other firms. The only two exporting firms that had reduced capital intensity did so in very minor ways: in one, by leaving certain guiding attachments off a class of sewing machines; and, in the other, through omission of packing machines.

6

Maintenance, Durability,
and Secondhand Equipment

In Mexico and Puerto Rico the use of old machines is the most widespread way of adjusting production methods to scarce capital and abundant labor. Expenditure for maintenance and repair permits capital goods to stay on the production line longer so that more labor is added to, and more output produced with, an initial investment. The equipment may have been bought new years ago or be secondhand.

This chapter begins by noting some differences and similarities in repair, maintenance, and other spending for equipment longevity. An analysis of a few aspects of rational choice among these alternatives follows. It is then shown that actual choices in Mexico and Puerto Rico, however, tended to be skewed by entrepreneurial misconceptions and flaws in economic organization. A similar discussion of attitudes and access to secondhand equipment ends the chapter.

I. The Economics of Equipment Longevity

Equipment can last longer if its quality is higher or if it receives better care. The higher quality refers only to resistance to wear, tear, and corrosion, not to quality in general. To get durability, other qualities—speed, accuracy, versatility, convenience, and appearance—may be sacrificed. Savings from greater durability can mean that equipment is also cheaper. It could easily be more labor-intensive as well if automatic controls and attachments have been left off for manual operation. But greater durability for equipment with given operating characteristics generally means components of better construction, made out of more expensive materials, and more carefully assembled and inspected. Labor-intensive maintenance and repair will then be less needed than for more perishable equipment used equally long. The capital-labor ratio of operation rises.

But alternative equipment of low durability need not be used equally long and therefore need not require more maintenance and repair work. Entire plants can be replaced more often. If they last half as long at half the investment, they would be a bargain; funds released can bring a return from investment elsewhere. Faster replacement also gives entrepreneurs an earlier chance to correct mistakes and to apply recent technical advances.

Aside from the rise in flexibility given by that chance, any replacement merges with repair and maintenance, that is, the replacement of parts. "Repair" is the replacing and mending of parts *after* equipment has ceased to function properly. "Maintenance" offsets deterioration before that point; it adds what time and the process of production wear away and removes what is deposited or altered unfavorably. Worn-out moving parts, insulation, lubricants, or furnace linings are replaced; rust, lint, and grit are cleaned out. Many of these tasks can be accomplished with more than one degree of labor intensity: manually or with mechanical aids, mending breaks or replacing the part, fabricating the replacement or keeping an inventory of imports. As with hollow Japanese dolls, little alternatives wait inside bigger ones.

But obviously not all cleaning, lubricating, and adjusting is optional spending on maintenance to lengthen equipment life. Where these expenses depend on the volume of production, they are ordinary variable costs. Some equipment must be disassembled and cleaned daily, weekly, or monthly if production is to go on at all. Tiny impurities can spoil processed foods; slag and ashes may clog furnaces; and the grit from stone and clay products can quickly destroy machines. Where volume makes no difference and no option exists, the expenditure on cleaning may be a fixed cost. Maintenance outlays, properly defined, do not begin at once, can be delayed or foregone, and lengthen equipment life.[1]

The amount of longevity that is worth the expense of more durability or more maintenance (or some combination of both) depends on the scarcity of capital and maintenance skills. An initial outlay for greater durability means that spending for replacement in the future can be postponed. This postponement and successive postponed replacements amount to a stream of savings with a present value determined by the interest rate. The higher the interest rate, the less the present value of the stream. Since interest rates are higher in capital-scarce underdeveloped countries, one would expect less insistence on durability. *How* much less would first depend on the marginal cost of greater wear resistance. If marginal cost per year of extended life falls and then rises, as suggested by Blitz,[2] spending should rise to the point where the extra cost matches the addition to the future stream of savings, properly discounted. Of course, if a rise in interest rates is expected, spending on durability may rise in anticipation. Firms may spend more now to stock up on durability. As a result they need spend less on maintenance and replacement later. They will therefore have more funds to invest when the expected higher interest

---

[1] Rudolph C. Blitz, "Capital Longevity and Economic Development," *American Economic Review*, June 1958, pp. 320–22.

[2] *Ibid.*, pp. 315–18.

rates materialize, *cet. par.* An expected fall in interest rates has a reverse effect.

Spending on maintenance is an alternative way of postponing replacement. A cost is incurred that must be compared not only with a changed replacement rate but also with lower durability outlays. There is a new set of future saving streams with present values that must be compared with those of combinations of various possible maintenance and durability outlays. Since maintenance is likely to be labor-intensive and therefore cheap in underdeveloped countries, a slower rate of replacement than elsewhere might be expected. Inadequacies of supervision and knowledge may, of course, keep maintenance productivity low enough to offset any wage differential. Preventive maintenance —attending to adjustments, dirt, wearing parts, insulation, leaks, and oiling—is technically easy but hard to supervise and therefore takes great self-discipline. Good maintenance is not immediately obvious and properly rewarded, hence negligence is common in newly industrialized areas. But low preventive maintenance means more breakdowns and repairs. Trouble-shooting broken-down equipment takes not only high technical skill and persistence but confidence that all snags and breaks can be found. This skill and confidence are likely to be scarce and expensive. In any case, a breakdown is at least a clear call for action. Not to stop for preventive maintenance may, how-ever, be rational in some highly seasonal industries like sugar-grinding, if there is a good chance that the machines will last until slack months.

In 1959 the Bureau of Economic Affairs of the United Nations estimated depreciation and maintenance costs and com-pared them for a nitrogenous fertilizer plant used for ten or fifteen years in the United States and in Central America. The data were partly hypothetical but not unrealistic. An identical plant would cost $1,000,000 in the United States but $1,350,000 delivered at a Central American site. Maintenance and repair expenditures would average 4 per cent annually in the United States for a 10-year life and 8 per cent for a 15-year life. Half would be spent for labor and half for spare parts. Columns 1 and 2 of Table 15 give the results: A 15-year life in the United States costs 5 per cent more per year than a 10-year life.

Table 15. Comparative cost data on depreciation and maintenance for a nitrogenous fertilizer plant with alternative lifetimes of ten or fifteen years, United States and Central America

(Thousands of U.S. dollars per one million dollars of investment in the United States)

Item equipment life	United States		Central America			
			Same techniques in maintenance and repairs as in the United States		Greater relative use of labor in maintenance and repairs	
	10 years	15 years	10 years	15 years	10 years	15 years
Depreciation	100	67	135	90	135	90
Maintenance and repairs	40	80	35	70	29	58
(Labor)	(20)	(40)	(8)	(16)	(14.5)	(29)
(Spare parts)	(20)	(40)	(27)	(54)	(14.5)	(29)
Total	140	147	170	160	164	148

Source: This table appears in "Problems of Size of Plant in Industry in Underdeveloped Countries," *Industrialization and Productivity, Bulletin 2,* March 1959, p. 22.

Similar maintenance and repair techniques would affect Central American costs differently. If wages and salaries are one-fourth of United States levels and productivity is two-thirds, labor costs per unit of work fall to 40 per cent. On the other hand, imported spare parts (like the plant itself) will cost 35 per cent more. On these assumptions, columns 3 and 4 of Table

15 show that depreciation and maintenance for a 15-year life in Central America cost 6 per cent less than for a 10-year life.

But what if, given these price and productivity ratios, the labor input to maintenance can be increased and the use of imported spare parts reduced until these two costs are once more equal? Implied is that their marginal products are equal at this point. Depreciation and maintenance costs fall almost to United States levels for a 15-year life and gain a 10 per cent advantage over a 10-year life in Central America.

In this example, plant design and performance were constant, merely one of several options. One can design a plant to be more or less durable and, for either case, easier or harder to repair. Relative factor costs would seem to point toward cheap construction, cheaply repaired. If not at the expense of one another, greater ruggedness and reparability combined are likely to come at some other cost such as higher investment or inferior operation. Faced with this choice, a German engineer concluded that in underdeveloped countries one should keep voltages, temperatures, and pressures as low as possible:

By demanding little, one should try to make a plant as safe as possible, as uncomplicated to service as possible. But control devices should be the latest available. The new arrangements are easier to see, easier to service, and if necessary, simpler to replace. Fewer well-trained people, inhabitants of the country or Europeans, who know how to care for such layouts, need be on hand. In the long run these are cheaper and make fewer mistakes than a larger number of less well-trained people, who, in this sense, would be replaced by relays and servomechanisms. The latter I consider more reliable.[3]

At tropical temperatures, under extremely high or low humidities, and perhaps with voracious insects or rodents, electrical installations will have their own maintenance problems

---

[3] B. Plettner, "Erfahrungen aus der Auslandsarbeit eines grossen Unternehmens," *Der Ingenieur und Seine Aufgaben in Neuen Wirtschaftsraümen* (Düsseldorf: VDI Verlag, 1959), p. 145. My translation.

to which hot and running machinery is not subject. In my sample I found that electronic equipment was generally considered a maintenance disadvantage and that secondhand equipment with such devices was especially avoided. On the other side, however, an American steel engineer thought:

Lack of experienced and technically skilled workers can best be offset by using methods and processes in which the operations requiring skill are entrusted to machinery to the greatest possible extent. Skill in maintenance, mechanical and electrical work seems to be more easily found or developed than that required for complicated manual operations such, for example, as in sheet or tinplate rolling.[4]

By contrast Russian engineers altered the design of the Gorky Automobile Plant (GAZ) in the early 1930's from that of its model, the Ford River Rouge plant, in order to reduce the need for skilled maintenance and repair workers. For example, sandslingers were rejected for molding cylinder blocks because the slingers would have required frequent repairs and would have worn out molding patterns faster, thereby putting pressure on that rare skill, patternmaking.[5] Relative costs vary with time, place, and industry.

II. Maintenance in Practice

Variations in cost must pass through the filter of entrepreneurial attitudes. Almost all Mexican sample enterprises kept equipment going longer than would have been true in a high-wage, capital-abundant economy. But the emphasis was on re-

[4] William A. Haven, "Selection of Steelmaking Processes and of Locations for Integrated Iron and Steel Works," *A Study of the Iron and Steel Industry in Latin America* (New York: United Nations, 1954), Vol. II, p. 356.
[5] David Granick, "Organization and Technology in Soviet Metalworking: Some Conditioning Factors," *American Economic Review*, May 1957, p. 632.

pair, not preventive maintenance. Out of fifty-one plants, only one small pump maker checked wiring, painted, disassembled, and cleaned his machines more often than could have been done economically in the United States. Most firms with any conscious maintenance policy considered it a great achievement and something of a luxury if they merely equalled foreign preventive standards. More often decisions to repair or replace were made *ad hoc* whenever a machine was down, and not in accordance with any general policy to achieve greater longevity. That good preventive maintenance is hard to supervise and reward has already been mentioned. Current pressure to spend money elsewhere also plays its part where little can be borrowed and that only at high interest. Postponing maintenance is part of the general heavy discounting of the future, almost a way of life. As one American maintenance engineer said,

These people are great hopers, the greatest hopers in the world. They always hope a worn part will last another week or maybe heal by itself. So the breakdowns are much worse than necessary. And when they run into trouble during the repairs, they give up after the first try. I was supposed to go on to another job long ago, but here I am.

Maintenance and repairs were more of a headache in Puerto Rico where about half the sample firms reported serious problems. A metal fabricating subsidiary had brought in four maintenance experts with the assignment of training their own replacements. Two were to give 4,000 hours of training in two years; two 6,000 hours in three years. Four years later the company decided to keep two home-plant mechanics at all times in Puerto Rico on a rotating schedule because "there's a ceiling to what our [Puerto Rican] workers are willing and able to absorb." An electrical manufacturer could never get a complex machine tool to function properly. He regularly sent one semi-finished part to the home plant for treatment. Batches of these were then returned to Puerto Rico for assembly. A plastics maker sent his electronic timers to the United States for repair. He tried unsuccessfully to have shafts for presses locally reground with sufficient precision. An engineer at a nonmetallic mineral processing plant said one- or two-hour breakdowns happened daily either in mixing, washing, drying, weighing, heating, or transfer equipment.

Yet frequent breakdowns are not bad *per se*. They are extravagant only if their cost is more than that of possible prevention. Indeed, the cost of breakdowns is often exaggerated by managers who view it as that of all production lost during down time. But while equipment is down, costs are down too. Materials are not being used, and some parts of the plant get less wear. The cost of breakdowns is largely in the wages of idled operators,[6] and these are low in developing countries.

Exaggerated fear of breakdowns and an underrating of the value of preventive maintenance lead to an undue preference for sturdy equipment, for new instead of secondhand machines, for American instead of European equipment. In the early 1960's European machines tended to be more complex, harder to disassemble, more delicate, and more easily damaged by small overloads than American machines. "Delicate machines perish under Mexican treatment," said one German manager. "American machines can stand it because they are built for their own savage treatment. I have seen the way they mistreat machines in the U.S.A. just for speed. I could hardly believe it." On the other hand, an American technician thought German machines stood up well in Mexico if they were not too electronic and if the workers were allowed to handle them with only nonadjustable wrenches and babbit metal mallets.

[6] For an arithmetic example, see Rudolph C. Blitz, "Maintenance Costs and Economic Development," *Journal of Political Economy*, Dec. 1959, pp. 568–9.

If maintenance and repairs cause unusual problems, perhaps unusual solutions are in order. The improvements in vocational and managerial training mentioned in Chapter 3 will help. But what about a special maintenance service? Some manufacturers in Northern Mexico thought their inclusion in the California or Texas districts for service was a clear locational advantage and a reason for buying new equipment. Branch plants of big corporations receive good service in Puerto Rico, but others found breakdowns meant lengthy correspondence, questions answered with more questions, and finally visits by salesmen instead of technicians. Some concluded the best source of help was the friendly competitor. A better answer might lie in directions explored by the service departments of the Singer Sewing Machine Company and the United Shoe Machinery Company. Around Mexico City these companies had reputations for promptness and efficiency, even for making occasional inspections on their own initiative. "Why should I get more English, German, Swiss, or Danish machines when they don't save me all the trouble and confusion when things go wrong?" asked one provincial general director. Perhaps specialized industry-wide services can remedy the inadequacies of maintenance at plant level.

A joint approach to repair problems may at least assure the supply of spare parts. Some countries allow easy import of sufficient spare parts only on the condition that each firm's supply be available to others if the need arises.[7] If each company has its inventory list and if other records are kept by customs authorities, the main problem is pooling and distributing already recorded information. In the United States the availability of spare parts is much less of a problem since they can often

[7] United Nations Department of Economic and Social Affairs, *Management of Industrial Enterprises in Under-developed Countries* (New York: United Nations, 1958), p. 23.

be ordered and delivered overnight. Anything more than a two-day delay for a gasket or a belt is unusual. But parts flown to Mexico City took ten days before they were received, properly classified, and cleared through customs. For real emergencies, smuggled parts made it overland in five days or less. Of course, such emergencies should not occur after a company has gained experience and ability to predict both replacement needs and delivery times. A common practice is to restore inventories of specific parts to a predetermined maximum whenever they have been depleted to a predetermined minimum. What these minima and maxima should be cannot always be taken from United States or European experience. "No kidding," said a Puerto Rican general manager, "I see parts broken around here that I never even heard of before."

III. Trade of Secondhand Equipment in Theory

If it pays to maintain equipment longer in low-wage econ-omies, then importing equipment that high-wage economies are replacing must also be advantageous, assuming similar trans-port and related import costs for new and used equipment. High-wage, low-interest, large-market economies abandon equipment earlier because of different marginal replacement conditions—as Terborgh called it, earlier "operating inferior-ity," which is loss of productivity compared with technically improved alternatives.[8] Maintenance and repair are least ad-vantageous where wages are high and rising and where tech-nological change is labor-displacing. Earlier replacement means higher resale or salvage value and more years for collecting in-terest on funds so realized. On the other hand, postponed re-

[8] George Terborgh, *Dynamic Equipment Policy* (New York: McGraw-Hill, 1949). See also Vernon L. Smith, *Investment and Production* (Cam-bridge: Harvard University Press, 1961), pp. 128–61, for a review of the literature.

placement and successive later postponements lead to a stream of savings, mentioned in Section II, that has a higher present value at lower interest rates.[9]

But even without obsolescence and fading efficiency, older machines would still be a better buy for low-wage, scarce-capital countries—except to the degree that the lower price is offset by the higher (more frequent) transportation costs implied by a shorter life. As long as the relative prices of old and new machines are mainly determined where they are usually traded, in the advanced countries, the older the better should be the policy for underdeveloped countries (under these assumptions). New machines retain more years of output and profit in their future. All this expected income raises the current price of a machine more if the future is discounted by the lower profit rate of the advanced area. The profit rate is lower because the assumption of equal efficiency means equal material costs for equal output values in both areas, but a larger share of net output goes to wages in the advanced areas. Each additional year of machine life bought by an underdeveloped country puts capital into a high-priced outlet with a corresponding submarginal rate of return, given the greater capital scarcity of the poor country.[10]

---

[9] Assume that the difference between the investment cost, W, of a machine and its salvage value, S, are the same in a developed and an underdeveloped country, but that the rate at which initial operating costs fall per year for new equipment due to technical advances, α, and the rate, β, at which operating expenses for any given machine rise with age, are both four times as high for the developed country. Then machine life, L, that minimizes the annual equipment cost will be twice as long in the underdeveloped country because it varies inversely with the square root of α plus β:

$$L = \left[\frac{2(W - S)}{\alpha + \beta} \right]^{\frac{1}{2}}$$

For the derivation of this equation, see Smith, *op. cit.*, pp. 134–52.

[10] For a simple mathematical proof, see Amartya Kumar Sen, "On the Usefulness of Used Machines," *Review of Economics and Statistics*, Aug.

IV. Secondhand Equipment in Practice

About half of the Mexican and three-fifths of the Puerto Rican sample firms used secondhand equipment for major processes. Some equipment had been completely disassembled and "reconstructed"; some had merely been "reconditioned"; and some was sold "as is." Two-thirds of those citing relative prices had paid 25 to 50 per cent of the comparable new-machine price, and one-third only 10 to 24 per cent. Of course, lower price does not always mean worse condition. It could mean less disposability (lower demand), faster obsolescence (greater supply), or both.

Preference for secondhand equipment was influenced by the physical characteristics of processes, their rate of obsolescence, size of firm, type of ownership, and location. As may be seen in Table 16, only 29 per cent of nondurables producers used secondhand equipment, compared with 65 per cent of durables makers. Secondhand equipment is especially rare in chemicals. One chemical subsidiary had bought a scrapped plastic-making unit from its parent, but temperature and pressure could no longer be controlled accurately and leaks were common. The unit was replaced with new equipment. The less mechanical the processes, one might almost say, the more irreparable is deterioration. In Nuevo Leon all secondary and tertiary shaping of metal was done on secondhand machines, but complex electronic controls were avoided or bought new. A nonferrous metal fabricator near Mexico City had secondhand equipment throughout his plant except for a special vacuum furnace, a continuous oven, and an electronically controlled strip rolling

---

1962, pp. 346–8. Members of the United States Machinery Dealers National Association reported that in 1964 exports represented only $22.4 million, or 5.5 per cent, of total sales (*Report of Expert Group on Second-Hand Equipment for Developing Countries, 7–22 December 1965* [New York: United Nations, 1966], ST/CID/8, p. 5).

Table 16. Secondhand equipment policy in major processes of seventy Mexican and Puerto Rican manufacturing firms

Type of firm	Began and replaces or expands with used equipment	Began and replaces or expands with new equipment	Began with used equipment but replaces or expands with new equipment	Began with new equipment but replaces or expands with used equipment	Undecided or no response
Small	10	6	1	—	5
Medium	11	7	2	1	—
Large	7	16	3	1	—
U.S. subsidiaries	17	10	—	—	1
European subsidiaries	1	1	—	—	—
Immigrant	1	6	1	—	1
Private national	9	8	5	1	3
Public national	—	4	—	1	—
Nondurables producers	9	20	4	1	1
Durables producers	19	9	2	1	4
Nuevo Leon	13	6	1	—	4
Central Plateau	5	16	5	1	—
Mexico (total)	18	22	6	1	4
Puerto Rico	10	7	0	1	1
Total	28	29	6	2	5

process. In general, necessities of volume, speed, and quality influence choice. Equipment used intermittently for a few low-precision items is most likely to be secondhand.

Either a very high or a very low rate of technical advance works against exchange of secondhand equipment. A high rate can make new equipment save so much labor and materials or so improve a product that old equipment even if obtained free can be used only at a loss. Of course, advances may also make equipment more complex and fragile, requiring unavailable materials and operating and maintenance skills. Lack of advance, however, means that equipment is replaced when physically worn out, so that trade depends mainly on the rather dubious comparative advantage for repair work in the poorer country. If technical stagnation is a sign of a declining, "sick" industry, as suggested by Schmookler,[11] then equipment might have been undermaintained as a misguided or desperate economy measure before bankruptcy, making it an especially poor secondhand buy.

Preference for secondhand machines is associated with small scale. Table 17 shows that three-fifths of small firms but only two-fifths of large firms used secondhand equipment in major processes. Credit and finance are relatively scarce for small firms; therefore, at times these firms have no alternative but to buy equipment that is initially cheaper but actually wears out at a rate that amounts to higher costs per unit of output. These firms are forced to be uneconomically economical. Six Mexican-owned private firms began operations with used equipment but, once established as profitable and creditworthy, changed to expansion and replacement policies with new equipment.

[11] Jacob Schmookler, "Changes in Industry and in the State of Knowledge as Determinants of Industrial Invention," *The Rate and Direction of Inventive Activity: Economic and Social Factors* (Princeton: Princeton University Press, 1962), pp. 195–232; and Schmookler, *Invention and Economic Growth* (Cambridge: Harvard University Press, 1965).

Table 17. Percentage of secondhand machinery as a percentage of total investment in fixed assets in Japanese firms of various sizes during the 1950's

Number of employees	Per cent				
	1954	1955	1956	1957	1958
4– 9	48.8	40.2	34.3	n.a.	n.a.
10– 19	44.1	40.8	29.9	n.a.	n.a.
20– 29	39.5	34.3	28.7	n.a.	n.a.
30– 49	35.0	28.9	26.1	26.8	26.5
50– 99	31.5	22.0	22.3	21.9	20.9
100– 199	23.0	16.3	16.8	14.5	13.8
200– 299	15.2	9.1	9.9	9.3	10.0
300– 499	13.9	10.1	9.1	7.4	7.6
500– 999	11.2	5.2	4.2	4.6	6.3
over 1000	4.6	4.1	4.9	3.3	3.1

Source: M. Shinohara, *Sangyokozo* (*Industrial Structure,* 1959), p. 120, as reproduced by Amartya Kumar Sen, "On the Usefulness of Used Machines," *Review of Economics and Statistics,* Aug. 1962, p. 346.

As a Mexican paper mill owner said, *"Compro como rico para que me dure como pobre"* ("I buy like the rich to get a poor man's wear").

Growing firms often find it profitable after a certain point to change to larger-scale processes (new or secondhand) and to sell their old equipment to newcomers. If growth has a tendency to decelerate, or if technological returns to scale increase at a decreasing rate, one would expect a larger supply of small-scale than of large-scale secondhand equipment. Hence small firms would be more likely to use it. Finally, as described in Chapter 4, small firms tend to pay lower wages and therefore to benefit more from (or be penalized less by) the labor-intensive characteristics of old machines. As an illustration, Table 17 shows the extent to which Japanese firms of various sizes bought secondhand machinery during the 1950's.

Type of ownership—whether foreign or domestic by immigrants, old stock, or government—also influenced preference for secondhand equipment, at times inverting the effect of size. Table 16 shows that only one-third of locally-owned firms, but three-fifths of foreign subsidiaries, preferred secondhand equipment. Even small firms occasionally bought new equipment to get the technical assistance and guarantees of machinery makers, as mentioned earlier. Scarcity of knowledge takes precedence over capital scarcity.

Among American subsidiaries, 79 per cent of those in Mexico and 57 per cent of those in Puerto Rico used secondhand machines. None had reversed its initial equipment policy, switching from secondhand to new, or the opposite. Compared with local entrepreneurs they had greater confidence in their ability to avoid trouble with old equipment, and they knew more about the used equipment market abroad, not to mention the possibilities for buying equipment from their own parent plants. If purchases from parents are excluded, the proportion of American subsidiaries with secondhand equipment policies falls to one-half. But to assume that subsidiaries are generally equipped with the obsolete machines of their parents would be wrong. In international comparisons, age of equipment is not necessarily closely associated with modernity, nor modernity with mechanization. Their correspondence may be suggested by Table 18, based on questionnaires sent by the National Industrial Conference Board to American companies with seventy plants in Latin America. Although 84 per cent of

Table 18. Age of equipment, modernity, and mechanization compared with home plants in seventy Latin American plants of U.S. companies (percentage distribution of replies)

	More in U.S.	Same	More in Latin America
Age of equipment	34	50	16
Modernity of technology	38	59	3
Degree of mechanization	88	12	0

Source: Theodore R. Gates and Fabian Linden, *Costs and Competition: American Experience Abroad* (New York: National Industrial Conference Board, 1961), p. 117.

the Latin American branch plants had equipment as new or newer than the home plants, only 62 per cent were equally, or more, advanced in technology, and only 12 per cent were as mechanized. Preference for new equipment did not mean a comparable preference for latest methods, especially for purely labor-saving devices.

Finally, preference for new equipment is influenced by distance from heavily industrialized, machinery-producing areas. Preference for new equipment on the Central Plateau in Mexico was greater than the relative emphasis on nondurable production would imply. Even some metal-working firms preferred new equipment, a preference never found in Monterrey. The greater delays in obtaining spare parts far from the border (and in Puerto Rico) have already been mentioned as a factor. Indeed, less contact with American markets of secondhand machinery, which results in a smaller supply, led in some cases to efforts to reduce the supply even more. A few executives said they destroyed or exported their own replaced equipment to forestall competition. Some even bought such equipment from others to destroy or export it at a loss. At least one had a contract with the original machinery supplier to destroy rather than resell machinery in usable form. But in some other branches, especially in metal working and around Monterrey, machine shops bought and reconditioned or reconstructed equipment.

Secondhand equipment has disadvantages that are easily overstated, but general prejudices probably do not greatly influence entrepreneurs. If they read about it at all, managers know how to discount a Russian's insistence at the United Nations that developing countries should "be equipped with the most contemporary, up-to-date techniques and not merely with secondhand plants."[12] They will understand that their

---

[12] Professor Plotnikov, quoted in *World of Opportunity, Science and Technology for Development,* Report on the United Nations Conference

own political leaders can welcome foreign investment only if, associated with local management and labor, it will "stimulate introduction of the most advanced techniques." They know enough about public relations to disbelieve other entrepreneurs who tell reporters a new plant is the latest available, a true innovation, a patriotic advance in his region's justly famous progress. Secondhand machines have as much glamor in this context as hand-me-down clothes have for a teen-age girl.

Nevertheless, when secondhand equipment is rejected the basis is usually a calculation, possibly pessimistic and incomplete, but not a prejudice. In only seven Mexican firms of the sample was all secondhand machinery unacceptable for non-economic reasons of sheer pride. Six of these were large firms not apt to be severely penalized by the decision. Some were in sectors into which entry by less modern, lower-cost competitors would be difficult or impossible. Others were in industries in which the main process *had* to be new, and in which avoiding secondhand machines for minor auxiliary equipment added little to costs.

Fear of production losses through many sudden interruptions in an integrated plant was the reason given by about half of the companies that avoided secondhand equipment. Willingness to buy used equipment was determined largely by confidence in one's own maintenance and repair abilities. A metalworking plant can grind a bearing or shaft for its own machines; an electrical manufacturer is as good at rewiring circuits for his own use as at wiring those for sale. When repair services have to be bought from the outside, higher costs and uncertainties often make the secondhand second-best.

A widespread feeling thus exists that repairs by one's own employees, if possible at all, are the only worthwhile repairs. The question then arises as to whether this attitude creates a

on the Application of Science and Technology for the Benefit of the Less Developed Areas (New York: United Nations, 1963), Vol. I, p. 121.

preference for one's own antiquated equipment over replacement with apparently better secondhand machines. What sense
can one make of the following statement by a Mexican metal
furniture maker?

It is not our policy to buy used equipment. We used to do that when
we couldn't afford new equipment. But it is generally not advisable
to keep on buying used equipment. We do all our own maintenance
and we have no problems with it. We try to keep our machines in
good condition a long time, as long as utterly possible.

Perhaps the answer is that machines are their own training
school. As machines grow older, workers grow wiser in the
ways of maintaining them. They are introduced to the problems of maintaining them a step at a time; they are not immediately confronted by all the problems. By the time the
machines are old, they are thoroughly understood, and knowledge of the case history of each is a good substitute for a broad
knowledge of all the problems that might afflict that entire
family of machines. There is economy in the development and
use of skills; excess capacity in human capital is kept to a
minimum. If this is the answer, it might even give a clue for
improving the channels for trading secondhand machines.

V. International Channels for Trading Secondhand Equipment

The reluctance to buy secondhand equipment that has cost
advantages over new machines stems from fear, not pride.
Hence, to improve channels of trade, this fear and the underlying uncertainty must be reduced. Buyers must have ways of
learning more about used machines; sellers need to know more
about buyers. But to gain a reputation and to win confidence
takes time and a stable organization. Simply because secondhand equipment comes on the market sporadically from scat-

tered places is no reason for it to be sold in a casual way as indeed it is not in developed countries.

To lower uncertainty about machines, information can be provided relatively cheaply for either large, very expensive machines or for inexpensive, but often-traded, machines. Very expensive machines justify special treatment—compilation of a detailed history, careful inspection and appraisal by independent authorities, and the checking of its operation in accordance with standard test patterns, such as those used by the U.S. Defense Department. In the United States several well-known and reliable companies specialize in certifying equipment in this manner.[13]

Frequently traded machines may justify standardized procedures for selection and grading. Age must be determined for those machines (usually European) that do not have the year of manufacture on a plate or stamped into the body.[14] Normal decline in operating characteristics and increase in maintenance needs that can be anticipated with age must be given. Buyers must know if the original manufacturer still exists and can supply spare parts and accessories. Records should be kept and distributed about the experience of buyers of used machines of various grades and ages. Since 95 per cent of used machines are traded in developed countries, records need not depend on keeping track of machines overseas. If a history for each machine is too costly, at least the name of the last user will be helpful to uncertain buyers. In any case, more is needed than the monthly *Used Equipment Directory's* "rebuilt . . . reconditioned . . . guaranteed . . . excellent . . . good . . . fair . . . as is." But even this publication is not widely known abroad.

[13] Albert Waterston, "Good Enough for Developing Countries?" *Finance and Development*, Sept. 1964, p. 95.

[14] *Second-Hand Machines and Economic Development*, Publication 15/58, Netherlands Economic Institute, Division of Balanced International Growth, Rotterdam, May 1958, p. 24.

Once good used equipment has been found, a single organization should be responsible for disassembling, packing, reassembling, and getting it back into working order. For some buyers, the main advantage of new equipment is simply knowing that it will be well-packed because performance is guaranteed. Key parts may come in vacuum cans to avoid corrosion. If equipment is dropped thirty feet to the dock and then left for days in the rain, it will survive because it was packed to withstand such treatment. Or it will be replaced.

The uncertainty of used machinery exporters is a different problem. They can expect to get less government financial support for customers, such as the U.S. Export-Import Bank gives, than sellers of new machines can get because they do not contribute as directly as new machine sellers to home output and employment. Yet customers of used machinery exporters are likely to be greater credit risks—one reason why they cannot afford new equipment. Here development banks have an obvious role to protect machinery traders against bad debts. But it may be more likely that governments will add to uncertainty by threatening to prohibit imports of used machinery. Encouraging such prohibitions is one tactic used by established manufacturers for discouraging competition. Especially public enterprises find the bad publicity from breakdowns and idle factories worse than somewhat higher payments for new machines.

If a manufacturer's sales agent takes on used equipment as a sideline, he may worry about his reputation. Markets may not be large enough to support a separate organization for selling used machines to many industries. Without an organization, joint or separate, how can the exporter know if complaints from buyers are valid? If a discount is sought because of unexpectedly poor condition, should he grant it? If a motor is said to have broken within weeks, should he send another? The discount and the replacement may cost less than sending a technician to check up, and the exporter realizes that the buyer knows that. Perhaps sales contracts should make buyers liable for technicians' travel expenses where claims prove unjustified.[15] By eliminating these uncertainties by preventing abuses or through absorbing their costs, governments can foster use of secondhand machines, hence a more productive allocation of capital. For example, they can hire sellers of new machinery as consultants in sales and servicing, thus allowing these to contribute without much risk to their reputation.[16]

Such inspecting and underwriting services, aided by government, rise in importance with the distance of the developing country from those sending the machinery. Even though used machines were more eagerly sought in Monterrey than in Mexico City or San Juan, neither Mexican nor Puerto Rican industry was sorely out of touch with the United States secondhand equipment market. Occasional flights to New York, Chicago, or Los Angeles let industrialists keep up with trends. Further away, contacts are less close, and more assistance is needed to overcome uncertainties. Under a "Tools for Freedom" program, over \$1.6 million worth of used machine tools have recently been given away by American manufacturers, largely to schools in the Philippines and to a United Nations advanced technical

[15] *Ibid.*, pp. 27–8.

[16] At its annual meeting in 1963 the United States Machinery Dealers National Association decided to draft a code of ethics and procedures to be followed by all member firms interested in exporting to developing countries. This code would be a counterpart to the guarantees already given with United States sales. Of these, most common is the 30-day money back guarantee, with the buyer paying the cost of return transportation. Relatively safe are the sales of excess U.S. government equipment to other governments via the Agency for International Development. In 1964 these sales amounted to \$50 million. Among other recommendations to the United Nations, a group of experts in 1965 suggested the establishment of a clearing house to facilitate the international transfer of secondhand equipment (*Report of Expert Group on Second-Hand Equipment,* pp. 6, 17, 22).

and vocational training center for developing nations in Turin, Italy.[17] Such gifts are admirable, but they may be a sign that marketing channels are underorganized and the mutual advantages of ordinary commercial transactions undervalued at both ends of the channels.

VI. *Summary and Conclusions*

Lower wage levels and higher capital costs in underdeveloped countries make a strong a priori case for using equipment longer than in developed countries and for importing second-hand machines. If maintenance is labor-intensive, labor-abundant countries should buy more of it. In addition, labor-displacing inventions can make old machines inferior for high-wage countries without doing so for low-wage countries. But even when new and old machines differ only in life expectancy, the old will be a better buy for underdeveloped countries if price is determined mainly by the demand in developed countries. The capital not spent can be invested at a higher rate of return.

Practice and the a priori case agree widely but not universally in part because assumptions are not universally met. In some industries obsolescence or deterioration occur so fast that wage rates cannot be low enough to make spending on maintenance, repair, and transportation a bargain. Here labor-capital substitution through old machines is not an option.

In other industries and regions, abundance of labor may have no relation to the supply of key maintenance skills so that new equipment, often replaced, is more efficient than is keeping or buying old equipment. At the same time, imperfections in capital markets may allow more funds to flow into new equipment and at lower interest rates.

[17] *New York Times*, March 6, 1965.

But even in cases where old machines are a feasible choice, Mexican and Puerto Rican experience suggests that entrepreneurs may reject or abandon equipment too soon. They may be unduly afraid of breakdowns, an inclination often given the ethically neutral label of "taste for risk-avoidance." Of course, they may simply be estimating that breakdown costs per day are equal to production per day, which is an error and not a matter of taste. Also, entrepreneurs may not know how to mobilize their staffs to attain better maintenance, though the skills may be available. Uncertainty about the quality of machines may be compounded by uncertainty over spare parts supplies and shipping methods. In the secondhand equipment trade, these uncertainties are compounded by the fears of suppliers about the credit of buyers and about the future tolerance of governments for secondhand imports.

Governments should not only tolerate secondhand imports but encourage them as much as any other way of saving capital. Undue financial penalties imposed on used machinery imports should be offset by the government. At the risk of being itself victimized by both buyers and suppliers, government can underwrite the risks of both, guaranteeing quality to the buyer and protecting suppliers against unfair claims and bad debts. It can hire or set up a regular organization to collect on a continuing basis an amount of uncertainty-erasing information that would have exorbitant cost if collected spasmodically for this or that transaction by ever-changing sets of partners. Government can support both education for executives in maintenance policies and training for mechanics in specific maintenance and repair tasks. In some cases it may foster industry-wide service-and-repair organizations. Finally, government can give preferred treatment to imports of spare parts and can encourage the pooling of spare parts. But government should neither force the use of truly inferior, obsolete equipment for the sake of employment nor discriminate because of national pride against maintenance and secondhand machines. Economic development has a place for up-to-date gadgets, even for original experiments and innovation, as suggested in the next chapter, but no place for prejudging opportunities on the basis of false premises.

7

Innovation, Technology, and Economic Development

The last two chapters looked at ways of spending more on workers and less on equipment. The sorts of equipment discussed were generally standard types available new or second-hand from developed countries. In this chapter discussion will center on the possibilities of innovation for the small markets, little capital, low wages, and social and natural environments characteristic of underdeveloped countries but different from the North Atlantic region. Are special innovations in fact possible to create a whole new technology for this setting? How much does science offer, and must it be involved in any major innovations? What kinds of attitudes and organization are needed to put an innovation across?

Technological innovation in this context should be defined from the entrepreneur's viewpoint as a world-wide novelty: He knows of no model that might be copied. This is not to say that all copying is simply predictable duplication, devoid of novelty. An activity might be novel for a region, an enterprise, or an individual, and therefore retain its uncertainty. The challenge is to fit the model properly to one's own case. In a given region, channels of supply, public services, regulations, and habits of customers may at first be unsuitable. Even after the region has been prepared, an imitating firm may still have to expand and reorganize itself in ways novel to the entire staff. Any amount of labor turnover means that some people have to learn tasks new to them. Obviously, if too many orders of novelty are dared at a time, the chance of success fades. Can one train an inexperienced group of men to organize a firm, rig out an economic system, explore nature, and hammer out inventions, all at once? Brave, but inconvenient for diagnosing trouble. An engineer at an innovating Mexican firm said the hardest thing during start-ups was extricating negligence (always well-alibied) from process deficiencies as a cause of breakdowns and poor quality.

At the same time, an experienced firm in a developed region may innovate without assigning to anyone a truly novel task. Its top executives have made such decisions before; its engineers have worked other ideas through from sketch to blueprint to production line; and when fundamental problems arose, the research laboratory knew how to sift nature with hypotheses. Carefully isolating variables is the essence of scientific research; novelty is rendered familiar by unweaving its component strands and inspecting each in fairly routine ways. In the language of Herbert A. Simon and his group, search activities are made to reach "a level of concreteness where known, existing programs (generalized means) can be employed to carry out the remaining detail."[1] The pilot plant and development phases of innovations are often the most difficult because here the tangle of variables cannot be reduced. Even in a developed country only the most experienced workmen will regard clearing the inevitable blocks and muddles of the pilot plant as just another variation within a familiar class of activities. As Burton Klein observed: "There is quite a difference between knowing that some idea, say for a communications satellite system, does

[1] James G. March and Herbert A. Simon, *Organizations* (New York: John Wiley, 1958), p. 191.

not violate any known scientific principles, and knowing when it can be ready for use, how much it will cost, how well it will operate, etc." [2]

I. Terms

Discussions have usually broken down the early phases of technological change into science, invention, and innovation; or basic research, applied research and development. I doubt that any useful purpose could be served by redefining either trinity in an unconventional way. "The choice must be between discussing these matters with concepts that are necessarily somewhat vague and not discussing them at all"; [3] and one might as well be vague in a familiar way.

Most vague is the term "innovation" itself. Sociologists often define it as any "idea perceived as new by the individual," [4] but economists prefer to think of it as the first attempts to introduce a new commodity or process on a commercial scale. If these products and processes always came to the entrepreneur in fully ripened technical form, then innovation could be "purely a matter of business behavior," as Schumpeter thought.[5] In practice, however, both scientific and inventive work may have to follow the entrepreneurial choice, and the foreseen cost

[2] Burton Klein, "Rejoinder" to Frederic M. Scherer in *The Rate and Direction of Inventive Activity: Economic and Social Factors* (Princeton: Princeton University Press, 1962), p. 508. Scherer had said, among other things, that such causes as failure by contractors to bring adequate human resources to bear on a problem, rather than unforeseeable and unavoidable technical difficulties, accounted for over 70 per cent of variances from original development time and cost estimates ("The Decision Making Problem in Development," p. 500).

[3] John Jewkes, David Sawers, and Richard Stillerman, *The Sources of Invention* (London: Macmillan, 1958), p. 13.

[4] For example Everett M. Rogers, *Diffusion of Innovations* (New York: Free Press of Glencoe, 1962), p. 13.

[5] Joseph A. Schumpeter, *The Theory of Economic Development,* Redvers Opie, trans. (Cambridge: Harvard U. Press, 1934), p. 86.

of this work will affect that choice. The technical work called for will be directed by a business estimate of the features which the product or process will need to assure commercial success.[6] For economists, therefore, the process of innovation may subsume applied research, invention, and development while excluding imitation or diffusion.[7]

Widely accepted is the definition of "science" as the development through logic and observation of verifiable, general "truths." Within the concept of science, the distinction between "basic" or "fundamental" and "applied research" is vague. "Basic research" is directed toward fuller understanding and is not prompted by specific commercial objectives. "Applied research" aims at solving problems for designated commercial products or processes. Yet basic research *may* lead directly to saleable materials and instruments, while applied research *may* yield a better understanding of nature but no commercial application. Laboratories like good fairies reward the chosen in unexpected ways, but the probability is that findings will fit motivation. The reins that keep one on the path toward application lessen the chance of stumbling on fundamental truths.[8] There is also a borderland of "technically justified science," "exploratory science-invention," or "background applied re-

[6] Abbott Payson Usher, "Technical Change and Capital Formation," *Capital Formation and Economic Growth,* A Conference of the Universities, National Bureau Committee for Economic Research (Princeton: Princeton U. Press, 1955), pp. 533–8; Harold C. Passer, *The Electrical Manufacturers, 1875–1900* (Cambridge: Harvard University Press, 1953), pp. 1, 66–7, 180–1, 356–60; W. Paul Strassmann, *Risk and Technological Innovation: American Manufacturing Methods during the Nineteenth Century* (Ithaca: Cornell University Press, 1959), pp. 8–10.

[7] Fritz Machlup, *The Production and Distribution of Knowledge in the United States* (Princeton: Princeton University Press, 1962). Machlup would have called "new-type plant construction . . . 'innovation' had not so many of my colleagues run away with this word" (pp. 179–82).

[8] Charles V. Kidd, "Basic Research—Description versus Definition," *Science,* Feb. 13, 1959, p. 370, quoted by Machlup, *op. cit.,* p. 147.

search," where fundamental knowledge is produced with the confident expectation of some kind of early but unspecified application.[9]

Finally, there is the problem of setting "development" apart from "applied research" and deciding where "invention" belongs. "Applied research" leads to knowledge that seems to have practical application but does not include the application itself, working out the blueprints and operating instructions for commercial use. This last step is "development." After applied research shows what is possible, development solves remaining problems with "design, construction, and testing of preproduction prototypes and models and 'engineering follow-through' in the early production phase."[10] Development ends when testing becomes routine quality control not aimed at improving further the product or process. Of course, the development of a new product or process can follow inventions made without related scientific advances.

Then, what is an invention? Most agree that it is the idea that some useful product or process can be contrived and made at least workable, if not yet efficient—a more than routine step forward. Invention is an activity that may take place in applied research laboratories, in engineering divisions concerned with development, in the two jointly, or independent of either. Inventions may or may not be patented and published. At some point patent offices and others interested must draw a line between inventions and the minor improvements or "sub-

[9] C. F. Carter and B. R. Williams, *Science in Industry: Policy for Progress* (London: Oxford University Press, 1959), p. 9; Robert S. Merrill, "Some Society-Wide Research and Development Institutions," *Rate and Direction of Inventive Activity: Economic and Social Factors*, pp. 416–8; Michael Polanyi, *Personal Knowledge* (University of Chicago Press, 1958), p. 179; Pierre Auger, *Current Trends in Scientific Research* (Paris: Unesco, 1961), p. 245.

[10] National Science Foundation, *Science and Engineering in American Industry: Report on a 1956 Survey*, NSF-59-50 (Washington, 1959), p. 98.

inventions" that make up much of development. Obviousness, effort required, or significance may be the criteria.[11]

II. Innovations without Science?

A country can progress industrially without innovating and can innovate without advancing science. The raising of productivity without innovation is widespread and has been the main topic of this book. To search for the techniques and experience of others is cheaper than to work out one's own. Troublesome enough is suiting one's work habits to borrowed techniques, and the techniques to one's markets and resources. Of course, as outlined before,[12] resulting problems have a better chance of identification and solution in a country with creative scientists and inventive engineers. One can borrow most effectively if one also has the capacity to be original. Still, countries can develop, though at a slower rate, on the basis of passive, even haphazard, borrowing.

In other words, higher productivity may result from various changes in production methods. First, equipment already installed may be used more effectively through better organization and training. Second, a better layout in strict accord with advanced foreign practice may be adopted. Third, a new layout may be adapted to local markets and resources by selectively including or omitting standard equipment and staffing intensively, especially for inspection and repair. Part of the equipment may be secondhand, even obsolescent. Fourth, equipment may be ordered that has been specially adapted to the local situation but without the application of newly-discovered principles of nature. Fifth, fundamentally redesigned or completely new equipment may be developed in order to apply

[11] Simon Kuznets, "Inventive Activity: Problems of Definition and Measurement," and Jacob Schmookler, "Comment," in *The Rate and Direction of Inventive Activity*, pp. 19–24, 43–7.

[12] Chapter 2.

new scientific findings. At times, these findings can be applied to standard equipment without change in design by specifying different materials, temperatures, speeds, pressures, or voltages.

Information for making all five kinds of changes may come from abroad, as discussed in Chapter 2, but only the adoption of four and five have been defined as technological innovation. Applying science or not is the difference between these two.

The mere presence of eminent scientists in national laboratories, especially at universities, obviously does not assure any connections with industry. Factories may borrow science from abroad, while national scientists may shun applied research or, more rarely, export their own discoveries for application elsewhere. A Puerto Rican process for making yeast out of blackstrap molasses was installed commercially, not in Puerto Rico, but in Taiwan and Costa Rica.

Some examples of equipment adapted independently of scientific advances were noted in the section on local machinery production.[13] Most of these must be classified as subinventions —a change obvious to any technician whenever the need for it arises. A Mexican tire maker found that for the small local volume, his machines had to operate so slowly that, after certain stages, premature cooling rather than excessive heat of the rubber, as in the United States, was a problem. His engineers replaced the cooling equipment with heating lamps. A Puerto Rican ammonia plant had to develop standby devices to keep gas heated during breaks and fluctuations in the public electric power system. No advance in knowledge about properties of materials at various temperatures was needed in either of these cases.

But genuine inventions, based on mechanical rather than scientific ingenuity, do occur. An example is the glass-tumbler molding machine made by Fabricación de Máquinas, S. A. for Cristalería, S. A., of Monterrey. The machine allows six types

[13] Chapter 5.

of molds to be used at a time and to be replaced with others so easily that six mold changes per day are possible. Each day thirty-six different types of tumblers can be made—an adaptation to the comparatively small but heterogeneous Mexican market.

A mosaic tile machinery maker of Monterrey had changed the arrangement of tools and supports and tried to make his machines sturdier, but (although not sure) doubted that any of his changes were worth patenting. "What do I care about novelty? I'm a plain type like this, my old brown sweater. Patenting and theory is for college engineers. When my sons take over, I'll be happy back in the shop where they talk my language and where practical experience counts." His machines were especially suited for small production runs and were advertised as occupying half the space of their closest competitors.

Without recourse to scientific research, a Puerto Rican enterprise developed unusually thin mosaic tile and the machinery for its production. The essence of the innovation appeared to lie in careful selection and mixing of ingredients and in meticulous control of temperature and timing of dips in a continuous oven. To keep the secret, the owners had not applied for patents. The company had also tried to design and build its own mixers, vibrators, grinders and polishers, but finally gave up on many stages and bought French equipment. But even these machines operated so intermittently that a continuous production line became impossible. One complex polisher began breaking a large fraction of tiles one November, but not until June did the French send a mechanic to correct the operation. Unable to help, the mechanic was followed in August by an engineer who had no greater luck. The scrappage rate stayed high. The managers had not anticipated these problems with assistance, repairs, and delivery of spare parts—especially important in an innovating firm where more things are likely to go wrong. It was also obvious that no time-and-motion engineer had ever synchronized work elsewhere in the company, for example, among four men around a hand press. Mere noise reduction from adding routine mufflers to the locally made equipment might have raised output a few percentage points. But as long as the major troubles lasted year after year, treating these minor ones was postponed. The firm has nevertheless survived on the basis of unexpectedly good prices from local contractors who are building offices. Yet the original plan had been to export tiles from the island.

No firm came closer to daring all levels of novelty at once, a remarkable display of spunk—though perhaps fitting Leonardo da Vinci's observation that, "those who are enamored of practice without science are like a pilot who goes into a ship without rudder or compass and never has any certainty where he is going." [14]

All in all, the chance for a major invention without some exploration and development of the scientific base seems slight, especially in underdeveloped countries. This view differs from that of John Jewkes and his associates, who hold that:

In many fields of knowledge, discovery is still a matter of scouting about on the surface of things where imagination and acute observation, supported only by simple technical aids, are likely to bring rich rewards. . . . It may be that the flow of inventions is just as likely to be increased by stimulating the fuller exploitation of the myriads of technical possibilities inherent in the existing stock of scientific knowledge as by increasing that stock. [15]

But among the fifty case histories of inventions selected as "important" or "representative" of the twentieth century by Jewkes, hardly a dozen were not directly related to advances

[14] *The Notebooks of Leonardo da Vinci*, Edward MacCurdy, ed. (New York: Reynal & Hitchcock, 1938), Vol. II, p. 238.

[15] Jewkes *et al.*, *op. cit.*, p. 224. If the definition of "surface" is not too shallow, and if "fuller exploitation" includes scientific research, then our statements could be reconciled.

in science made shortly before the inventor's first hunch or in the course of inventing and developing. This dozen naturally had a mechanical bias and included a few producer's goods—the cotton picker, Sulzer loom, and shell molding—as well as some consumer's gadgets such as the ball point pen, safety razor, zipper, and self-winding wrist watch. Others of the dozen were the gyrocompass, power steering, automatic transmission, and cinerama. As Jewkes noted, these were theoretical advances in a sense because they had to be "thought of from the beginning as a system, and designed as a whole," perhaps to an even greater degree than some new chemical products and processes.[16] Yet as such they added little to our knowledge of nature. Certainly none of them was in a class with radio, television, the transistor, catalytic cracking of petroleum, jet engines, rockets, DDT, penicillin, and nylon—not to mention atomic energy and the servomechanisms of automation, excluded by Jewkes.[17]

[16] *Ibid.*, p. 68.
[17] *Ibid.*, p. 75. The reason for their exclusion was the wish to avoid premature assessment. The remaining inventions listed by Jewkes are bakelite, cellophane, continuous casting of steel, continuous hot strip rolling, crease-resistant fabrics, cyclotron, diesel-electric traction, electric precipitation, fluorescent lighting, freon refrigerants, hardening of liquid fats, helicopter, insulin, Kodachrome, long-playing records, magnetic recording, methyl methacrylate polymers, neoprene, polyethylene, radar, silicones, stainless steels, streptomycin, synthetic detergents, synthetic light polarizer, polyester fibers, tetraethyl lead, titanium, tungsten carbide, and xerography. An additional eleven are mentioned but not given case studies: acrylic fibers, air conditioning, cellophane tape, chromium plating, domestic gas refrigeration, Duco lacquers, electron microscope, krilium, modern artificial lighting, polaroid Land camera, and quick freezing. Of course, Jewkes' main point is not to show that many inventions occur independently of scientific advance, but rather that large organized groups employed by business and government cannot replace the independent inventor with little assistance and resources but more freedom. The independent inventor may, however, use and contribute to scientific advances. See also John Jewkes, "How Much Science?" *Economic Journal*, March 1960, pp. 1–16.

III. Science-dependent Innovations

To hold that major inventions are likely to involve some scientific exploration is not to say that the rate of invention will be determined by, and be proportionate to, the rate of scientific advance. Leaving problems of measuring aside, surely some knowledge will lie dormant until complementary discoveries are made; some discoveries might never be applicable; and some findings will have more applications than others. The relative proportions of these results probably vary from period to period and field to field. Fluctuations in the rate of application are likely to depend on the state of an industry more than on the state of related knowledge, although causes and effects are thoroughly entangled.[18]

But should the fraction of major inventions needing scientific exploration be even larger for underdeveloped than developed countries? Why is the comparative disadvantage of the underdeveloped country least in this area? Since underdevelopment has become a synonym for widespread poverty, low wages and a small market, inventions intended to accommodate high priced labor and large volumes of sales, especially of comparative luxuries, will find more use in developed countries. On the one hand, producers there are under more pressure to replace labor and to consider the economies of continuous processing; and on the other, opportunities for selling novelties and embellished models are wider. Their income elasticity of demand is higher. By contrast, cheaper substitutes for materials used in production and for consumers' necessities could do well in poor countries. If rising-income-related inventions are less

---

[18] Jacob Schmookler, "Changes in Industry and in the State of Knowledge as Determinants of Industrial Invention," *The Rate and Direction of Inventive Activity*, pp. 195–232; Richard R. Nelson, "The Economics of Invention: A Survey of the Literature," *Journal of Business*, April 1959, pp. 105–7.

dependent on science than inventions intended purely as substitutes, then the case is clear.

The fact is, however, that rising-income-related inventions may be either relatively science-dependent, such as Kodachrome, or relatively science-independent, such as self-winding wrist watches. If higher incomes and nothing else occasioned inventions, then technical progress for lagging countries could be pure trickle-down, augmented by an occasional gap filler with no particular science-dependent or science-independent bias. But rising incomes are not the only stimulus. Developed countries also make inventions which create substitutes, some of which can be used immediately all over the world, which means that all users are on the technological frontier, ready for the next step. The molecular and crystalline structure of materials is still less well understood than are principles of mechanics; and since climate, soils, and minerals vary, the technological and scientific frontier will also vary from place to place. Some discoveries and inventions for one latitude have different implications at another.

There is in addition more international heterogeneity among necessities than among luxuries. For the poor, food, clothing and shelter must often be related to a myriad of local differences in resources and traditions to be both cheap and respectable. Inventions for Bedouins may not suit Bengalis. As incomes grow, however, the effect of example spreads acceptance of alien fashions so that more inventions are internationally apt. Possibilities for borrowing technology therefore rise with income.

As incomes and labor costs come to each higher level, moreover, it is also likely that science-independent inventions for that level will already have been made: the cotton pickers, automatic transmissions, and self-winding wrist watches. After all, mechanics were not a scientific frontier even in the nineteenth century when such devices as turret lathes and typewriters were invented.

In short, inventions that are combinations of long-existing knowledge are likely to occur where the economic setting first becomes favorable. The more others lag the fewer combinations of the known will remain unmade by the time they reach that stage. Especially the easiest and clearly productive combinations will be thoroughly complete. But a surprising scientific advance can erase the advantage of early arrival at high income levels and temporarily set the speedometer back to zero for the whole planet. Developed countries will usually regain momentum faster, but they cannot explore all directions at once.

IV. The Choice of Tasks

That scientific research is likely to be needed for innovation, especially in underdeveloped countries, is not to say that it is the pure scientist who is most likely to try to solve problems of poverty and low productivity. Much of the frontier of science today lies in the area of extreme conditions: abnormally high and low temperatures, high and low pressures, short time intervals, extreme electric and magnetic fields, extraordinary purities, intense or zero gravitational or acceleration fields. Economic conditions in the lands of *favelas,* monsoons, and deserts are also extreme, but it would be unreasonably lucky if understanding physical extremes were the best way to abolish economic extremes. Nor do ocean depths, Antarctica, or outer space seem the best progenitors of new production methods. Although any exploration of the unknown will have unexpected byproducts, the pure scientist working with lasers or DNA molecules has neither the interest nor the competence to look toward a new industry within a decade or so.

To deal with the need for innovation, in underdeveloped countries particularly, therefore, the purity of seeking truth about nature must be sullied by considerations of practical problems, though not as much as might appeal to the ordinary rather tightfisted and fainthearted bureaucrat or businessman. Their craving for certainty and fast results can easily match the pure scientist's indifference. Scientific work should, however, be guided neither by fashions in curiosity, which might perhaps be stimulated by new laboratory techniques and measuring devices, nor by predictable commercial payoffs. The work should and can be guided at first by the general contours of poverty: bad health, hunger, and poor housing. To apply science to manufacturing here means to lower the cost of processed food and to raise the content of proteins and vitamins, perhaps through new types of food including animal feeds, and through new methods of preparation, preservation, and packaging, as well as by new pesticides and fertilizers. Local raw materials can provide new medicines as well as building materials of many types. Various countries have different advantages for the development of cheap and effective new hardboard plastics, paints, resins, and adhesives, whether macromolecular compounds of carbon and hydrogen only, polyurethane foams, or polyacrylic compounds. Other, perhaps simpler, materials can be produced in the field of traditional ceramics, which the most highly advanced countries are reported to have practically abandoned.[19]

As development proceeds and the consumption of manufactured goods proliferates, innovations in more and more lines grow feasible. Scientific research can advance the acceptability for local production of many imports that reach wide local sales. It is possible, although unrealistic, to suppose that the growth of manufacturing will tend to promote exports rather than import-substituting, but this tendency will not be explored here.[20]

The point here is that research is likely to be initiated by the notion of making a specific product, not by the hope of exploiting a general condition. One hopes to substitute one material

[19] Pierre Auger, *Current Trends in Scientific Research*, pp. 183–8.

[20] A. O. Hirschman, *The Strategy of Economic Development* (New Haven: Yale University Press, 1958), pp. 120–5.

for another or one process for another to make the price and performance of the domestic line as acceptable as, if not preferable to, the import. The scientist looks at the function of the product: is it warmth, lubrication, adhesion, flavor? He looks at the materials conventionally used to see if their key elements (a certain oxide here or a cellulose fiber there) may not be better obtained from unconventional local materials. He looks at the way the physical and chemical changes— always the essence of any manufacturing process—take place with these materials, how they bring out the special properties sought and what elements interfere. He thinks about filtering, sintering, extruding, engraving, stitching, annealing, roasting and countless other operations.

Unlike the economist, the applied scientist does not live in a world of generalities. He cannot identify his task with global concepts like "land, labor, and capital," nor even with aggregative notions of "energy." Economists have long insisted that the net result of a myriad of spending and lending decisions is different from their arithmetic sum, that certain interactions cancel the effects of some decisions and multiply those of others, and that crude adding often means a "fallacy of composition." But this line of reasoning works both ways. A "fallacy of *de*composition" may be committed if analysis of technological change in every industrial branch from pillows to barometers is reduced to the interplay of capital and labor. True, materials and processes are irksomely heterogeneous, a fact that for generations blocked rational economizing. And insofar as they are not imported, materials do tend to cancel out in the aggregate, by one firm's output being another's input, except for inventory changes which become part of capital. But this approach solves the economist's problem, not the scientist's, engineer's, or entrepreneur's.

The scientist, whether pure or applied, hunts for the great simplifying breakthrough—that singular discovery or elegant formulation that cuts through the patchwork of earlier methods and views, a grand simple design that overwhelms or eludes a host of irritating obstructions. His ideas have their origin in careful thought about the properties of some material and in close observation of its behavior. With a feeling of self-denial he may keep himself from following some intriguing hunches because the chance for their industrial utility is too slight. This would be the extent of his concern for industrial utility: How can he think of detailed costs of buildings, equipment, and workers before he knows what materials are to be treated and in what sequence of steps? If a pilot plant is worth building, something can be learned then—but at a time when much of the freedom to pursue alternatives may be gone.

I asked a few directors of scientific research institutes about innovations to use more workers and to save capital for the economy. Answers were uniformly indignant. "If industrial engineers can't do that when their turn comes, why are they getting paid?" said one. "No señor," said another, "I see things in a completely different light from you. When you pray or work for miracles, you do not make terms." Anyone who thought an invention less meritorious because of capital intensity was like the fisherman's wife who, when turned into a queen by the weird halibut, complained of not being empress. When you are pushing out a production function, you do not worry about its slope until you are through.

Like capital-labor ratios, energy use is a feature of all industrial processes and on a per capita basis is often thought to be an index of economic development. Unlike the abstract capital-labor ratios, fuels and prime movers are fields of direct scientific research. Yet, when applied in manufacturing this common denominator—the need for flaming chemical reductions or whirling shafts—is again dwarfed by uncommon elements. Heat and power are important in making steel, aluminum, cement, glass, and certain chemicals; but in most lines the cost of fuel and power comes to no more than 1 to 3 per cent of value added. A dramatic change in energy sources together with a sharp fall in costs per calorie or kilowatt could therefore have only limited repercussions. There would be a bit more mechanization; some energy-intensively made materials would be substituted for others; and concern for insulation could decrease. The elasticity of substituting energy directly or indirectly for other elements of production will vary from process to process and is bound to be low in many lines. Energy research is no nostrum that, if successful, allows neglect of other subjects: Larger amounts of energy used with fewer advances in complementary knowledge than before would clearly be an unreliable index of progress. Finally, it appears that unless controlled nuclear fusion becomes a reality, energy research will probably do well just to keep costs from rising as fossil fuels grow scarce.[21]

Another candidate for cross-industrial innovation might be "miniaturization," the adaptation of basic industrial processes to smaller volumes. Large volume has often been a prerequisite for the development and use of radically new ways of processing, but as these new ways are perfected, possibilities for relaxing that prerequisite can arise. The dimensions of the process can be reduced most easily where dimensions of the product are small per unit, and perhaps reducible. Least reducible are the many products from bathtubs to binoculars for which the human consumer physically sets the minimum scale. More amenable are the materials out of which these are made. These

[21] Palmer Putnam, *Energy in the Future* (New York: Van Nostrand, 1953); Hans H. Landsberger, Leonard L. Fischman, Joseph L. Fisher, *Resources in America's Future* (Baltimore: Johns Hopkins for Resources for the Future, 1963); Paul W. McGann, "Technological Progress and Minerals," in Joseph Spengler, ed., *Natural Resources and Economic Growth* (Washington: Resources for the Future, 1961), pp. 74–97; Richard L. Meier, *Science and Economic Development* (New York: John Wiley, 1956), pp. 76–138.

materials themselves are often made by processes in which economies of scale have been relatively more important. Yet, cross-industrial application of these generalities is blocked by the heterogeneity that makes most answers to casting problems irrelevant to weaving.

That common elements exist in all production is true and basic to the most valuable insights of economists and scientific managers. No doubt engineers and research scientists with a better grasp than most have today of economic reality, particularly of the principles of scarcity and substitution, could make more effective contributions. Nevertheless, as in other cases, mistaking models for reality can be a handicap. In pondering the connection between science and innovation, one must not generalize out of existence the overruling diversity of tasks.

V. *Attitudes and Organization*

The tasks of innovation cannot be characterized only in terms of materials, processes, and products. Thrusting a novelty into the routine affairs of others must by definition be distinguishable from those affairs: hence an extraordinary feat. Can only extraordinary people carry out such feats, and what is really extraordinary about the feats and the people? A little cussedness or fast talk may give the chance to bring in a degree of novelty in one society or decade that in another would take risk of martyrdom. The difference in societies lies not only in their tolerance of novelty—high where many changes are taking place anyway so that routines and positions are unsettled and therefore less sacrosanct; low under reverse conditions. Novelty can, however, be fostered through techniques of organization that make up both for possible disturbances and for the rarity of extraordinary vision, facility, and boldness.

Lack of vision means greater uncertainty: failure to see both difficulties and opportunities. Incompetence can waste the opportunities, when they come, and leave the difficulties unmastered. Timidity embroiders on these dangers and inhibits action even more than is justified by the poor vision and incompetence. The result of this unhappy combination is that not enough resources are allocated to innovation. Appropriate organization can lower uncertainty and the penalty for failure, and raise capacity and rewards for success so that more men and funds are tempted to try innovation. The result in these circumstances is that some extraordinary tasks are not delayed by the lack of equally extraordinary men.

"Appropriate" organization, of course, means more than better markets. The same dilemmas of inappropriability and increasing returns, and the paradox of the demand for information, that keep pure markets from transferring enough *old* knowledge internationally,[22] hamper spending for *new* knowledge from laboratory to pilot plant. No wholly unequivocal system for kindling technological creativity has been widely accepted even in developed countries. It is generally agreed that subsidies to scientific and managerial education are necessary, but how far should subsidies for research go? Research also educates: Does the public therefore not have a right at least to the knowledge bought with taxes? If so, should patent royalties be paid and for how long? Must patents be used to stay valid? What gambles are discouraged by any given obligation to share returns or knowledge at early stages? Large research organizations can balance failure with success, avoid duplication, and coordinate related work. But without direct or indirect public support, must they not be part of huge private firms, raising doubts about maintaining competition? Whether public or private, where does large size imply procedures and standards that rule out madcap schemes, the demented as well as the brilliant? Inability to answer these questions has kept many developed countries using all approaches,

[22] See Chapter 2.

public and private, large and small organizations, open and closed. And these countries still do not know whether the balance is near an optimum.

Cultivating the social garden for the planting of innovations is far more difficult in underdeveloped than in developed countries. The planters are less experienced; and the owners suspect them of sowing weeds, or in any case less pretty flowers than are grown beyond the wall. Innovation gets less support in the underdeveloped countries, and what support there is seems subject to higher risks. The veracity of this supposition should be tested, however, by comparing the incidence of loss in various countries. The risks appear higher not only compared with developed countries today but with conditions there in the last century.

Hard to evaluate is the production risk of not attaining and keeping enough technical efficacy, compared with alternatives, to amortize the investment while earning the going rate of profit. More foreign expertise is available to help with recalcitrant problems than was true a hundred years ago; but by the same token, competing innovations from abroad are more likely. Such competition may not always be thwarted by tariffs because a foreign process or product can be licensed to a domestic concern behind the tariff wall—if, indeed, it cannot be copied without license.

In general, however, the wider use of protective tariffs lowers customer risks that a product will not sell because of ignorance, inertia, and prejudice. Customers are simply deprived of foreign alternatives. Even domestic competitors may be discouraged through tax, selective credit, and licensing policies.

Whether the risks of unlucky timing are higher or lower in the early stages of development in this century compared with the last depends on the country. The extremes of political stability and instability are now too far apart, as are the patterns of economic stability (determined by one or two export crops in some countries), to allow much generalization. But depressions because of internal demand deficiency and credit contraction are less likely than before World War II. Any uncertainties affect all investment, of course; but they bear down more heavily on those novelties which have a longer gestation period. Science-dependent innovations usually take more time because they involve more stages; and, though such innovations have grown more common, any comparable stage can usually be despatched faster than in the last century.

The clearest increase in the risks of innovation comes from deliberate interference by hostile groups, particularly in government. One branch of a government may finance research carried out by another while a third withholds the permits needed for full-scale application of resulting discoveries and inventions. Nobody can be against science in this century. Not to have a few landscaped, glassbrick research institutes is like not having a modern Labor Code or an Economic Planning Commission: a national disgrace. But the laboratories, if well-staffed and equipped, can produce unpredictable and embarrassing results. A proposed innovation can upset government plans for spreading employment, for mitigating income inequality, or for decentralizing industry. It may aggravate the losses of a competing government-owned enterprise. As is true of patents, any guarantee given to an earlier innovation means greater interference risks for the next step. If an innovation threatens private firms or a group of organized workers, these will find a branch of government that will plead their cause in terms of the general welfare and precedent. Moreover, it is entirely possible that abuses can be committed in the name of technological advance or that some genuine innovations could lead to so much confusion and divert such energy and attention from other tasks that the net result would be a loss to society. Unable to tell one case from another, to sift valid evidence from trumped up claims and charges, the minister in charge will procrastinate, hope in vain for a compromise, and finally decide against. Why should he stake his career on something untried? The national laboratory will be content to have its budget renewed, and the private sponsors can surely find some other way to stay rich. Small innovations have a better chance.

In this chapter the difficulty of generalizing because of such things as wide heterogeneity of industries and the idiosyncrasies of governments and talented individuals could not be overcome. It therefore seems proper to include a few case studies that illustrate the possibility of science-dependent innovations, their relation to local peculiarities of markets or materials, the role of government as supporter or thwarter of innovations, and the parts played by certain key personalities in this context.

VI. Cases

A. *Stabilized Tortilla Flour.*   One of the best possible innovations in a poor country is to make the staple food easier to prepare, less perishable, and of higher nutritive value. It can release people for tasks besides food preparation and gives them more energy for all work.

From the hot lowlands to the sierras, maize has traditionally been the main crop of Mexico, accounting for over half the acreage in crops and for about one-fourth of total crop value. Over half the maize eaten by humans is in the form of tortillas, thin cohesive pancakes of pre-Columbian origin. Tortillas are formed out of a paste called *masa,* obtained by precooking the grain in a lime solution to make *nixtamal* and grinding the result. Making an average family's daily supply of tortillas with the traditional clay jars and hand grinding on stone *metates* would take one woman six to eight hours. Since the nineteenth century, thousands of small mills, *molinos de nixtamal,* have done the precooking and paste grinding in Mexican towns, mechanizing the primitive process in a relatively unsanitary fashion. Their product is a *masa* that easily decomposes and must therefore be bought daily for each household.

The advantages of a nixtamalized flour that could be stored and mixed with water to make *masa* are clear. During the first half of the twentieth century, a number of Mexicans tried to develop such a flour but with trial and error methods. The results either lacked cohesiveness, the right flavor, or the desired stability. In 1946 the Banco de Mexico began sponsoring a more scientific study of the problems involved, first directly and then indirectly through the Instituto Mexicano de Investigaciones Tecnológicas (IMIT), the applied research institute set up in 1950 with the help of the Armour Research Foundation. Such factors as the optimum proportions of corn, water, and lime for maceration, the right pH level, temperatures and times for cooking, cleaning, and drying were determined[23] as well as possibilities for enriching the product. After further study in a 7.5-ton-per-day pilot plant, patents were obtained, and a 300-ton plant was designed by IMIT and installed at Tlalnepantla outside Mexico City in 1954 for Maiz Industrializado S.A. This was a new company financed entirely with 19 million pesos from Nacional Financiera, hence a public sector enterprise. In the United States, the Quaker Oats Company obtained the patent rights and built plants in Texas and California to sell the flour as *Masa Harina*. The novel part of the plants is not the equipment itself but its arrangement and the manner of handling water, steam, lime, and corn. Technical success from the beginning in the laboratory to the final product came from systematic teamwork rather than from the vision and drive of any one indispensable personality.

[23] The process is described in Guillermo Salorio, Jorge García Arroyo, and Mario Velarde, "Substitución de los Procedimientos Primitivos en la Elaboración de Maíz Nixtamalizado, Artículo de Consumo Básico en la Población Mexicana," United Nations Conference on the Application of Science and Technology for the Benefit of the Less Developed Areas, Geneva 163, E/Conf.39/D/159.

Whether finding such a person and keeping him in charge would have helped in later stages of this innovation cannot now be determined. In 1960 tortilla flour was still considered IMIT's greatest success, yet even sympathetic observers were disappointed and others called it a "white elephant." Four years later I heard that,

The trouble with our research institutes is the same as with our football teams. There's much finesse—but where are the goals? Talk about experience and this and that is fine, but what counts is can you put yourself in a position to kick a goal?

In 1960 the plant at Tlalnepantla operated at only 42 per cent of capacity using two shifts for about three months and one shift for the rest of the year. The profit rate was only 1.2 per cent of sales. The government controlled price of maize was 750 pesos a ton, which meant 810 pesos per ton of tortilla flour since 1.08 tons of maize are needed per ton of flour. At 42 per cent of capacity, other production costs per ton came to 425 pesos. Total cost per ton of tortilla flour was 1,235 pesos. The controlled price of the tortilla flour was 1,250 pesos. If the plant could have operated at full capacity, other costs would have fallen to 210 pesos per ton, leaving profits of 230 pesos per ton, or 18.4 per cent of sales, and a much higher percentage of the original investment.

Why the plant did not sell enough to allow full-capacity operation is not clear. Were the succession of managers noted more for their political connections than their talents as aggressive promoters? I do not know. One often finds the same busy hum in the offices of government-run plants as in those privately owned. Probably more significant is that maize prices were subsidized to the *molinos de nixtamal* so that they could sell *masa* at only 35 centavos per kilo. The equivalent amount of *masa* from less subsidized tortilla flour cost 56 centavos per kilo. Maiz Industrializado, S.A., was not successful in getting the subsidies reduced even to *molinos de nixtamal* near the high income Pedregal and Lomas de Chapultepec sections of Mexico City. Most sales were in the sparsely populated northern states where distances from *molinos de nixtamal* were great. But soon the process was copied in Sinaloa, Nuevo Leon, and perhaps elsewhere, all without paying patent royalties to IMIT. The Banco de Mexico found that plants with 25-to-50-ton daily capacities were entirely feasible.

Of course, one cannot be sure that the government has been wrong in protecting thousands of *molinos de nixtamal*. How quickly could these resources have been shifted to other uses? What price tag can be put on political repercussions? But as far as IMIT and its public sponsors were concerned, the tangible rewards for their innovation came from Quaker Oats.

B. *Direct Reduction of Iron Ore with Natural Gas.* Steel is conventionally made from iron ore in two steps: ore is first smelted with limestone and coke in a blast furnace to make pig iron; this pig iron is then refined in converters, furnaces, or crucibles. Direct reduction eliminates the blast furnaces —enormous and costly structures that cannot be scaled down to low volumes. In direct reduction, two or more basic steps may remain between the mine and the rolling mill, but the ore is typically reduced at temperatures below the melting point of iron and without limestone. Exceptions are the electric furnaces developed in Scandinavia after 1910. Attempts to reduce iron with hydrogen, carbon monoxide, or solid carbon fines also date back to 1910 in Sweden. Most of the processes developed (Höganäs, Wiberg-Söderfors, Basset, Avesta-Domnarvet, Krupp-Renn, U.S. Bureau of Mines) used horizontal rotary kilns as in cement plants. Although few of the kilns reached capacities above 30,000 tons annually, a number of European countries and Japan found them economical during World War II. Most of these kilns were quickly abandoned afterwards except for some types which have advantages for making sponge iron out of very pure ores, for high quality alloys or for powder metallurgy. (The term "sponge iron" can be traced back to the Greeks and refers to the porous appearance of masses of iron particles reduced from oxides at less than melting temperatures.)

During the 1950's interest in direct reduction was taken up by countries eager to industrialize but lacking both coking coal and markets large enough for blast furnaces.[24] Although Mexico has both, Hojalata y Lámina, S.A., (HYLSA) of Monterrey was first to develop a commercial direct reduction process using natural gas on high-grade hematite lumps to make sponge iron as a substitute for scrap in an electric furnace. A 66,000-ton plant using the "HyL Process" was built in 1957, a 165,000-ton plant in 1960, and another in 1964.

Hojalata y Lámina was founded in 1942 as part of an industrial empire of banks, breweries, glass plants, paper mills, machinery builders, and other firms, some dating back to the late nineteenth century, and all largely owned and controlled by the Sada and Garza Sada families of Monterrey. Assets were said to be worth over seven hundred million dollars in the early 1960's. During the Korean War, scrap prices rose and the quality available to HYLSA's electric furnace fell. The Ontario Research Foundation of Toronto was retained to try its rotary tunnel kiln, developed by Patrick E. Cavanagh. A pilot plant at Monterrey made 20 tons of sponge iron per day and achieved things Cavanagh had believed impossible: using coal instead of coke, and labor "in a way that could not be imagined in Canada, giving rise to quite different possibilities."[25]

[24] Economic Commission for Latin America and Technical Assistance Administration, *A Study of the Iron and Steel Industry in Latin America*, Vol. II, Proceedings of the Expert Working Group held at Bogotá, Oct. 1952 (New York: United Nations, 1954), pp. 167–230.

[25] *Ibid.*, p. 230.

In spite of talk about tripling output or even raising it to 5,000 tons monthly, HYLSA abandoned the tunnel kiln. Unlike similar processes it had sharply decreasing, not increasing, returns to scale. The larger the diameter, the greater the difficulty of keeping gas velocity high enough in the kiln center. The final innovation meant a change to natural gas from coal and was not at all labor intensive.

But first another failure occurred. The 1952 Bogotá Conference in Latin American iron and steel production was attended by Bernardo Garza Sada, a young engineer and assistant manager of HYLSA. There he heard a paper about experiments at Longview, Texas, in the mid-1940's, using reformed natural gas in a shaft furnace, in batch reactors with a pulsating "butterfly valve" that varied pressure from atmospheric to 40 pounds per square inch. The pulsating pressure was to give a higher rate of reduction through better gas distribution.[26] Ross Compton, who had been at Longview, was hired as consultant by HYLSA, and a pilot plant was built at Monterrey in late 1953. Although the design was improved to keep temperatures higher, performance was unsatisfactory. In July 1954, the M. W. Kellogg Company, a large New York firm of industrial process engineers, was hired to build a better gas reforming unit. But even this failed to improve matters enough, and in the winter of 1955 the pulsating pressure system was given up.

There was no doubt but that the carbon monoxide and hydrogen made from desulfurized natural methane and steam could reduce iron ore. That had been shown in 1918 by Martin Wiberg in Stockholm. The problem was to make it pay—to get a lot of reduction out of a little gas without consuming the plant. As with tortilla flour, it meant finding the right temperatures, times, sequences, and balance of materials. But new equipment had to be designed, too; hydrogen could not be heated enough in the usual tubular preheaters because of ex-

[26] *Ibid.*, p. 220; and sources cited p. 227.

pansion problems. This, and other problems seemed to be solved primarily by a brilliant young Mexican engineer, Juan Celada, to whom HYLSA gave an unusually free hand. Celada originally came from Torreón, Coahuila, and received a Master of Science Degree from the Massachusetts Institute of Technology in 1944. M.I.T. was also attended by Eugenio, Roberto, Armando, and Bernardo Garza Sada, a rather important link in the chain of events. Soon Celada was Chief Engineer and then Technical Director of HYLSA and a cluster of related firms. By September 1955 the improved pilot plant made 30 tons of sponge iron per day with enough reliability to warrant bringing back the Kellogg Company to collaborate in the design and construction of the 200 ton per day (66,000 tons per year) plant. The unit was started up in November 1957, one reactor at a time, the last of five in March 1958. As one Kellogg official put it later, "Thank God for the Mexicans, that they had the guts to sink millions into this process."

The separate batch reactors in the HyL process go through phases that, in effect, have gas and charge moving in opposite directions. For three hours hot, partially spent gas from other reactors preheats the reactor newly charged with crushed and screened ore ($\frac{1}{2}$ to 2 inch lumps, about 45 per cent hematite and 20 per cent magnetite). Reduction begins. When it has reached the point where thermodynamic equilibrium limitations become important, richer unspent gas is passed through for a second three hours. This gas has been preheated for three hours in a third reactor in which a previously reduced charge is cooled while acquiring some 2 per cent of combined carbon. The sponge iron never reaches melting temperatures, which keeps refractory maintenance low—mostly for abrasions.[27] The

[27] Juan Celada, Gunther H. Muller, Earl W. Riblett, "HyL Sponge Iron Production," *Chemical Engineering Progress,* Sept. 1960; Juan Celada, C. K. Mader, R. Lawrence, "The HyL Sponge Iron Process," *Iron and Steel Engineer,* Jan. 1960; Gunther H. Muller, "Sponge Iron in Mexico," *Metal Progress,* Jan. 1960.

500 ton (165,000 tons per year) plant cost about six million dollars. It converted ore into sponge for $6 to $9 per ton operating costs, excluding capital charges. Steel ready to be rolled into plates and sheets was made for about $70 a ton. Import-protected Mexican prices for the finished product averaged U.S. $177 during 1955–59.[28]

Of course it took months before either the 200-ton or the first 500-ton plant worked well. For two months the first plant operated at less than 50 per cent of capacity because of fouling of waste heat boiler tubes. A better water supply had to be installed. Teamwork in manipulating the reactor cycles was slow in coming. Hydraulic mechanisms functioned poorly. The electric furnaces had trouble melting the less conductive sponge together with scrap, and a way of melting sponge first and adding scrap later had to be developed. With inexperienced supervisors and workers, repairs took days instead of hours.

The second plant was made a showpiece of automation, partly to impress possible clients for the process from other countries. Only eight men are needed per shift. Safety levels are raised and crude devices eliminated. For example, to load and unload the sponge iron it is no longer necessary to disconnect the lower part of the reactor, move it out, and tilt it for emptying into a hopper. The reactor stays together and is loaded from above and emptied through its base. A novel 24-inch valve, patented by Kellogg, eliminates a step in which gas was quenched to make it cool enough for existing valves, only to be reheated after passing through.

Innovations in the use of oxygen in blast furnaces made the HyL process relatively less advantageous than expected for

[28] *Steelmaking with Gas*, M. W. Kellogg Company brochure (undated), pp. 14–17; David G. Greene, *Steel and Economic Development: Capital-Output Ratios in Three Latin American Steel Plants* (East Lansing: Michigan State University Institute for International Business and Economic Development Studies, 1967), pp. 100, 105.

many locations. At the 1963 Geneva Conference on Science and Technology, two British experts insisted that, "Beyond all doubt the orthodox blast furnace must be selected as the proven and reliable means of iron making for the emergent country with normal rather than unique conditions." [29] Nevertheless, HYLSA built a second 500-ton plant at Monterrey in 1964 and a third near Puebla in 1965. A maker of seamless tubes, Tubos de Acero de México, S.A., signed a contract to build a 500-ton plant near Vera Cruz in the spring of 1965 and was planning another in Argentina.[30] A $250,000 feasibility study was under way for a plant in Northeast Brazil. Other plants were considered in Saudi Arabia and Iraq.

The way in which Hojalata y Lámina achieved success shows what vast resources and great patience innovation may require: willingness to spend and to wait, to borrow at some time and to be original at others, to work alone and to hire help, to be persistent, yet finally ready to abandon one approach for another. In the United States, Standard Oil, U. S. Steel, Republic Steel, National Lead, Allis-Chalmers, and others were experimenting with direct reduction at the same time, hoping for a more continuous process than HYLSA's, but they were unable to marshal better scientific resources for superior results.

C. *Paper from Bagasse, Yuccas, and Tropical Hardwoods.* Tortilla flour makers must begin with corn, and steelmakers have few material options besides scrap, magnetite, and hematite. But for paper making a wide spectrum of cellulosic materials can be pulped, matted together, and dried into sheets. Over 85 per cent of the pulp still comes from long-fibered

[29] G. B. R. Feilden and A. G. Raper, "A New Concept of a Low Cost Integrated Steelworks for Emergent Countries," United Nations Conference on the Application of Science and Technology for the benefit of the Less Developed Areas, Geneva, 1963, E/Conf.39/D/151; see also D/41, D/77, D/105, D/154, and D/191.

[30] Royalties were to be U.S. $1.00 per ton, subject to negotiation.

spruce, fir, balsam, and some other conifers. Soft and with little resin, these are most suitable for grinding, while their lack of phenolic heartwood makes them fit for tried-and-true sulphite cooking. Yet outside of the northern latitudes, other plant materials are more abundant. Economic development means more people reading and more things to wrap up at a pace that should double world demand for paper from the early 1960's to the mid-1970's.[31] Hence, experiments with other fibers are under way in many countries.

Odd materials are nothing new. Fine paper has been made out of the esparto grass of southern Spain and North Africa for nearly a century. The very first paper is said to have been made in China by T'sai Lun in 105 A.D. out of the inner bark of the mulberry tree, its beaten fibers mixed with linen and hemp rags. Paper has been made commercially out of eucalyptus in Australia, Brazil, and Israel; out of bamboo and hardwoods in Japan; from sabai grass in India; out of poplars, willows, and straw in Italy and Argentina; and out of the resinous pine trees of the lower latitudes. Also considered have been sisal, banana stalks, cotton stalks, and most appropriate, papyrus from the Nile.[32] The different morphological and chemical characteristics of various materials have helped stimulate about a dozen new processes in addition to the pre-World War II groundwood, calcium-based sulphite, caustic soda, and sodium sulphate techniques.

That Mexico would be in on all this is not surprising. An examination of innovations attempted with three kinds of materials—bagasse, yuccas, and mixed tropical hardwoods—showed the same patterns as those in the development of tor-

[31] Food and Agriculture Organization of the United Nations, *World Demand for Paper to 1975: A Study of Regional Trends* (FAO/WPPC–59/2; Rome, 1960).

[32] United Nations, *Science and Technology for Development,* Vol. IV., *Industry* (New York, 1963), p. 113–15. A 2,000-ton pulping plant for banana stalks, La Sobana, began operations near Mexico City in 1959.

tilla flour and sponge iron. Innovating takes years of creative flexibility, which can be provided under either government or private auspices. But in late stages government is more likely to be an enemy than a friend; hence, less involvement means a better chance of success. The higher the official the more likely he is to feel accountable to those who lose as well as to those who gain by an innovation, and it will be safer for him to forbid than to promote. Expectations of a small loss of long held things by innocent laggards is more outrageous to the public than a large loss of things never had but only hoped for by up-starts, especially if foreign. Diffused social returns are usually not clear, large, and quick enough to counteract these feelings, and innovation, other than the small or the import-substituting, is not politically smart.

Sugar cane bagasse—the stalks left after milling—was first turned into pulp with a soda chlorine process in 1922 by Humberto Pomilio, an Italian engineer. After a few more years of research, commercial application began in 1939 with limited success in a W. R. Grace and Company plant at Paramonga, Peru. Fifteen years later woodpulp still had to be added in the Grace process, though less than 25 per cent.[33]

The Food and Agricultural Organization of the United Nations considered bagasse pulping definitely established by 1953, but economic elimination, and subsequent use, of pith, which impairs paper quality, remained a problem.[34] It was solved by the first company to make bagasse paper in Mexico, the Compañía Industrial de San Cristóbal, S.A., which also introduced some other innovations and which by late 1964 had the largest bagasse process in the world.

[33] Eugene W. Burgess and Frederick H. Harbison, Casa Grace in Peru, Case Study No. 2, *United States Business Performance Abroad* (Washington, D.C.: National Planning Association, 1954), pp. 29–32.

[34] Food and Agriculture Organization and Economic Commission for Latin America, *Possibilities for the Development of the Pulp and Paper Industry in Latin America* (New York: United Nations, 1954), p. 7.

The entrepreneur behind San Cristóbal was Dr. Dante Sandro Cusi, son of a Mexican-Italian who had owned large farms that were expropriated by the Mexican government. Dr. Cusi had studied engineering in Milan, Italy, and had investigated various food oils and wild palm nuts before shifting his interest to bagasse in 1951. The first plant at San Cristóbal was set up in 1952, but research continued. In 1955 a fifty-fifty association was formed with the Scott Paper Company for making fine papers with the Cusi process. A new plant was finished in 1956, though formal inauguration was delayed until 1959. In 1963–64 this 80-ton per day batch process plant was replaced by a 200 ton per day continuous process.

To eliminate the pith, Dr. Cusi bought the patents of Dr. E. G. Lathrop of the U.S. Northern Regional Research Laboratory and turned the ideas into working equipment. He developed a stabilization process that turns pith saturated with molasses into dry feed. But the main invention involved a special kind of screen that separates "A-fibers" from "B-fibers" after depithing. A-fibers come mainly from the central vascular bundles of the cane; B-fibers from the rind bundles. A-fibers can be pulped at low temperatures with relatively little caustic soda, but they lack the rigidity of wood fibers and make paper that is easily torn unless blended. Making B-pulp takes more heat and chemicals but gives a product much like sulphite softwood pulp, a pulp that can be used for high grades of paper. A mixed cook of the two types of fiber yields 470 kilos of pulp with 118 kilos of caustic soda per metric ton of bagasse. Cooking A- and B-fibers separately gives 557 kilos of pulp with only 104 kilos of soda per ton.[35]

In the summer of 1961, I visited an International Paper Company bagasse plant near Arecibo, Puerto Rico, designed and built by W. R. Grace and Company in 1959 and sold in January

[35] Dante Sandro Cusi, "New Bagasse Process," *Pulp and Paper International,* March 1959, pp. 42–9.

1961. This plant already used a continuous digestor but sold the pith as fuel to a nearby steam plant. A four-stage vibratory screen process for removing the pith was considered too secret to be shown to visitors. The plant mainly produced corrugating medium for packaging, a product which, unlike most, can incorporate "fiber-A." By now, the Paramonga plant in Peru was also making white paper out of "fiber-B." In spite of the publicity given to him in the trade literature, no one at Arecibo could remember having heard of Dr. Cusi and his Mexican process. Unique at Arecibo was a German paper machine equipped with both a six-cylinder and a Fourdrinier wet end.[36] To prevent bagasse decay during storage, the company was experimenting with soaking bagasse in a lactic acid culture of bacteria to turn sugars into lactic instead of acetic acid. If successful, savings could come to $300,000 per year.

By the early 1960's Dr. Cusi and his organization were looking for ways of making newsprint out of bagasse. Making pure bagasse newsprint had been attempted without success in Louisiana around 1950, and with doubtful results by Técnica Cubana in a 30,000 ton plant at Cardenas, Matanza, that was expropriated shortly after opening in 1959 and then left idle for some time.[37] Also in 1959 the Mexican government opened a 30,000 ton newsprint plant using pine at Tuxtepec, Oaxaca. In the fall of 1962, managers at Tuxtepec announced that they would start making printing and writing papers with bagasse alone and would expand newsprint capacity, perhaps using 40 per cent bleached bagasse pulp. Dr. Cusi quickly put large advertisements in Mexico City newspapers saying his company had been first to use bagasse in the country and still made 80

[36] John C. W. Evans, "W. R. Grace Pioneers with Bagasse Corrugating Medium Mill in Puerto Rico," *Paper Trade Journal*, Jan. 9, 1961.

[37] F.A.O., *Pulp and Paper Prospects in Latin America* (New York: United Nations, 1963), pp. 49, 51, 65. Equipment for the plant had been furnished in part by the Webster Manufacturing Company of Tiffin, Ohio.

per cent of all Mexican bagasse pulp. He warned against giving import protection to mixed bagasse and mechanical woodpulp newsprint:

Experience in all countries has shown that newsprint can only be produced using the international price as norm. The process of the Compañía Industrial de San Cristóbal permits fabricating newsprint under optimum technical-economic conditions; that is to say, adequate quality, and production costs less than those of specialized makers.[38]

He described his process in a lecture to the Mexican Association of Paper and Pulp Industry Technicians on November 30, 1962.[39] In the summer of 1963 he organized Mexicana de Papel Periódico, S.A., as an affiliate of San Cristóbal, with an initial capital of 1,500,000 pesos (U.S. $120,000). Meanwhile the Crown Zellerbach Company had also developed a process for pulping bagasse mechanically for newsprint purposes but delayed plans to build a 60,000 ton plant in India and to license others in Latin America.[40]

---

[38] *Excelsior*, Oct. 4, 1962.   [39] *Novedades*, Dec. 1, 1962.

[40] F.A.O. (1963), *op. cit.*, p. 51. Crown Zellerbach became interested in bagasse pulping in 1952, after its association with a research project started by the Hawaiian Sugar Planters Association in 1951. Over one and a half million dollars were spent in eight years developing many grades of paper—writing, corrugating, packaging, greaseproof, and finally newsprint. Newsprint made only from untreated ground bagasse could be run on modern presses at speeds well over 40,000 copies per hour; nevertheless, adding 30 per cent softwood kraft was recommended for optimum strength and capacity. Prospects were good enough to make a detailed feasibility study for a Hawaiian newsprint plant, but the conclusion was against building it in competition with mainland imports. For countries with tariffs, however, the company offered its patents, technical services, and capital. See S. B. Knapp, J. D. Wethern *et al.*, "Sugarcane Bagasse as a Fibrous Papermaking Material," *TAPPI*, Aug. 1957, pp. 595–645; W. G. Meyer and J. T. Henderson, "The Production of Bagasse Newsprint," paper contributed to the ECA-FAO Conference on Pulp and Paper Development in Africa and Near East, Cairo, March 8–20, 1965; and various brochures of the Crown Zellerbach Corporation. By 1963, sixteen

If one branch of government seemed to limit the scope for innovative activity in the eyes of Dr. Cusi, others fostered novelties greater than bagasse paper. The Laboratórios Nacionales de Fomento Industrial, supported by the Ministry of Industry and Commerce, worked out a process for pulping three palm-like species of yuccas called filifera, carnerosana, and brevifolia. In the arid Mexican northeast, millions of such yuccas grow in stands resembling vast forests. By 1961 their pulping properties had been tested in laboratory and pilot plant with caustic soda, monosulphite, and sulphate methods. In 1964 a private group was ready to build a 60 to 100 ton per day plant near Salado, San Luis Potosí. A remaining uncertainty was whether or not the government-supported Ejidos in the area could raise yucca prices to uneconomic levels. An impasse at this stage had blocked introduction of a novel process for making carnuba wax out of henequen waste in Yucatán, a process that had taken IMIT five years to develop. The private group was ready to give assurances that, if yucca carnerosana were to be used, only moribund plants would be cut. Otherwise semi-annual harvesters and processors of the 100 gram tips for bag and brush fibers would surely protest. But all these negotiations came to nothing, and therefore plans for a government plant were announced in February 1965. Difficulties in finding water further delayed construction.[41]

Finally, there was Maderera Maya, S.A., the company that spent 20,000,000 pesos on an unsuccessful project for making high grade papers out of tropical hardwoods. The possibility of pulping mixed tropical broad-leaved species had been established in the Paris laboratories of the Régie Industrielle de la

---

plants with daily capacity above 15 tons were making bagasse paper of various types in Brazil, Colombia, Cuba, Taiwan, India, Mexico, Peru, the Philippines, Puerto Rico, South Africa, and the United States.

[41] Salvador Carrasco N. and Rafael Rojas G., "Estudio Quimúrgico del Género Yucca," *ATCP*, Oct. 1961, pp. 82–92; *El Día*, Feb. 17, 1965.

Cellulose Coloniale of the French Government and tested in a small pilot plant at Abidjan on the Ivory Coast. It was found that "the consumption of chemicals by a mixture of species is almost the same as if only the species which consumes the smallest quantity of dissolving agents were treated."[42] Other experiments were started in the Philippines, Malaya, and central Africa.[43] An 18,000 ton plant for making corrugating medium opened at Yumbo, Colombia, in June 1959, and another of 17,000 tons was built at Puerto Isaacs in 1964.[44] The Mexican plant would have been about as large as both combined and would have made high grade sulphite pulp.

As in Colombia, however, research had begun with sulphate methods at IMIT in 1952, using wood samples from Yucatán. In 1956 the Vancouver Plywood Company became interested in the work, and Maderera Maya, S.A., was organized. Along the Usumacinta River in northeast Chiapas, between Palenque and Tenosique, the company controlled 425,000 hectares of jungle. Export of tropical hardwoods was the original purpose, but it seemed that innovating to produce a byproduct, paper, which was imported in large quantities, would be good public relations, especially if government-supported laboratories were engaged for part of the work. The late Mr. Thomas H. Mills, general administrator and entrepreneur behind Maderera Maya, told me in 1961, in his small, idol-filled office that only later did he learn to admire the quality of IMIT's work and the energy of Ing. Ignacio Deschamps, the director. IMIT undertook the entire research project, which cost Maderera Maya about 3,000,000 pesos, supplemented by 750,000 pesos from Mexican government banks.

Eventually Mills realized that the government itself was get-

[42] *Possibilities for the Development of the Pulp and Paper Industry in Latin America*, p. 4.

[43] *Science and Technology for Development*, Vol. IV, p. 114.

[44] *Pulp and Paper Prospects in Latin America*, pp. 39, 54.

ting more involved in paper making, not only directly at Aten-
quique and Tuxtepec, but indirectly through heavy Nacional
Financiera support of Celulosa de Chihuahua (Mexico's largest
pulp mill), a mill he had wrongly expected would supply not
paper but rayon factories. He decided fine sulphite pulp would
be less competitive, and research shifted in that direction. The
French and Swedish consultants who were engaged doubted
that a feasible process could be developed until Ramiro Vil-
lareal, one of the best of IMIT's own men, solved the main
problems.

Conventional acid sulphite cooking takes a pH of 1 to 2;
neutral sulphite cooking occurs at pH 7 to 9. Most bisulphite
cooking is slightly acid at pH 3 to 5. IMIT's process involves
a pH 2 to 3 and a faster cooking time. A Chiapas deposit of
dolomite (hydroxic calcium magnesium carbonate) could become a cheap source of magnesium sulphite if it could be
separated from calcium sulphite. The Armour Research Foundation put IMIT in touch with Dow Chemical for that. Also
developed was a way of drying the pulp to allow recovery of
original properties after rehydration. By the end of 1961 every
aspect of the process had been worked out in a Mexico City
pilot plant.[45] Maderera Maya was ready to spend eight million
dollars on a 100 ton per day (1 shift) pulping plant and nine
million dollars for the dolomite process, saw mill, plywood
plant, and other facilities. All that was lacking was presidential
authorization.

"If you know Mexico," Mills had told me, "you know you
can't buck the government." The policy of Maderera Maya was
described as "unconditional surrender from the start." If 25
per cent foreign ownership was all that was allowed, they
would sell 75 per cent to Mexicans whenever funds appeared.
Mills had already taken the initiative in lining up Mexican in-

---

[45] Institute Mexicano de Investigaciones Tecnológicas, A.C., *12 Años
de Labores* (Mexico, D.F., 1962), p. 16.

vestors committed to subscribe to 75 per cent of the capital stock, given presidential authorization of the project. He realized that exports of plywood would be allowed only after further domestic sales of plywood were impossible and that exports would be subject to higher severance taxes in accordance with existing law. The project would proceed as long as the Vancouver Plywood Company had first option on the exports. Fire prevention methods and reseeding of the forest were guaranteed, as well as schools and hospitals for people in the area.

At first delays came from several of the government administrative departments. Successive reports were found inadequate. Further details were needed; reports were not in the proper form. But nothing seemed to be basically wrong, and the company proceeded with the construction of access roads until 1961. Eventually Mills heard that the decree was prepared and would be signed almost any day; if the President did not leave town, it might be that week.

Then trouble began. Squatters from Tabasco settled along the access roads and burned the forest to grow corn. More roads meant more squatters and more destruction. Soils were too thin and leached for more than one or two crops, and the squatters moved from place to place. The governor of Chiapas, one of Mexico's poorest states, grew worried about losing a large taxpayer and a new industry. The squatters were evicted by force. A boundary dispute arose with Tabasco. The squatters returned, and Maderera Maya offered to give them as much corn as they could grow, provided no trees were burned. But reports of brutal evictions were already widely publicized, and the Department of Agrarian and Colonization Affairs (independent of the Ministry of Agriculture) mobilized opposition against Maderera Maya as the instrument of unjust foreign exploitation. Many joined this opposition: Those who saw a threat to the *ejido* system and agrarian reform; those who thought any cutting of the forest was a national loss; those who hoped to skim the cream off the jungle in a far more primitive and wasteful way; and others. Former supporters of Maderera Maya began to worry. Perhaps it would be better if the company were reorganized under a different name.

But Thomas Mills was opposed to that. Seriously ill with ulcers, he had one operation in Los Angeles and another in Mexico City. When recovery did not occur, and his blood pressure remained too low, a doctor in desperation told him the decree had been signed. For the first time, Mills' blood pressure rose from 90 to 130, but early in 1963, he died. With the entrepreneur gone, Maderera Maya, now called Industrial de Palenque, lost momentum. Permission was finally granted to cut trees for ordinary sawmills built by Mexicans during 1964–65. Plywood and paper mills remained in the indefinite future.

Perhaps President Adolfo Lopez Mateos was right not to sign. If the symbol of the Mexican Revolution was crucial to the country's strategy of development, and if Maderera Maya had rightly or wrongly come to be seen as a threat to that symbol, then perhaps his duty was to protect the symbol. By 1964 a regular campaign against "latifundism in forests" was under way. In August 1964 alone, 284,000 hectares including sawmills were expropriated from five companies in Guerrero.[46] Meanwhile, the Undersecretary of Nonrenewable Resources, Ing. Peña Slane, said it was "tragic that private initiative was not making the necessary investments in exploration in a country like Mexico with a vast territory and richly endowed."[47] A man regarded as a spokesman for the incoming President, Gustavo Díaz Ordaz, announced that the Department of Agrarian Affairs and Colonization would probably be abolished since it had often interfered with the work of the Ministry of Agriculture,

[46] *El Día*, Aug. 26, 1964; Oct. 30, 1964; Jan. 23, 1965.
[47] *El Día*, Sept. 3, 1964.

and a thirty-year plan for rational exploitation of forests was under study.[48]

VII. Conclusions

It hardly needs saying that where government assumes the roles of economic planner and arbiter of conflicts, support of innovation calls for men with both economic and technological sophistication near the highest level of government. Such men must have neither romantic illusions about what science can deliver within the decade, nor undue pessimism about the potential of local research, compared with foreign work. They must possess a willingness to wait and to defend a few failures and delays; they must understand the difficult maneuvers that lie between laboratory proof and first commercial sales. Mexico has been fortunate in having a few such men high in the Banco de México and the Nacional Financiera, institutions somewhat independent of the political game; yet in key positions to back decisions with funds, even if unable to get the needed permits in every case. In a different setting, these supporters of change and experiment against timidity and vested interests illustrate Carter's and Williams' observation of British industry that the receptiveness of a firm to innovation is correlated with the participation of scientists and engineers in policy making, preferably on the board of directors.[49]

[48] *New York Times,* Aug. 23, 1964; *El Día,* Sept. 21, 1964. Completely successful innovations begun at IMIT include one plant in Chiapas making high quality starch out of yucca tubers and one in Mexico City making an agricultural fungicide out of an allotropic form of cuprous oxide.

[49] C. F. Carter and B. R. Williams, *Industry and Technical Progress: Factors Governing the Speed of Application of Science* (London: Oxford University Press, 1957), pp. 34, 129–35. A leading Mexican economist, Dr. Miguel S. Wionczek, nevertheless, regrets the "very low priority given to domestic research and development." He estimates that only "something like 0.15 per cent of national income is dedicated in Mexico for

Governments must therefore not only support the education of technologists but must absorb a few into tasks other than in laboratories or drafting rooms. Just as radio reception needs more than antennae, such high administrative appointments mean little if they are not an expression of a basic attitude. This attitude must be one of leading without detailed control, of recruiting soldiers of innovation with great promises and then letting each squad choose its own weapons and terrain, of taking a large share of the risks and a smaller share of the direct gains. A group of experts meeting at Geneva agreed that gov-

---

pure and applied research as against 2 per cent in the developed countries," meaning 1/60 or less in per capita terms. Dr. Wionczek also regretted the scantiness of information on the aggregate costs of importing (licensing) foreign technology. The higher these costs might be, the better the case for substituting domestic research and development. For many firms, however, the gain from unpatented, free domestic know-how would not offset the monopolistic advantages of patented foreign knowledge, regardless of how expensive (Miguel S. Wionczek, "Transfer of Technology to the Developing Countries through Enterprise-to-Enterprise Arrangements: Issues Arising in the Case of Mexico," mimeographed paper prepared for the Fiscal and Financial Branch of the U.N. Secretariat, Oct. 1966, pp. 8, 10, 19).

A National Meeting of Science and Technology for Economic and Social Development in Mexico took place in October 1967. The most active group behind the meeting was the National Productivity Center. A declaration of the group stressed that emigration of Mexican scientists and technicians should be averted, that private sources should finance a larger share of research, and other generalities. A smaller group was charged with drafting a national scientific and technological policy (*El Mercado de Valores*, Oct. 16, 1967, pp. 867–70).

In 1966 the Laboratorios de Fomento Industrial had a budget of two million pesos and employed twenty full-time researchers. The Instituto Mexicano de Investigaciones Tecnológicas (IMIT) employed forty-five full-time researchers on a budget of eight million pesos. There were an additional twenty-five technicians on fellowships. Both institutes earned about a quarter of their income from private industry. The Instituto de Investigaciones Industriales of Monterrey employed thirteen researchers (eight with degrees) and received only 12 per cent of its budget from government (*El Mercado de Valores*, Aug. 28, 1967, pp. 723, 726).

ernments would have to take a central role in promoting innovative activity, but first and foremost governments had to take measures to arouse the initiative and interest of those in daily contact with industrial operations from skilled workers to engineers. The Geneva group called for vigorous and sustained national campaigns, nonpecuniary incentives as well as highly attractive financial rewards, public technical and material assistance, release of talented men from routine and normal duties without loss of pay, and special units for coordination and sponsorship of some experimental projects.[50]

Aside from subsidizing education, technical libraries, and applied research institutes, however, it appears that protection is most needed for inventors and innovators against patent infringers and retaliation (other than better economic performance) from obsolete or slow competitors. Independent researchers or entire firms can be stimulated to innovate with loans and a well-known, cheap, and dependable patent system; but government cannot effectively reach inside a firm and make a part progressive against the spirit of the whole, whether the firm is publicly or privately owned. Socialistic economies, incidentally, have yet to find a good way of encouraging the sort of individualistic, aberrant, inventive work that can be financed as a patent gamble in sophisticated mixed economies.

Some creative work has become potentially routine, awaiting only the application of sufficient resources, because the lack of good technologists is still greater than the inherent difficulty of solving the most common problems. But certainly not all exploration is that predictable. There comes a point where further contriving of routines, information systems, and safeguards on spending grow less productive than giving elbow room and

---

[50] International Labor Office, *Employment Objectives in Economic Development: Report of a Meeting of Experts* (Geneva, 1961), p. 74. In Russia workers who invent can hope to become instructors at institutes of advanced practice (E/Conf. 39/I/33).

hope of empire to those extraordinary personalities that drive and beguile themselves, their associates, and their backers toward one obsessive target innovation. Perhaps these types received too much stress from Schumpeter; but Mexican experience suggests that they do exist and should be welcomed as a not wholly obsolete cavalry in the campaign for progress.

Yet the main point of this chapter is more general. Although long-industrialized countries can more easily discover, invent, and apply, they will not and cannot do enough for poor countries. Important opportunities for innovation exist in underdeveloped countries; and in a greater proportion of cases, possible innovations there depend on scientific work, though not of the most fundamental type. Worthwhile in these nations, therefore, are: one, an educational policy that generates creative scientists and engineers; and, two, a national science policy that puts these people in a setting both intellectually satisfying and financially attractive compared with work abroad. Scientists must be high-paid and left alone to sow discord with inventions that benefit many but may harm some.

To achieve this setting demands courage from the policy maker. He knows the top scientists would cause less trouble if they were set to unravelling a half dozen small current emergencies. Yet the policy maker must let these be solved by clumsy mediocrities. He cannot go into the esoteric details of what the scientist is doing nor promise net gains with certainty. He must even live with the suspicion that the scientist's loyalty to the international scientific community, his hope for rank there, may be greater than his pride in the homeland. Should he recruit the scientist for the small emergencies anyway, it will be his fault if the man fades into dusty inconsequence,[51] and

---

[51] Edward Shils, "Scientific Development in the New States," in Ruth Gruber, ed., *Science and the New Nations: Proceedings of the International Conference on Science in the Advancement of New States at Rehovoth Israel,* Aug. 1960 (New York: Basic Books, 1961), p. 225.

national science policy becomes a matter of grand input and trivial output. For the policy maker, therefore, wisdom is knowing what to overlook and remembering that, little by little, mulberry leaves become satin.

8

Conclusion

Technological change has many facets. To understand why a firm has taken up a more efficient technique one may have to study changes among managers, consultants, machinery suppliers, national patent incentives, licensors of foreign patents and techniques, vocational teachers, tax and credit schemes, import restrictions, labor legislation, conditions of scientific research, to mention only a few possible causes. Economic trends in general play their part but not to the point of making technological change simply an endogenous, dependent variable. Some of the causal agents may stagnate while the economy grows, and others may improve in spite of economic catastrophes.

Nevertheless, the agents are not so independent that they can be appraised in isolation, one at a time, and then added for the total effect. They may interact or go their own way with all the diversity possible in human affairs. To say that fertilizer of a different chemical composition will be adopted by a peasant when yam prices double leaves two crucial questions unanswered: Who developed the fertilizer? How did the peasant learn to appreciate its effect? In the more complex business of manufacturing, the stream of inventions and the skills of application do not approach a routine until the sector involved is thoroughly modernized and industrialized. While industry is young, few developments could be more affected by the idiosyncrasies of persons and institutions than technological change.

Early industrialization has been the context of this book, of course, and almost every chapter has either dealt with the stream of inventions, more precisely, with the origin and nature of alternatives available to the entrepreneur, or has treated his ability to appraise and to apply, that is, the firm's absorptive capacity. Reports from many countries have been cited, but firsthand observations were limited to Mexico and Puerto Rico. Since the importance of personal and institutional idiosyncrasies as obstacles or spurs to change have been stressed, do conclusions also apply to Asia, Africa, and the rest of Latin America? To an extent they do not. For example, the effect of political and economic instability on technological choice could not be studied in Mexico and Puerto Rico, both stable during 1940–1965. On the other hand, their very stability and progress have made for a great diversity of industries and types of firms, large and small, public and private, domestic and foreign, which exploited or avoided nearby North American technical resources. Other countries may have less diversity or as much in different proportions.

Where a particular firm or sector does have a Mexican counterpart, similar conditions seem to lead to a similar response. Although Latin preindustrial culture traits differ from those of Africa and Asia, there exists a large area of overlap. New private firms of national origin will usually show traces of authoritarianism in personal relations, characteristically in the form of family dominance and paternalism. Former importers or artisans are typical founders. Immigrant entrepreneurs and branch plants stand out everywhere and tend to have the characteristics of their countries of origin. State-owned plants may be managed by an engineer, a soldier, or a politician near the end or near the beginning of his career, and these plants show perhaps the greatest range in levels of efficiency.

The Puerto Rican tax-exempt relation to the American market is no doubt unique, but that is why the Puerto Rican experience was studied—to see what Mexican patterns fit nevertheless. In general, the distinctive traits of Mexican and Puerto Rican managers, workers, and government procedures affected the stream of possible techniques, to be reviewed in the next section, less than they affected absorptive capacity.

I. The Changing Set of Techniques

If poor countries are to be more productive in manufacturing, entrepreneurs must learn that better techniques are possible and that changes in organization go with their use. Teaching all this cannot be left to schools, libraries, trade journals, and catalogues. As brought out in Chapter 2, these impersonal or general sources of information will not make an inexperienced owner stake much money on unfamiliar equipment and materials. He needs the help of organizing experts who have experience, which is that species of information mainly embedded in the tissues of human participants because of its complexity and scattered applicability. In past centuries the need for experience, such unpublished and perhaps unrecordable information, extended to the ranks of skilled labor. Technological change then called for migration. But now the organizing expert with jet and transoceanic telephone can assure that tolerable equipment is bought and at least started up properly.

These experts may be consulting engineers, but they might also be employed on a firm's staff, or representatives of a licensor of foreign patents and know-how, or machinery salesmen, or even industrial research institute officials. Often these different experts supplement one another's knowledge by working together. The analogy of the relay stations was used in Chapter 2 to suggest that assembling an answer is usually an imperfect process. Each link in the system tends to add irrelevant elements to a problem and to overlook promising alternatives. Thus distortion is cumulative. Distortion shows the pressure of time on each link, the inability to explore conditions thoroughly, and the lack of coordination among similar projects in different places. Not enough resources are allocated to technological diffusion; and the alternatives brought to a firm's attention are often too few and poorly tailored to its needs.

This conclusion could have been inferred as at least probable from the inherent economic circumstances of diffusion. Using information more widely leads to falling "unit costs" or increasing returns to scale since knowledge once produced cannot be used up. By the same token, knowledge is not property that is easily kept from those users who simply will not pay to cover the costs of knowledge-producers (or diffusers). Finally, there is the paradoxical uncertainty of having to contract in advance for what one hopes to learn, that is, before knowing its actual value. As a result, not enough resources are bid toward the production of knowledge. Patent royalties cannot, and public subsidies have not, come close to correcting the underallocation. Foreign subsidiaries do not procure technical information in this fashion, but they often have even less freedom of choice.

But drawing on foreign techniques is not the only way of adding to available alternatives. The example of some bold Mexican firms and research institutes, which invented their own, cited in Chapter 7, may be irrelevant to tiny countries but it is worth pondering elsewhere. Probably some objective opportunities for improving production methods can be found and will be within a poor country's financial capacity. Techniques borrowed from abroad, it is true, will not inevitably turn the herbage of arid and humid tropics into oils, thread, and papers at low cost. Using some unusual clays, coals, and ores also takes more than routine adaptation. The occasional sight of abundant, homogeneous, but area-specific plants and rocks gives tropical industrial research a material-directed push, and results could be called the special underdeveloped-country technology. Far more common, however, are the uses of universal principles of mechanics, hydraulics, metallurgy, chemistry, thermodynamics, electromagnetism, etc., and reckoning that only photosynthesis makes plants, air is air, rivers are water, and that eight elements make up 98.18 per cent of the earth's crust. Innovations that depend on high income levels for a market and that involve widely understood principles of nature are likely to have been quite well explored by old industrial countries. As a result, the application of altogether new discoveries to the creation of local substitutes for materials and for products needed early in development is likely to be more fruitful.

No doubt, diffusion and unadaptive copying are safer than innovation. Copying avoids many risks and expenses of testing (once conditions are proven similar) and is therefore cheaper. But innovation is complementary with diffusion. Any country that lacks the kind of technical community that can innovate, lacks one channel to foreign expertise—the ability to identify problems clearly and to ask the right questions. The "know-where" (to find the answer) of a research institute, via its library and overseas contacts, may be far more productive than its "know-how," but the two go together. Moreover, an ability to ask questions and to theorize, to experiment, invent, and apply must be used to be preserved. Hence, although direct yields to innovative activity may seem low, that is part of the cost of being receptive to diffusion from abroad, of being able to copy creatively, to minimize the filtering out and distortion of good technological options.

Economists have often supposed that less complex additions could be made to the set of techniques. Are there no ways of using more workers instead of equipment without elaborate prior research or international consultation? Chapter 5 tried to appraise the possibilities. If people alone were sensitive and versatile enough for some jobs, and only machines strong and fast enough for others, how extensive was the range of tasks in which the two could be substituted or combined in varying proportions? This range was shown to be mainly determined by production volume. As volume rises, ever lower wage-capital-cost ratios are needed to make given amounts of labor an economic substitute for capital. The elasticity of substitution falls and virtually disappears. Using more workers makes sense only if enough other resources can be saved per unit of output, and beyond a certain volume (varying with the nature of each industry), the productivity of capital cannot be raised by hiring more workers, no matter how low the wage rates.

Although the sample of firms was not designed to be a cross-section of manufacturing in Mexico or Puerto Rico, it did show that labor-capital substitution was possible in a limited way. At Mexican cost ratios, half the firms had made practically no substitution; and at the higher Puerto Rican wage levels, two-thirds were satisfied with unadjusted American methods. More telling was the character of the firms that had made adjustments: all small Mexican firms, but only one-third of large ones; three-quarters of Puerto Rican firms that produced only for the island market substituted, but only 18 per cent of the exporting firms. Only when volume does not steal the show, do factor prices come on stage. Nor was it therefore surprising that capital-saving techniques were often not so much labor-substituting as volume-substituting through the lowering of output diversity by standardization or more flexible, multiple-purpose machines.

But perhaps most significant was the fact that many labor-intensive techniques make large demands on training and organizing ability. Without this ability, elaborate subcontracting, intensive staffing, multiple shift-working, better maintenance, and longer repairs easily become too costly. At this point, therefore, any discussion of the set of alternatives becomes a consideration of absorptive capacity.

II. Absorptive Capacity

If a technique is to be absorbed by an economy, the entrepreneurs of public and private enterprises must be able to create and manage the kind of organization implied. This ability to create and manage without bankruptcy is partly determined by law. One cannot successfully adopt a process rendered unprofitable through tax, credit, labor, and trade legislation. Chapter 4 described in detail how labor-intensive methods were penalized in Mexico through the system of reinvestment tax incentives, payroll taxes, easier credit for new than for secondhand machines, costly retrenched worker indemnification, and certain other labor laws and practices. In Puerto Rico, the Federal Minimum Wage Boards pushed firms toward capital intensity at a pace condemned by both liberals and conservatives in the Commonwealth. Such distortions of market scarcity signals have many counterparts in the poor countries of the world. Policies for growth are aimed at making investment (not production, per se) more lucrative for the wealthy, and work more secure and remunerative for the poor. As a result, where substitution is possible, some investment is made in unduly capital-intensive techniques at the expense of employment, and output grows less than it might.

More important, however, is raising absorptive capacity beyond simple avoidance of laws that render some techniques unprofitable. What matters more than distorted prices is ability in the sense of capability. Relatively experienced Mexican and Puerto Rican entrepreneurs and foreign consultants compounded already imperfect market signals with further misinterpretation and miscalculation so that capital intensity was again reinforced.

Inability to organize, to instruct, and to motivate subordinates, is, however, the main barrier to labor intensity. Shift-working lets machines run double and triple time but requires the creation of a respected and reliable alternate management. Intensive maintenance of old and secondhand equipment requires workers who wish to perform well, for these tasks can be done carelessly without immediate detection. A more elaborate system of supervision is always needed where many workers take the place of a few mechanisms or where intensive staffing of given machines is used to raise output more than cost. Mexican and Puerto Rican evidence in Chapter 3 supported findings from other developing countries that poor labor productivity with given equipment was not so much a matter of poor manual dexterity (seconds per task), but of poor motivation and consistency (tasks per day or month).

The capacity to absorb technology, in other words, is limited by cultural factors. These factors do not necessarily affect rich and poor in a society in the same way. Are workers culturally so conditioned that they cannot adjust well to impersonal factory routines? Or are managers and owners too rigid to give workers enough upward mobility and other incentives? The evidence of Chapter 3 suggests that traditionalism of managers and owners is the greater problem. Their reluctance to grant status to people outside of a family or ethnic group, to give promotions, and to delegate authority to subordinates, undermines the will to learn and to produce. Above all, their reluctance in these matters inhibits growth of a necessary social stratum lacking in preindustrial societies: the foremen. Mexican and Puerto Rican firms giving adequate training and tying upward mobility to knowledge and performance had no intractable problems with low productivity. The requirements of training and participant experience for developing a modern manager are more varied and less easily specified. A perhaps typical Puerto Rican estimate was that "it takes mainland training and five or ten years of experience to make entrepreneurs with relatively strong, traditional Puerto Rican culture into effective operators in a business world of hierarchical organizations, cooperative teamwork, and abstract systems of control."[1]

Managerial rigidity and labor's resultant undependability lower absorptive capacity more for local adaptations than for unmodified foreign techniques. Product-flow and machine-adjustment decisions can be avoided with machines precoordinated in the factory. Need for training nightshift management and staff can be eluded by having machines with enough capacity to turn the goods out in one shift. Raising capacity in this fashion not only lowers needs for internal supervisory skills; insofar as the number of firms in the economy is reduced, it also lowers the need for Japanese-style inter-firm coordination of schedules and standards in subcontracts. More durable machines lower the need for training in maintenance and repair.

Thus, when firms in poor countries buy equipment that seems too automatic, large-scale, and durable, they dodge organizational problems by the same means that advanced country firms dodge high wages. Put differently, large-scale automatic machines allow both high wages to persist in developed countries and organizational incompetence to continue in the less developed countries. Since ability to organize and function at all must precede marginal adaptations to factor scarcities, the capital-intensiveness of organization-saving techniques is secondary. In Mexico, foreign branches tended to operate more labor-intensively, with older equipment and more shifts, than locally-owned plants. But among Mexican-owned plants, the least adaptive and most capital-intensive were generally more efficient. On the basis of the labor theory of value, Soviet industry during the 1930's followed the same organization-saving

[1] Thomas C. Cochran, *The Puerto Rican Businessman: A Study in Cultural Change* (Philadelphia: University of Pennsylvania Press, 1959), p. 73.

strategy. Organization saving may be organization building where that task would otherwise be too complex to be profitable.

III. The Role of Government

Public action can accelerate technological change best by indirect means. The diversity of problems and opportunities in all the branches and twigs of manufacturing is too great to be known fully on the outside. Government action can therefore speed up the flow of alternatives and raise the absorptive capacity of firms in general but must leave the specific choice of technique to management. Government should always consider incidental effects on absorptive capacity for new technology as an aspect of changes in taxes, credit policy, and labor legislation. More important is the encouragement of managerial training through schools, visits abroad, productivity centers, and the like. Enlightened managers can then cooperate with ministries of education to establish in-plant training courses to raise the productivity of labor.

Government action can speed the flow of alternatives by encouraging international diffusion in all its phases, as already summarized above in Section I. Usually, the main effect is that firms gain access at a lower price but through more complex procedures to channels of information that could have been hired all along. Effective use of these channels presupposes a supply of well-trained scientists and engineers. How many scientists and engineers a country should train can hardly be precisely estimated. Perhaps one scientist and nine engineers per thousand people, as suggested by Unesco, will do. With enough technicians a country can add a channel that would otherwise be lacking, a public industrial research institute, that would in turn contribute to training. A shortage of technicians may not even be apparent, however, if the few on hand are used ineffectively. Maximum effectiveness assumes that discovery and invention under the auspices of the research institute or of particular entrepreneurs will be tolerated and furthered commercially.

Unfortunately, innovation is costly, uncertain, and disrupting. Research institutes must get strong government support and weak control, a frequently distasteful combination for political leaders. Scientific and inventive work has a long gestation period, and its chips are much more likely to land on productive chances if allowed to fall where they may. Research institute directors must therefore be allowed to mobilize their apparently overpaid teams on targets that cannot be justified indisputably or even clarified. Their secrecy about contract work for private firms must be inviolate, though publicly subsidized. The institutes must even solicit contracts with salesmanship traditionally thought unworthy of an eminent national institution. They must be encouraged to search for help and prestige internationally, which is sure to strike some as unpatriotic. Meanwhile, Schumpeterian engineer-entrepreneurs must be granted their patent monopolies and the right to horn in on obsolete but vociferous competitors. Without such incentives for wealth and fame, these streams of technological alternatives will dry up. Both the potency of long-suffering generosity and the risk of intervention were illustrated in Chapter 7 by the varied Mexican and Puerto Rican experiences in research, development, and innovation.

IV. Summary

When natural science, factories, and economic theory were all in the nursery in the reasonable days of Adam Smith, technological backwardness was thought to be no problem. No country was far behind, and the only barriers to catching up seemed to be curbs on trade and migration. But a century of mass migrations, nearly free trade, and lavish capital movements brought no well-balanced global advance. On the contrary, in a later era of depression and world wars, technological backwardness seemed to be the hopeless fate of the tropics. Without coal, chilly weather, pure Caucasian genes, or the incommunicable catalyst of Western values, many thought mass production technology could not germinate. Six generations had brought the world from no problem to no solution.

Experience with development programs since the late 1940's has shown that the major impediments to high productivity in manufacturing can often be specified in detail and assailed with clear-cut measures. But the network for diffusing technology from advanced countries is not well coordinated. It distorts the questions that arise in the course of adaptation and then further warps the answers. Whatever plants are then installed are often run by managers who have not learned how to schedule production well or how to train and motivate subordinates, especially at intermediate levels. They misinterpret costs of labor and capital that inept taxes and regulations may in any case have brought to unrealistic levels.

This is not to say that modern production methods allow labor to be substituted for capital in a fairly elastic way. Only at very low volumes can the capital-labor ratio be greatly lowered, and in many branches even then only with much improved supervision. Novel ways of substituting labor for capital and other more important inventions are not often attempted in poor countries because the supply of technicians and the tolerance for delay and uncertainty are low. In some industries, moreover, old-fashioned producing groups are strong, and so is resistance to giving new privileges as incentives to innovators.

A general government agency cannot plan in detail the release of industry from these impediments. But if those actually responsible for manufacturing are given information, training, and time, repayment of public support will be ample enough, though perhaps surprising in form. With better use of conventional and improved information channels, routine problems will be solved more effectively. With the fading of tradition-alism, the right number of workers will operate machines properly, on two or three shifts, and for extra years with extra maintenance. With special support and tolerance, scientific research and development, drawing on international expe-rience, will pay in poor countries because technicians in advanced countries are sure to neglect some opportunities. In this respect, whether or not creative people are on a public or private payroll makes little difference.

Industrialization in Mexico and Puerto Rico

Mexico and Puerto Rico industrialized with such dispatch during the years between 1940 and 1965 that none could now call them typically underdeveloped. Their relative economic success was partly based on singular geographic, political, and social advantages. Precisely because of these advantages, they are suitable for observing technological choices: to see what dilemmas remain as obstacles fade, and what opportunities arise.

Many problems encountered and overcome by Mexico during the first two-thirds of the twentieth century are those that other developing countries are meeting and must solve in their own way. The political power of domestic and foreign land-owning and commercial oligarchies which had little interest in modernizing society had to be broken. Withdrawing power involved economic interference and deranged production. Workable political institutions and a wider sense of national identity emerged only after twenty years of partly barren strife among personalities at one level and abstract ideologies at another. As government finally became a pragmatic balancer of interests, economic growth picked up.

If other countries must complete a similar process of demolishing obstacles followed by self-education, they may find themselves industrializing under circumstances recalling those in Mexico a decade or two earlier—that is, under governments purporting to represent industrial workers, small farmers, and the lower middle class; now and then adopting conspicuous social welfare measures; operating a miscellaneous set of industries; but tolerating great inequality and private enterprise wherever these gave promise of pushing the economy forward.[1] Puerto Rico, with its United States association and special status as an industrial tax haven, appears to be a special case though in fact its development followed a similar path. Puerto Rican industries were studied as a check on conclusions from Mexico and to note the effect of differences, mainly economies of scale, in producing for a larger, more competitive market. Both areas had the advantage of easy contact with American technical progress through geographical proximity, and both could avoid acute inflation and balance-of-payments deficits through flourishing exports and an inflow of tourists. To ease the frictions of great social transformations, few lubricants have ever been as good as earned foreign exchange. A very brief sketch of the growth of manufacturing and the related political setting in Mexico and Puerto Rico should support these broad statements.

I. Mexico

A. *Growth from 1900 to 1940.* As early as 1830 Mexico had a government minister, Lucas Alamán, who sought economic development through a variety of subsidies to manufacturing. By 1843 fifty-seven power-driven textile mills had been founded, but until the dictatorship of Porfirio Díaz (1876–1910), political flux was too great for much further development. Foreign

[1] India appears to have made a transition from ideology toward pragmatism. Five-year planning has been downgraded as risky and overly rigid. The Cabinet post of Minister of Planning was eliminated. Abandoned were all new public industrial projects, except for the Soviet-aided Bokaro steel mill. Instead, temporary concessions to foreign fertilizer manufacturers, first introduced in 1965, were put on a permanent basis (New York *Times,* Sept. 17, 1967, and Jan. 2, 1968).

enterprises in mining, railroads, and electric power and factories (Mexican or foreign) making beer, glass, cigarettes, matches, soap, cloth, paper, cement, steel, and other goods thrived under Díaz. Mexican statistics before the late 1930's are not very reliable, but such indices as exist point toward a manufacturing growth rate of 3 to 4 per cent annually from 1900 to 1910.[2] Gross national product seems to have grown at a similar rate, and population at something like 1.2 per cent annually.

The Mexican Revolution of 1910 began with calls for political reform—"Effective Suffrage and No Reelection"—and took up anticlericalism, economic nationalism, agrarian reform, and socialism in lumps of various sizes. The way its many leaders made deals, changed sides, were ambushed, and replaced will not be reviewed here.[3] Prerevolutionary levels in manufacturing, mining, and agriculture were not regained until some time between 1922 and 1926. Until 1940 agricultural production indicated no clear trend up or down; the population grew at 1.7 per cent annually; and manufacturing increased at about 5 per cent annually.

Although statistics of output growth were not impressive, the late 1920's and 1930's were nevertheless years of change. Under President Calles (1925–28) the Agricultural Credit System, the National Irrigation Commission, and the Central Bank began operations. During the Presidency of Lázaro

[2] Gonzalo Robles, "El Desarrollo Industrial" and Enrique Pérez López, "El Producto Nacional," in *México: 50 Años de Revolución, Vol. I., La Economía* (Mexico: Fondo de Cultura Económica, 1960), pp. 197, 587–9; George Wythe, *Industry in Latin America* (New York: Columbia University Press, 1945), pp. 298–308.

[3] Charles C. Cumberland, *The Mexican Revolution: Genesis under Madero* (Austin: University of Texas Press, 1952); Miguel Alessio Robles, *Historia Política de la Revolución*, 3d ed. (Mexico: Ediciones Botas, 1946); Alberto Morales Jiménez, *Historia de la Revolución Mexicana* (Mexico: Instituto de Investigaciones Políticas, Económicas, y Sociales del P.R.I.).

Cárdenas (1935–40) redistribution of 18.6 million hectares of land, added to the 8.3 million split up earlier, irrevocably ended the large landowners' chances for regaining power. Expropriation of British and American oil companies in 1938 under tense circumstances gained international recognition of Mexico's right to undertake a comprehensive social revolution. These two actions stood out among many as giving life to earlier Revolutionary slogans, thus reinforcing that patriotic "self-discovery" needed for national integration. As a result unavoidable inequalities and sacrifices of development could be tolerated.[4] Add the relative stabilization of the political process and the energetic building of schools, roads, irrigation systems, and other public works, partly to counteract unemployment, and Calles and Cárdenas can well be credited with setting up many of the preconditions for the rapid growth that followed.[5] But Cárdenas and his associates hardly sought nor expected urban industrialization on the scale which occurred. Some even shared a Gandhi-like dream of village industries electrified and sanitary but small scale and cooperatively organized, and, like the *Ejidos* themselves, linked to pre-Columbian customs. Urban industry was largely promoted indirectly through demand for supplies by public works projects.[6]

[4] Frank Tannenbaum, "Toward an Appreciation of Latin America," in *The United States and Latin America* (New York: The American Assembly, 1959), pp. 52–3; Edmundo Flores, "The Significance of Land-Use Changes in the Economic Development of Mexico," *Land Economics,* May 1959, pp. 115–24.

[5] Sanford A. Mosk, *Industrial Revolution in Mexico* (Berkeley: University of California Press, 1950), pp. 53–61; Robert E. Scott, *Mexican Government in Transition* (Urbana: University of Illinois Press, 1959); John J. Johnson, *Political Change in Latin America: The Emergence of the Middle Sectors* (Stanford: Stanford University Press, 1958), pp. 128–52, with annotated bibliography, pp. 240–51.

[6] Ramón Beteta, "Economic Aspects of the Six-Year Plan," in *Economic and Social Program of Mexico* (Mexico, 1935), pp. 44 ff., quoted at length by Mosk, *op. cit.,* p. 58.

B. *Growth during 1940–1965.* A turning point in economic growth often comes with the simultaneous occurrence of changes in several pertinent but unconnected fields. As a result it is often hard to tell necessary from merely helpful factors. If preconditions had in fact matured before 1941, what would have happened had President Ávila Camacho not reversed economic policy to favor urban industrialization? Were his policies freely chosen or forced by a need to lessen accumulated strains? Or were they a response to the effects and opportunities of World War II? Did the War prove the benefits of increasing export industries for speeding growth, or was its lasting effect the birth of infant, import-substituting industries?[7]

Whatever the contribution of internal preparation before 1940 compared with openings in the foreign market afterwards, the Mexican economy began growing at unprecedented rates during 1940–60. Nor was World War II the best period. If power generation, petroleum, construction, and manufacturing are combined, as is Mexican statistical practice, industrial and agricultural production both rose in marvelous harmony at rates somewhat above 6 per cent from 1945 to 1960. Stagnation in mineral exports was offset by growing foreign agricultural sales, particularly in coffee and cotton. Exports of these two products rose from one-tenth of agricultural production in the early 1940's to almost one-third in the late 1950's. Annual receipts from foreign tourists (including purchases along the border that were practically commercial exports) more than quintupled from 1940 to 1959, accounting for 26 per cent of the country's import capacity in 1940 and 46 per cent in 1959. Under these circumstances gross fixed investment could rise

[7] From 1939 to 1945 manufacturing exports showed an almost tenfold expansion, rising from 1.7 to 6.0 per cent of manufacturing production from 1939 to 1945, but they fell to 2.3 per cent by 1950 (Combined Mexican Working Party, *The Economic Development of Mexico* [Baltimore: International Bank of Reconstruction and Development, 1953], pp. 62, 276).

from 10 to 14 per cent of gross national product, with rates of inflation averaging only 8 per cent annually during the 1940's and 7 per cent during the 1950's. Meanwhile the population increased by a yearly 2.9 per cent and reached 35.2 million in

Table 19. Mexican manufacturing in 1955: number of establishments, employees, wages and salaries, value added, and value added per worker

Products	Number of establishments	Number of employees (thousands)	Wages and salaries including fringe benefits (thousands of pesos)	Value added per annum (thousands of pesos)	Value added per worker in U.S. dollars ($1=12.50 pesos)
Processed foods, beverages, tobacco	28,500	338	1,630	11,833	1,420
Textiles	4,300	283	1,380	6,400	960
Apparel [1]	6,300	74	321	1,320	750
Furniture and wood products [2]	4,485	76	518	1,220	840
Paper products	400	34	207	1,500	1,560
Printing and publishing	2,200	45	258	978	950
Chemicals [3]	1,828	120	850	1,920	1,090
Petroleum products	43	12	150	2,000	6,000
Rubber and plastics [4]	672	55	339	1,920	1,650
Leather products [5]	6,100	62	297	1,489	920
Stone, clay, glass products	2,500	58	308	1,300	1,260
Primary metal products	400	80	1,077	10,900	4,000
Fabricated metal products	3,505	73	351	2,034	1,130
Nonelectrical machinery	2,200	33	141	532	810
Electrical machinery and equipment	2,300	65	345	2,100	1,230
Transportation equipment	2,400	40	261	2,700	2,600

Source: Dirección general de Estadística, *Censo Industrial 1956* (Información Censal 1955; México, D.F., 1959), Vol. I, pp. 35–56. To make Mexican statistics comparable to SIC groupings, the following changes were made: (1) shoes were excluded from apparel; (2) fabricated metal furniture was included in furniture and wood products; (3) chemicals excluding plastics; (4) plastics were included in rubber and plastics; (5) shoes were included in leather products.

December 1960. In twenty years per capita gross domestic product grew from about 150 to 336 (1960) dollars. From 1963 to 1967, population grew at 3.3 per cent annually and reached 44 million in 1967. Gross domestic product rose at an average 6.0 per cent during 1960–65 and came to 393 (1960) dollars per capita in 1965. The pace was maintained during the following two years, and in 1967 per capita product reached 420 (1960) dollars or 500 (1967) dollars.[8]

In 1965 manufacturing output reached a level 6.3 times that of 1940, implying an average annual compound growth rate of 7.7 per cent for over two decades. As a percentage of net domestic product, manufacturing rose from 16 to 26 per cent during 1940 to 1960 and employed first 9.0 and finally 12.6 per cent of the labor force. Manufacturing employment rose from 525,000 in 1940 to 1,480,000 in 1960. Through the mid-1960's the share of manufacturing in output and employment failed to rise much further. Within manufacturing the structure of output changed. Processed foods and textiles lagged with 3 to 4 per cent growth rates from 1945 to 1960, while durables and chemicals grew at annual rates well above 10 per cent. During the years 1950 to 1958 alone, the share of foods and textiles in output fell from about 55 to 40 per cent; chemi-

[8] In addition to sources previously cited and official annual reports, see Victor L. Urquidi, "Problemas Fundamentales de la Economía Mexicana," *Cuadernos Americanos*, No. 1, 1961, pp. 75–103; Barry N. Siegel, *Inflación y Desarrollo: Las Experiencias de México* (Mexico: Centro de Estudios Monetarios Latinoamericanos, 1960); Adolfo López Romero, "Desarrollo Económico de México (1934–1959)" *El Trimestre Económico,* Jan.–March 1962, pp. 30–68; Oscar Lewis, "Mexico desde 1940," *Investigación Económica,* Second Trimester of 1958, pp. 185–256; Victor L. Urquidi, *Viabilidad Económica de America Latina* (Mexico, D.F.: Fondo de Cultura Económica, 1962), p. 161; Carlos Quintana, "México y Holanda: Dos Economías Complementarias," *El Mercado de Valores,* April 5, 1965, Suplemento, pp. 214–15; Victor Urquidi, *The Challenge of Development in Latin America* (New York: Praeger, 1964), p. 157; *El Mercado de Valores, Suplemento Especial,* Dec. 5, 1966, pp. 6–9, and Sept. 4, 1967, pp. 734–48.

cals, machinery, and metal products rose from 17 to 38 per cent.[9]

C. *Economic Policy.* Mexican policy during 1940 to 1965 was characterized first by measures courageously enacted and second by tolerance, however reluctant, of trends which occurred that were undesired, unplanned-for, and perhaps unexpected. One concludes that industrialization was fostered less with calculation than with desperate faith that gains to society as a whole would in time be decent compared with the resources and incomes transferred to factory owners. Certainly government leaders saw current inequalities and inefficiencies with regret. They knew that privileges were granted and accepted with little trust. But elaborate calculation was technically as unfeasible as administration of any possible alternatives. Many of the expert consultants and administrators of the 1960's were themselves a product of development.

Specifically, tariff protection, credit manipulation, and tax exemptions greatly enlarged investment yields without a corresponding rise in private saving. Earlier calculations of profits rising from 27 per cent of national income in 1939–40 to 41 per cent by 1950 appear exaggerated, but few informed observers doubt that incomes of owners and salaried professionals grew faster than wages.[10] Private saving, however, only rose from 7 per cent of gross national product in 1939–42 to about 9 per cent in 1959–60. Even this growth may have been due more to the selective effect of monetary expansion rather than to an increase in general thriftiness at given or higher income levels.

[9] Robles, *op. cit.*, pp. 197, 202; Nacional Financiera, *Informe Anual: Correspondiente a 1960* (Mexico, D.F., 1961), pp. 28, 176–242; *El Mercado de Valores,* Feb. 11, 1963, p. 73; Ifigenia M. de Navarrete, *La Distribución del Ingreso y el Desarrollo Económico de México* (Mexico, D.F.: Instituto de Investigaciones Económicas, 1960), pp. 43, 47.

[10] Ifigenia de Navarrete, *La Distribución del Ingreso y el Desarrollo Económico de México,* pp. 55–66; Siegel, *op. cit.,* pp. 131–46.

Private investment, including inventory accumulation, meanwhile had increased from 6 to 10 per cent of gross national product. Thus private saving first exceeded, then fell short of, private investment. These differences do not correspond to flows to and from the public sector, which usually invested more than it saved, but showed that foreign loans and investment in Mexico had come to outweigh capital exports.[11]

D. *Planning.* Public investment rose from 4 per cent of gross national product in 1939–42 to about 5 per cent in 1959–60 and included about one-fourth for the construction of manufacturing plants for steel, cement, paper, chemicals, transportation equipment, food products, as well as expanded petroleum refining capacity. Although these projects fit the ideological preferences of many intellectuals and politicians, and the fears of conservatives, they could hardly be described as systematic moves toward socialism. Many were started or planned during World War II in response to shortages and in the face of private aversion to long-term, large-scale commitments. Planning techniques were learned step by step. First one had to learn that steel mills could not operate at capacity without adequate coke supplies, nor cement plants without ample electric power. After mastering elements of physical planning, the problem arose of coordinating expansion plans of government-controlled enterprises with their varying degrees of autonomy so that spending would be determined by prospective yields, not by accumulated cash and bargaining power. Beginning in 1947 a series of public investment coordinating commissions was organized and then reorganized as each in turn collided with vested interests in government. The last was finally absorbed by the Secretaría de la Presidencia.

Submission for approval of detailed plans became compul-

[11] Combined Mexican Working Party, *op. cit.,* pp. 183–7; Nacional Financiera, *Informe Anual Correspondiente a 1960,* p. 30.

sory as did subsequent adherence to authorized expenditures.[12] With its own house not in order, neat guidance of private investment, production, and income distribution by government would have been surprising.

E. *Protection from Imports.* Rising tariffs and import controls were the primary underpinning of Mexican industrialization from 1947 to the mid-1960's. Mexican tariffs, like others, have often reflected accidents of history, sudden wartime shortages, international exchange fluctuations, and political pressures. They have at times retarded development by making some industries or firms privileged, which then became bottlenecks.[13] Although since 1916 tariffs had become increasingly protective rather than revenue-oriented, the modern era of protection began with the decrees of 1947 which greatly raised the levels and introduced ad valorem rates. By 1959 manufactured imports not produced in the country but considered essential, such as pharmaceuticals and semiprocessed materials, carried duties between 9 and 15 per cent. Competing manufacturing imports, however, were levied at 36.5 per cent for canned foods, at almost 200 per cent for some luxuries, but typically around 100 per cent of value.[14]

More important than the tariff were the controls applied to about one-third of the items listed, or to 58 per cent of imports by value.[15] For importing products under control, a license from

[12] Decree, *Diario Oficial,* Aug. 2, 1961, reprinted in *El Mercado de Valores,* Aug. 7, 1961, pp. 396, 403; Urquidi, "Problemas Fundamentales de la Economía Mexico," *op. cit.,* p. 96; Ernest López Malo, *Ensayo sobre Localización de la Industria en México* (Mexico, D.F.: Universidad Nacional Autónoma, 1960), pp. 257–73; Combined Mexican Working Party, *op. cit.,* pp. 62–5.

[13] Combined Mexican Working Party, *op. cit.,* p. 80.

[14] Rafael Urrutia Millán, Director General de Estudios Hacendarios, "Aspectos Fiscales del Tratado de la Zona de Libre Comercio de Latino America," mimeographed, speech given April 19, 1960, at the Cámara de Comercio de la Ciudad de México.

[15] *Loc. cit.*

the Ministry of Industry and Commerce (formerly Ministry of Economy) was needed but usually refused if national necessity could not be shown. The policy originated in 1944 and was tacitly understood to apply to most products more than three-fifths of the sales of which were domestically produced.[16] Approval of an import license usually depended on a hostile review board consisting largely of representatives of domestic manufacturers who saw their task as "closing the border." To add a product to the controlled list, a manufacturer had to prove ability to produce an adequate volume of appropriate quality at a more or less reasonable price, a procedure said to be easier and involving less inspection of books than requests for a higher tariff. One manufacturer told the author in 1961 that only one week passed from the drafting of a suitable decree by his own lawyer to its publication in the *Diario Oficial*. Asked about ways of preventing possible abuse of such practice, a ministry official said a few days later,

The best sources of information, naturally, are the buyers of each industrial branch. They are the ones who know what prices and quality should be and are therefore in a position to be the first to report anything out of the ordinary. When that happens, once we have verified the facts, we can act quickly. Unfortunately the buyers do not often cooperate with us. That is a very peculiar but unfortunate fact. We collect information about prices and quality all the time and have a department for analyzing this information. Of course, they can make a thorough analysis of only a small sample of the total. We rarely go so far as to examine a firm's books. Usually after two chats, they lower prices all by themselves—unless, of course, they prove their case. If they don't, and don't lower prices or improve quality, then we permit imports, and the Secretaría de Hacienda cooperates very well with us in lowering the tariff, not a

[16] Stanford G. Ross and John B. Christensen, *Tax Incentives for Industry in Mexico* (Cambridge: Law School of Harvard University, 1959), pp. 32, 76–7; William A. Rafferty, *Licensing and Exchange Controls in Mexico* (Washington: U.S. Department of Commerce, 1958).

punishing amount that has to be raised again later, but a just amount.

Manufacturing was further aided, at least relatively, by keeping import duties on some inputs from abroad below the average level of about 15 per cent: an average of 5.6 per cent on raw materials and 10 per cent on machinery. Until 1948, moreover, General Rule 14 of the tariff allowed exemption of even very low rates on machinery for new plants or for output expansions of 10 per cent or more of existing plants.[17] These rates were alternative to the exemptions discussed below. Import permits covering parts and materials for making some products considered nonessential were granted only if the importer, usually through a broker at 1¼ per cent commission, arranged for exports (typically cotton) of equal value. From the manufacturer's point of view, resulting expenses were like a tax on the imports.

In general, tariffs and controls gave not only protection but monopoly power. Government surveillance could detect only flagrant abuses of such power, that is, behavior much worse than the collusion and monopolistic practice that were routine. Cooperation with government was probably limited because many victims were also offenders. Legislative and judicial machinery for applying the antimonopoly Article 28 of the Constitution of 1917 had not been developed. On the contrary, Article 28 was viewed as an unrealistic residue of nineteenth century liberalism because it failed to admit the inevitability of concentration and the possibility for regulation in the public interest.[18]

In 1964, however, it appeared that Mexican protectionism

[17] *Diario Oficial,* Jan. 20, 1956, translated in Ross and Christensen, *op. cit.,* pp. 241–3.

[18] Jesús Rodríguez y Rodríguez, "Los Monopolios en México," appendix to E. A. G. Robinson, *Monopolio* (México, D.F.; Fondo de Cultura Económica, 1942), pp. 290–6.

had passed its peak. The old protectionist line did not fit a country now vigorously pushing its own manufacturing exports with such means as the Fund for Promoting the Export of Manufactured Products, set up in 1963. A Treasury official introduced a generally revised import tariff system in August 1964 with comments in which he blamed some high duties on the "exaggerated protectionism that private enterprise is always seeking from us." By 1967 the import-substitution policy was officially described as "transitory" for sectors that could not bring costs down and quality up. High-cost industrial parts and materials producers were prime targets for reduced tariffs and lower quantitative barriers. Import protection and tax incentives were no longer to be granted to new plants that could not keep prices within 25 per cent of those prevailing in industrial countries.[19]

F. *Industrial Capital Formation.* High profits, whether or not monopolistic, can build a nation's capital stock by being reinvested where they originate or by bringing to a sector funds from other, less productive uses perhaps through a capital market or by raising the average propensity to save. Data on profits and internal reinvestment in Mexico are unreliable and not readily inferred through other information. The minute fractions of stocks exchanged during 1950–61 generated a price index that declined in real terms by 9 per cent, falsely implying general misinvestment or even disinvestment by companies that issued relatively few new shares but were leaders in multiplying their output and were, by all other standards, flourishing.[20] Most observers agree that reinvested profits and

[19] *Excelsior*, Aug. 6, 1964; *Comercio Exterior*, Aug. 1964, pp. 526–8; *El Mercado de Valores*, April 12, 1965; *New York Times*, Aug. 14, 1967, pp. 45–46.

[20] Ifigenia de Navarrete, "El Impuesto a las Ganancias de Capital en la Teoría y en la Práctica Fiscal," *El Trimestre Económico*, April–June 1963, p. 225.

depreciation reserves paid for two-thirds to four-fifths of private industrial investment.

The remaining one-fifth to one-third of investment funds were channeled to industry from abroad or redirected internally through controls or through ceaseless nursing of the capital market by government banks. Detailed regulations backed by heavy penalties fixed minimum amounts that commercial banks must lend to industry and even specified distribution of loans by maturity dates. As a result, net lending to industry by commercial and savings banks came to 45 per cent of their expanded loans during 1946–55, and, being allocated by law instead of by changing interest rates, necessarily amounted to a subsidy at the expense of the deprived sector. Since government banks lent to industry 73 per cent of all expanded public lending to the private sector, the total ratio of net industrial lending for the banking system rose to 60 per cent. By 1959, 48 per cent of outstanding loans by the banking system were industrial, and of these 55 per cent came from public banks, accounting for 53 per cent of public lending.[21]

Part of the public funds lent were diverted from other outlets favored by private savers, especially real estate, and channeled to industry through the Nacional Financiera, the government development bank, by means of securities with generous income and liquidity privileges (guaranteed repurchase at par). Announced but not applied was a strategy to accustom buyers to industrial investment by slowly reducing liquidity in successive issues, using increased industrial collateral, raising yields, but allowing a margin of fluctuation.

Finally, ever since 1941 privileges have been granted to private *financieras* or investment banks which usually sold their

[21] Raúl Ortiz Mena, "Moneda y Crédito," *México: 50 Años de Revolución,* p. 409; Banco Nacional de Comercio Exterior, *Comercio Exterior de México: 1961* (México, D.F., 1963), p. 67.

own bonds to get funds for buying stocks or relending to industry. Since most *financiera* obligations were both held by other (usually affiliated) banks and were customarily repaid on call, and since assets were backed by rediscounting privileges at the Nacional Financiera after 1945, *financieras* in effect monetized part of the capital market. This tendency was reinforced in the late 1950's when the Bank of Mexico curtailed direct support of government deficits, thus tightening credit for commercial banks while expanding it for nominally nonfinancial institutions. Throughout the period the *financieras* tried to shift their activities as much as they could from stocks to loans, and these from long term to short term. In spite of probable disappointments, government financial officials generally sounded pleased with what progress had been made, that is, the growth of the capital market so that it allocated 15 to 20 per cent of domestic investment, though still largely in nonindustrial construction.[22]

G. *Foreign Capital.*   Investment exceeded domestic saving by 9 per cent during 1939–50 and 14 per cent during 1950–59. Direct foreign private investment and foreign loans filled the gap. Foreign loans, mostly from the Export-Import Bank and the International Bank for Reconstruction and Development, made up 41 per cent of the saving deficit in the first decade and 42 per cent in the second. Although by no means all were specifically directed to the public sector during the 1950's, these loans on balance just made up the difference between public investment and public saving not financed through internal borrowing. It follows that net foreign resources flowing

[22] Alfredo Navarrete, "La Experiencia de México en el Uso de los Instrumentos de Política Financiera," *El Mercado de Valores,* March 11, 1963; Annual Reports of the Banco de México and Nacional Financiera; Mosk, *op. cit.,* pp. 223–54; Siegel, *op. cit.,* pp. 147–66; O. Ernest Moore, *Evolución de las Instituciones Financieras en México* (Mexico, D.F.: C.E.M.L.A., 1963), pp. 282–7, 383–99.

to the private sector matched the volume of direct foreign private investment, as defined in Mexican statistics.[23] But probably only half this volume was direct investment in the sense of funds imported for creating foreign-owned productive capacity. On the other hand, a substantial part of domestic savings were the reinvested profits of foreign subsidiaries, financing perhaps a third of expanded foreign-controlled capacity.

Over 90 per cent of foreign-controlled enterprises were United States or Canadian owned. Of $344 million dollars of United States private direct investment added during 1950–59, $222 million dollars or 65 per cent went to industry,[24] raising the American fraction of manufacturing value added to one-sixth. In general, foreign-owned manufacturing firms have received privileges and faced regulations exactly like those met by domestically-owned private firms. Indeed, since stocks are made out "to the bearer," amount of foreign participation is not always clear. A law of 1944 authorizing the government to require 51 per cent Mexican ownership in any enterprise seemed like a stringent mandate, but in its first three years the law was applied only to publishing and the production of movies and carbonated drinks.[25] Companies which came in later found government permits more readily forthcoming if they had "Mexicanized" themselves, if only through nominal stock ownership by a trusted employee or lawyer who might give the real owners both the securities and an undated letter surrendering the property. By the end of the 1950's, this practice was discouraged, and many foreign investors sought local equity financing, usually through a *financiera*. The foreign sector was sufficiently politically sensitive that it was subject

[23] Alfredo Navarrete, "El Financiamiento del Desarollo Económico," in *México: 50 Años de Revolución,* pp. 523–35.

[24] Urquidi, *Viabilidad . . . Economica de America Latina,* pp. 193–97; U.S. Department of Commerce, *U.S. Business Investments in Foreign Countries* (Washington, D.C., 1960), p. 110.

[25] Mosk, *op. cit.,* pp. 89–91, 255–61.

to slightly greater government pressure and was also more responsive to any given pressure than were domestic firms. Foreign firms usually paid higher wages, complied more strictly with social welfare regulations, and viewed much of its trade with public sector firms as investment in official good will.

H. *Taxes on Manufacturing.* The terms at which customers and lenders made payments to manufacturing firms in exchange for goods and income flows, respectively, were changed in favor of the manufacturers by the government. Import controls raised prices while divesting customers of alternate suppliers. Regulation of banks and financial markets made funds available to manufacturers at lower interest charges than they would otherwise have had to pay. If taxes and payments to labor and suppliers had risen by the same amount, industrialization would have meant no "disproportionate" gains to industrialists. But would industry have grown at all? And how many wage earners and others were really worse off than before?

Wages, fringe benefits, and labor legislation were discussed in Chapter 4. Little will be said about the complex and often revised tax system because only broad guesses are possible about that main variable, evasion. According to one estimate, 86 per cent of profits were hidden, more or less legally, for tax purposes in 1950.[26] In addition to import and export taxes and surcharges, Mexico has, among others, a federal stamp tax on a variety of transactions, commercial receipt taxes, and separate income taxes for different sources of income. Beginning in 1943, income taxes made up between 20 and 25 per cent of federally collected taxes, which themselves were three-quarters of all taxes. During the early 1950's, companies with incomes

[26] Carlos Andrade Muñoz, "Reformas a La Ley del Impuesto Sobre La Renta," *Problemas Económicos Actuales de México* (Mexico, D.F.: Escuela Nacional de Economía, 1954), p. 206, cited by Ross and Christensen, *op. cit.*, p. 23.

over five million pesos reported paying taxes between 30 and 40 per cent on income, although revised aggregate data indicate that the percentage of profits given up for taxes was no more than 15 per cent.[27] By the late 1950's large manufacturing companies, closely watched by the government, reckoned with a tax burden of 40 to 45 per cent, including the straight 15 per cent (after deductions) dividends tax that was collected before distribution.[28]

Taxes on manufacturing income with possible deductions for depreciation and reinvestment influenced choice of capital intensity and therefore technique of production. Mexican income taxes with rates not exceeding 4 to 8 per cent date back to 1921. But the era of modern, higher levels began with the law of 1941, in turn revised or replaced about every three years. The trend was toward higher rates offset by growing leniency for depreciation and reinvestment. For example, beginning in 1954 machinery could be depreciated annually at more than the standard 10 per cent with proof of replacement, and after 1961 merely with prior Hacienda authorization.[29] After this deduction, profits were taxed at rates rising to a marginal 33 per cent until 1955, and afterwards to 39 per cent on net income exceeding two million pesos. If remaining profits exceeded 15 per cent of net assets, they could after 1948 be taxed as "excess profits" but to no more than 10 per cent of net income. What still remained was subject to the 15 per cent dividends tax,

[27] Dirección de Estudios Hacendarios, *Estados Consolidados de Balance General y de Ingresos y Gastos por Actividades Económicas* (Mexico, D.F.: Secretaría de Hacienda y Crédito Público, 1951; Combined Mexican Working Party, *op. cit.*, p. 343; Navarrete, *La Distribución del Ingreso y el Desarrollo Económico de México*, p. 56.

[28] Ross and Christensen, *op. cit.*, p. 78.

[29] Hugo Margaín, "El Sistema Tributario," *México: 50 Años de Revolución, op. cit.*, p. 562; "Reformas a la Ley del Impuesto sobre la Renta," *Mercado de Valores*, Dec. 25, 1961, pp. 650–51.

mentioned above, after a 5 per cent automatic exemption for a "legal reserve," supplemented by a 10 per cent "ordinary reinvestment reserve" in 1949, and a further 20 per cent "extraordinary reinvestment reserve" after 1954, and rising to full 100 per cent dividend tax exemption with proof of actual reinvestment plans, granted as a matter of routine to all industries except alcoholic beverages. At the end of 1964 a new income tax law simplified this system and set up a framework for further reforms.[30]

There were, however, two other systems of tax exemption. One system involved key industries, especially steel. Under the label of "subsidy" import and export duties, production taxes and certain excises were forgiven. Perhaps the most important effect of this system was the furthering of raw material and machinery imports by the cancellation of duties that in the mid-1950's (ignoring demand elasticity) would have raised duty collections by 10 to 15 per cent.[31]

The other system granted exemptions to "new and necessary industries" which covered about one-tenth of the workers added to manufacturing payrolls between 1941 and 1957. The 1941 Law of Manufacturing Industries which replaced a vague 1939 decree was itself superseded by new laws in 1946 and 1955 and was amended by decrees in other years. At first five-year exemptions were granted for virtually all federal taxes on "totally" new manufacturing industries or those considered necessary for industrial development by the Secretaría de Economía. After 1946 industries considered "important" or "fundamental" could have, but seldom received, seven- and ten-year exemptions. Until 1955 some firms in "new" industries could extend their exemptions from two to five additional years by reapplying as "necessary." Collections under the applicable taxes

---

[30] *El Mercado de Valores,* Jan. 11, Feb. 2, and April 15, 1965.
[31] Ross and Christensen, *op. cit.,* pp. 38–9, 97–8.

apparently fell by about 6 per cent (or 2.8 per cent of all taxes) because of exemptions during 1949–1957.[32]

As early as 1949, however, there began a lessening of benefits and the enforcement of growing restrictions. Only 40 per cent or less of the profits tax could be forgiven, among other changes, and none of the excess profits tax. At the same time requirements for using at least 60 per cent supplies of Mexican origin, for contributing value-added of 10 per cent or more to imported materials, for training local personnel, and even for submitting to some price and quality controls were enforced with increasing rigor. By the late 1950's, tax exemption was generally regarded as payment for allowing some government inspection and regulation. About two dozen exemptions were granted annually. Enterprises receiving them would all have been profitable anyway, and they did not wait out the year or two between application and exemption before building and producing. On the contrary, the waiting would have made it hard to supply the information needed.[33] One must conclude, therefore, that Mexican tax exemptions during the 1950's—unlike the Puerto Rican system described next—did not foster industrialization by soothing the fears of entrepreneurs before investing. Gains went instead to enterprises already under way through favorable tariff and credit policies.

II. Puerto Rico

In spite of obvious differences, a few striking features of Mexican social and economic change had Puerto Rican counterparts. There were the landed oligarchs and foreign corporations said to be heedless of popular welfare, the harsh severance of tradition, the experiments with land reform and government enterprise, discord with the Catholic Church, the guarded

[32] *Ibid.*, pp. 43–52, 136, 191–208.   [33] *Ibid.*, pp. 52–105.

molding of new political forms, and the final acquiescence in a strategy of development which had little fastidious balancing of one group's profits with the related gains of others. What mattered was that there were some gains. A Puerto Rican difference in these various stages, however, was an occasional paradoxical overlapping of events.

A. *Literacy and Sugar Expansion: 1898–1928.* Conquest of Puerto Rico by the United States in 1898 was probably less traumatic, certainly less violent, than the Mexican Revolution. But the overhaul of public institutions and especially the expansion of schools, including the founding of the University of Puerto Rico in 1903, had a similar disrupting and renovating effect. That instruction had to be in English, first in high schools, then in all grades, then in all beyond the fifth, and finally again only in the high schools, was unsettling, and infuriating; yet more important was the drop in illiteracy from 80 per cent in 1899 to 55 per cent in 1920 to 31 per cent by 1940.[34]

But the first three decades of American rule also marked an expansion and modernization led by outsiders in a way reminiscent of Mexican growth under Díaz. In flowed 120 million dollars of American private capital, raising sugar production from about 60,000 tons a year to 870,000 tons and building a railroad for its transport. Over half the increase came after 1910 using a third more land and better varieties of cane but almost no more field workers. Meanwhile the population rose at a yearly 1.6 per cent from 950,000 in 1899 to 1,540,000 in 1930. The growth of manufacturing employment, other than home needlework, from 32,000 in 1910 to 53,000 in 1930, was

[34] Theodore Brameld, *The Remaking of a Culture: Life and Education in Puerto Rico* (New York: Harper, 1959), pp. 242–6; Harvey S. Perloff, *Puerto Rico's Economic Future: A Study in Planned Development* (Chicago: University of Chicago Press, 1950), p. 52.

not enough to relieve the general wretchedness, typified by the high, 24.4 per 1,000, death rate of the 1920's.[35]

B. *The New Deal and Agrarian Reform.* A Puerto Rican paradox is that the worsening of economic conditions with the hurricanes of 1928 and 1932, the drought of 1930–31, and the worldwide depression, coincided with dissension among liberals, leading to ultraconservative control of the legislature during 1932–40. Senator Millard Tydings, chairman of the Committee on Insular Affairs, wrote to President Roosevelt from Puerto Rico, "I am sorry to report there is no real independence sentiment here. . . . It would certainly be better for us if we were out of this place."[36] Instead, a number of leading New Dealers, including Mrs. Roosevelt, took a special interest in Puerto Rico, and through a variety of soon feuding agencies—the Puerto Rican Emergency Relief Administration, the Puerto Rican Reconstruction Administration, the Works Progress Administration, the Reconstruction Finance Corporation, and others—the Federal Government spent and lent from 1933 through 1941, some 230 million dollars.[37]

Schools, roads, hydroelectric plants, and the construction of other social overhead capital, as well as a cement plant for processing the raw material for these structures, were leading

[35] Victor S. Clark, *et al.*, *Porto Rico and Its Problems* (Washington: Brookings Institution, 1930), pp. 375–86; Perloff, *op. cit.*, pp. 25–30, 98, 401; Thomas C. Cochran, *The Puerto Rican Businessman: A Study in Cultural Change* (Philadelphia: University of Pennsylvania Press, 1959), pp. 20–42; A. J. Jaffe, *People, Jobs and Economic Development: A Case History of Puerto Rico Supplemented by Recent Mexican Experiences* (Glencoe: Free Press, 1959), pp. 61, 98; U.S. Bureau of the Census, *Puerto Rico: Census of Manufactures: 1958* (Washington, 1960), p. 2. In 1910, 11,200 home needleworkers were employed; in 1930, 42,100.

[36] Letter, Dec. 6, 1933, quoted by Thomas Mathews, *Puerto Rican Politics and the New Deal* (Gainesville: University of Florida Press, 1960), p. 107.

[37] Perloff, *op. cit.*, p. 32; Mathews, *op. cit.*, pp. 154–9.

New Deal projects. As early as 1933 all tasks were conceived in terms of a single economic plan, which was worked out during 1934 under Carlos Chardón, Chancellor of the University of Puerto Rico, and then approved by Roosevelt. Lack of supporting legislation by the territorial legislature and opposition by key U.S. Senators, by Governor Winship, and by some other Roosevelt appointees on the Island, blocked enactment of its main feature, agrarian reform.[38] Some large sugar estates were to have been expropriated and in part operated as "yardsticks" by a public corporation; others would have been subdivided into nontransferable plots (recalling the *Ejidos*) for agricultural diversification. What struck the planners as anomalous was that most foodstuffs had to be imported to an island where land was increasingly concentrated in the hands of sugar corporations with ever higher agricultural efficiency but ever lower incomes for the inhabitants.

Yet the proposed land reform had precedents in theory as well as in legal tradition. As early as 1900, reaffirmed by the Jones Act of 1917 and upheld by the Supreme Court in 1940, the U.S. Congress had prohibited corporate or partnership owning of more than 500 acres of Puerto Rican land. The fear was that, otherwise, "the condition of the people will . . . be reduced to one of absolute servitude." Nevertheless, two-thirds of sugar producing lands were held in units illegally exceeding 500 acres and averaging over 3,000.[39] Throughout the 1930's, industrialization, as a means to bolster agrarian reconstruction,

[38] Mathews, *op. cit.*, pp. 149, 166, 202–3, 218, 283.

[39] Congressman Jones, *Congressional Record*, April 24, 1900, p. 4619, quoted by Walter Packard, "The Land Authority and Democratic Processes in Puerto Rico," *Inter-American Economic Affairs*, Summer 1948, pp. 49–50; Rexford Guy Tugwell, "Report on the 'Five-Hundred Acre Law'," *Puerto Rican Public Papers of R. G. Tugwell, Governor* (San Juan: Service Office of the Government of Puerto Rico, 1945), pp. 291–316; Arthur D. Gayer, Paul T. Homan, Earle K. James, *The Sugar Economy of Puerto Rico* (New York: Columbia University Press, 1938), p. 103.

was to be encouraged either through the adoption of Puerto Rican tariffs or the elimination of American duties on materials. But in fact no action was taken and factory employment stayed below 56,000.

Agrarian reform became a reality with the winning of legislative control by Luis Muñoz Marín and his Popular Democrats in 1940 under a slogan borrowed from the Mexican and Russian revolutions, "Bread, Land, and Liberty." Rexford Guy Tugwell was appointed Governor in 1941. A Land Authority was created; the sugar industry was declared a public utility; and by the end of 1947, 36 per cent of illegal corporate lands had been condemned and purchased.[40]

The program coincided with World War II which raised net Island income originating in federal activities from $21 million in 1939–40 to a yearly average of $115 million during 1942–46, or from 9 to 24 per cent of total net income. Manufacturing output grew at an annual 11 per cent; manufacturing employment (not counting home needleworkers) rose from almost 56,000 to 73,000.[41] But changing conditions did not lead to reappraisal of land reform. On the contrary, Tugwell thought the contemporary Mexican shift in emphasis "merely pointed to another victory for the orthodox who feared that an experiment might succeed if allowed to continue."[42] By 1950, however, the Puerto Rican experiment with government-owned sugar mills and profit-sharing farms was no longer thought worth the price of expansion. In 1951 the designation of sugar production as a public utility was repealed; and later the resettlement program for the landless was cut and given a terminal date. As in Mexico, the reforms had served what came to be their main purpose: closing a political era.

[40] Packard, *op. cit.*, pp. 73–4.
[41] Perloff, *op. cit.*, pp. 383, 398, 401.
[42] Tugwell, *Puerto Rican Papers*, p. 311.

C. *Government Manufacturing and Political Reform.* With the population approaching two million at a natural rate of increase of 2.5 per cent annually by 1940, it seemed clear that insular well-being meant industrialization. The institutions that formed the backbone of the later "bootstrap" program, the Development Bank and the Industrial Development Company, were set up in 1942, although with quite a different initial orientation. Like the Mexican Nacional Financiera in the 1930's, the Bank's first task was facilitating government finance, and it had no regular policy of lending to private firms until 1945. The Industrial Development Company, based on a Chilean model, was mainly concerned with building and operating its own factories, which made bottles, paper board, structural clay products, and shoes, as well as taking over the cement plant of the P.R.R.A. War conditions perhaps made Puerto Rican investment, even in support of flourishing rum exports, submarginal for busy mainland corporations; but no doubt the government welcomed the chance to own industries. Government manufacturing fit the program of creating a Land Authority, Transportation Authority, Communications Authority, Water Resources Authority, Housing Authority, and others all under a Planning Board "to lock projected improvements into a logical whole that would be broken only with difficulty." The initial capital for these authorities was mainly derived from the extraordinary $160 million in rum excise taxes collected in the United States during the war and remitted. In 1944 the Governor pocket vetoed an income tax exemption law passed for all firms in new industries.[43]

[43] Rexford Guy Tugwell, *The Stricken Land: The Story of Puerto Rico* (Garden City: Doubleday, 1947), p. 259. According to Tugwell, Muñoz had no real interest in planning beyond fractionalizing sugar lands but nevertheless lined up legislative support at the Governor's insistence. Though not sympathetic to the claims of private enterprise, Tugwell was not determined to exclude it from Puerto Rican development. It was

About to resign after the war, Tugwell worried about ways of defending the government manufacturing industries against dumping by "mainland giants" and wondered "who would understand the economic structure we had planned and were building?"[44] Indeed all public manufacturing was soon in trouble. Mainland competition hurt the sales of government-made shoes, limited in variety of style and size, as well as the bathroom wares sales by the Puerto Rico Clay Products Corporation. The shoe company also had excessive training and startup costs. The clay products plant seemed unable to overcome technical defects and piled up still visible mountains of rejected bricks and building tile. Prolonged strikes and labor problems were difficult and embarrassing to handle for a labor-oriented government and closed the cement and glass plants for months. The owner of the local container board factory, publisher of an opposition newspaper, failed to buy from the government paper board mill, in part for political reasons, and the product had to be exported at a loss. To avoid further trouble, the government changed plans and decided to lease rather than operate a hotel (later the Carib Hilton) and a textile mill under construction.[45]

Assigned to appraise Puerto Rican economic policies, Harvey S. Perloff recommended in 1949 that the other plants, worth $10,700,000 and normally employing 992, be sold to create a

---

rather his view that private capital, especially that in Puerto Rican banks, lacked needed vision and courage. He recalled the Philippine experience of Governor General Burton Harrison (1913–1921) who, unable to attract industries with 5 per cent dividend guarantees, had launched government-owned enterprises in utilities, railroads, cement, iron, coal, and petroleum (*ibid.*, pp. 172, 253–5, 410–12).

[44] *Ibid.*, p. 683.

[45] H. C. Barton, "Puerto Rico's Industrial Development Program, 1942–1960," paper presented at the Center for International Affairs, Harvard University, October 29, 1959, reproduced by Economic Development Administration (San Juan, 1959), pp. 8–10.

"revolving fund for risk-taking investments" since Puerto Rico was "fighting against time" and could not "afford the luxury of industrializing at a leisurely pace," reinvesting profits and avoiding absentee ownership.[46] By the end of 1951 all plants were sold. To Tugwell, this sale, the abandoning of more land, and the expropriation of utilities seemed a costly anticipation of Republican control in Washington: "the giving up of state socialism as a gesture of appeasement." [47]

Perhaps Tugwell's most lasting contribution to Puerto Rico was his part in building new political institutions. During the 1930's Puerto Rican legislators and officials were notorious for corruption—"using every known ruse to increase their own income" and better at operating a vast nepotism than the ordinary functions of government.[48] Passing over some associates of Muñoz, Tugwell selected for top positions young Puerto Ricans, most of them educated in the United States, who could forget their Spanish *dignidad,* for "it was they who possessed the power to transform." [49] Still in charge of the major government departments in the mid-1960's, none of them had grown rich; expenditures were subject to independent public auditing with tiny inconsistencies feared as fatal to careers. Administrative excellence was thought a tradition. With the granting of power by Congress to elect a Governor in 1948 and the establishment of its unique Commonwealth status in 1952, the Island's political stabilization was virtually complete. The old issue of independence versus statehood had been circumvented.

The anachronistic conflict remaining was with the Catholic Church which was offended by the election of a divorced and remarried man, Muñoz, as Governor and by the distribution

[46] Perloff, *op. cit.,* pp. 374–5.

[47] Rexford Guy Tugwell, *The Art of Politics as Practiced by Three Great Americans: Franklin Delano Roosevelt, Luis Muñoz Marín, and Fiorello H. La Guardia* (Garden City: Doubleday, 1958), pp. 3n, 63.

[48] Mathews, *op. cit.,* p. 322; Tugwell, *Stricken Island,* pp. 78, 82.

[49] Tugwell, *Stricken Island,* pp. 489–90.

of contraceptive devices and materials at thirty-three public health stations. The birth rate had fallen from 42.9 per thousand around 1940 to 34.5 in 1957; or from 186 to 159 per 1,000 women aged 15 to 44. Meanwhile the death rate was down to 7 per thousand by 1957. Some 450,000 migrants to the United States kept population growth down to 150,000 during the 1950's or to an average annual increase of only 0.6 per cent. The total population reached 2,350,000 in 1960.[50] The rift with the Church lasted until an accord in August 1962.[51] The temporary fading of net emigration brought population growth up to its natural rate of 22 per thousand during 1963–64. But net emigration was back at 30,000 in 1966; meanwhile the population passed 2,700,000.

D. *Operation Bootstrap: 1947–1960.* The reversal in policy to bring in more absentee owners, this time in manufacturing, suited worldwide economic conditions and especially Puerto Rico's tax-immune access to the United States market. Exempted from the American tariff, from United States taxes, and for ten years from corporate and personal (if a resident) Commonwealth property and income taxes, and subsidized in other ways described below, 926 new manufacturing firms started producing during 1947–60. Ignoring some changes in ownership, 664 of these were still in operation on December 31, 1960. In 1963 a new Tax Incentive Act provided 17 years of tax exemption for the least developed parts of the Island and 12 years for most other parts. Firms could double their exemption period by choosing 50 per cent exemption

---

[50] Jaffe, *op. cit.*, pp. 56, 61.

[51] *New York Times*, Oct. 7, 1962. By contrast, the Mexican Revolutionary Party through the 1940's held that population growth reinforced economic development and rejected "the neo-malthusianism of the militarist and imperialist nations." During the 1950's growing awareness of demographic arithmetic coincided with improving Church-State relations, and the topic of population control was still given little official mention (Jaffe, *op. cit.*, pp. 253–4).

instead of 100 per cent. By mid-1967 there were 1,500 operating plants.[52] Manufacturing output during 1947–60 grew at an average yearly rate of 7 per cent compounded, which pro-

Table 20. Puerto Rican manufacturing in 1958: number of establishments, employees, wages and salaries, value added, and value added per worker

Classification	Number of establishments	Number of employees	Wages and salaries (thousands of dollars)	Value added per annum (thousands of dollars)	Value added per worker
Processed foods, beverages, tobacco	652	21,591	$41,718	$105,736	$4,900
Textiles	53	4,592	8,328	15,473	3,370
Apparel	353	17,901	24,518	44,005	2,460
Furniture and wood products	253	3,356	5,133	10,089	3,010
Paper products	10	631	1,875	3,902	6,180
Printing and publishing	109	1,484	3,572	6,145	4,140
Chemicals	68	1,513	4,179	9,330	6,170
Petroleum products, rubber and plastics	13	164	467	1,346	8,210
Leather products	32	2,837	3,984	7,544	2,660
Stone, clay, glass products	171	4,122	9,003	19,856	4,670
Primary metal products	14	416	1,157	1,760	4,230
Fabricated metal products	116	1,531	3,742	8,493	5,550
Nonelectrical machinery	26	1,180	3,365	6,439	5,460
Electrical machinery and equipment	48	3,006	6,766	21,321	7,090
Instruments and related products	15	1,148	2,342	3,932	3,420

Source: U.S. Bureau of the Census in cooperation with the Puerto Rico Planning Board, Bulletin MC-PR, *Puerto Rico Census of Manufactures: 1958* (Washington: Government Printing Office, 1960), p. 4.

[52] Office of Economic Research, Economic Development Administration, "Analysis of Discontinuances of Operations: 1960 Edition" (mimeographed), San Juan, April 1961, Table VI; *1966 Informe Económico Al Gobernador* (San Juan: Junta de Planificación, 1966), p. 158; *New York Times*, Aug. 3, 1967, p. 43.

duced a yearly expansion of real "gross Commonwealth product" (GCP) of 5.5 per cent, or 4.8 per cent per capita. In fiscal
1960 per capita GCP reached 677 (1960) dollars, compared
with 367 (1960) dollars in 1946–47 and 299 (1960) dollars in
1939–40.[53] By 1965 it was 920 (1960) dollars. The higher 1960–
65 GCP growth rate of 7.2 per cent offset the higher population
growth rate of 2.2 per cent.

Unlike Mexico, there could be no even growth of agriculture
and industry. Agricultural output grew 20 per cent during the
1950's, but manufacturing by 154 per cent. Rising productivity
allowed agricultural employment to fall by 42 per cent or from
one-third to one-fourth of total employment. But who would
have expected manufacturing employment to fall? It did, from
105,000 to 93,000. Factory employment grew from 55,000 to
82,000; but of 50,000 home needleworkers only 11,000 were
still sewing in 1960. Since emigration had cut the labor force
by 61,000, unemployment remained at 13 per cent.[54] Given
these trends, the government decided that the economic problem was the raising of incomes; unemployment was a "social
problem" to be solved by income transfers through government
channels.[55]

A large portion of the funds, some earmarked and others not,

[53] Junta de Planificación, *Puerto Rico: Indices Seleccionados de
Progreso Económico y Social: Años Economicós 1939–40, 1946–47 al
1959–60* (San Juan, 1961), pp. 1–2; *Idem, Income and Product: 1964*
(San Juan, 1965), p. 9; *Informe Económico Al Gobernador,* pp. 6, 151,
A-23.

[54] Puerto Rico Planning Board, *Economic Report to the Governor:
1960, Part II* (San Juan, 1960), pp. 40–43. In 1966 the labor force reached
800,000; unemployment seemed to have stabilized around 11 per cent.
In the first half of 1967 manufacturing employment averaged 123,000
("Employment, Hours and Earnings in the Manufacturing Industries in
Puerto Rico, June 1967" [San Juan: Bureau of Labor Statistics, Aug.
1967], p. 4).

[55] Alvin Mayne and Evelyn Ramos, *Planning for Social and Economic
Development in Puerto Rico* (San Juan: Puerto Rico Planning Board,
1959), p. 40.

for investment and income transfers to Puerto Ricans came from the United States. In fiscal 1958, not an atypical year for Puerto Rico, all government transfer payments to individuals less social insurance contributions came to $53 million. Net transfers from the Federal Government to individuals and agriculture were $68 million. The Commonwealth government received an additional Federal $46 million in grants-in-aid, returned customs, and rum excise taxes collected in the United States. The Federal Government spent a further $90 million in operational disbursements, largely for defense but including housing, the postal service, and others, for which no taxes were collected because Puerto Rico lacked a vote in Congress.[56] The total Federal contribution of 204 million dollars that year amounted to 15.5 per cent of gross Commonwealth product.

At a more aggregative level, one need not distinguish between the outside funds, public and private, that either reinforced Puerto Rican saving directly or released local funds from private and public consumption expenditures. One may estimate the extent to which development was financed out of Island resources (gross saving) by comparing gross domestic public and private investment with the import deficit. In fiscal 1950 gross domestic investment was 14.3 per cent of gross Commonwealth product, and the import deficit was 14 per cent. Gross Commonwealth saving, therefore, was 0.3 per cent. Investment rose to an average of 21 per cent for 1956–60, and the import deficit to 19.8 per cent. Gross saving was 1.2 per cent.[57]

Before concluding that the bootstraps of Puerto Rican development were a mainland import, one should note that much outside support of consumption, including private remittances

[56] Puerto Rico Planning Board, *Economic Report to the Governor: 1960, Part I* (San Juan, 1960), pp. A-7, A-17, A-18; Mayne and Ramos, *op. cit.*, p. 51.

[57] *Economic Report to the Governor: 1960*, Part I, p. A-2.

to relatives, supported investment in a spurious sense. Without these funds it would have been primarily consumption, not local saving or investment carried on by different groups, that would have fallen. During 1958–60 almost half of gross investment was locally financed, that is, without a directly associated inflow of outside loan or equity capital. Seventy per cent of the local share was equivalent to depreciation allowances.[58]

E. *Policy toward Manufacturing.* Since private manufacturing was to be the fulcrum of the whole development program, the fifth or so of gross investment that outsiders put directly into plant and equipment, about sixty million dollars annually in the late 1950's, was crucial. With an additional third accumulating in liquid assets, cash, and accounts receivable, this inflow left Puerto Rico each year on the average with sixty more operating factories. Attracting these funds was the target of economic policy.

Without sovereignty, the Puerto Rican government had to forego for the most part the two policies effective in Mexican industrialization: import protection and manipulation of money and private financial institutions. Climate and distance, reinforced by obligatory use of high cost United States shipping from the mainland, gave some protection, as did the "Buy American" policy of local military units. No doubt, also, the high excise tax on automobiles shifted some spending to Island products. But these were paltry stimulants to manufacturing which was necessarily export-oriented. Net income from new manufacturing promoted by the development program began to surpass that of older, not tax exempt, manufacturing in 1957. The following year only 36 per cent of shipments of taxable firms in old industries went to buyers outside Puerto Rico, but 68 per cent of shipments were exported by exempt firms. Exempt firms selling exclusively on the Island, that is, nonexport-

[58] *Ibid.*, pp. 31–33.

ers, had only 14.5 per cent of exempt-firm payrolls.[59] This export emphasis continued and made import protection inappropriate.

Producing only one-fifth of 1 per cent of United States industrial output, Puerto Rico faced a highly elastic export demand; and its industrialization has been described as close to a pure application of comparative advantage.[60] This is true in the sense that industries processing bulky materials with heavy equipment have not found shipping to and back from Puerto Rico attractive. But comparative advantage is not by definition absolute: Because the U.S. Department of Labor could raise wages during 1952–60 from an average $.45 to $.94 per hour by determining the legal minimum,[61] and because there is no exchange rate to devalue, mere comparative advantage does not assure trade.

Incentives to manufacturers had to be more direct. Hence, the government took responsibility for keeping business risks low by assuring liquidity and helping with startup problems;

[59] U.S. Bureau of the Census in cooperation with the Puerto Rico Planning Board, Bulletin MC-PR, *Puerto Rico Census of Manufactures: 1958* (Washington, D.C., and San Juan, 1960), p. 58; *Economic Report to the Governor: 1960, Part II,* pp. 8–9; Also, *Tax Treatment of U.S. Concerns with Puerto Rican Affiliates,* Hearings before the Select Committee on Small Business, U.S. Senate, Eighty-eighth Congress, second session, on The Economic Development Program, April 16–17, 1964.

[60] Hollis B. Chenery, "Comparative Advantage and Development Policy," *American Economic Review,* March 1961, p. 44; Werner Baer, "Puerto Rico: An Evaluation of a Successful Development Program," *Quarterly Journal of Economics,* November 1959, pp. 666–70; and Baer, *The Puerto Rican Economy and U.S. Economic Fluctuations* (Rio Piedras: University of Puerto Rico, Social Science Research Center, 1962).

[61] H. C. Barton and Robert A. Solo, "The Effect of Minimum Wage Laws on the Economic Growth of Puerto Rico," mimeographed, San Juan, 1959; Robert R. Nathan Associates, "Evaluation of Minimum Wage Policy in Puerto Rico," mimeographed, Washington, D.C., 1955. Puerto Rican wages and labor productivity are discussed in Chapters 3 and 4 above.

and when finally profitable, business was exempted from sharing social costs for the remainder of its first ten years. In the late 1950's the profit rate on equity before taxes was 50 per cent higher for exempt Puerto Rican firms than profits in the United States. After taxes, they were triple: 27.9 per cent compared with 9.3 per cent in 1959.[62] Firms were more profitable because they were in Puerto Rico, still a low wage area; but to a great extent causation ran the other way. Profitable, monopolistic, patent-protected firms had the greatest incentive to invest in the move. As recognition of this spread in the United States, more "blue-chip" subsidiaries moved in; and the industrial structure shifted from apparel toward technically advanced products such as electrical machinery which approached or exceeded profits of half the equity per year. By 1959 tax savings by the new companies came to some twenty-five million dollars annually.

Perhaps the tax savings alone have brought about the 7 per cent growth rate of manufacturing. Nevertheless, in 1950 the managers of the development program thought otherwise. The Economic Development Administration was created, and expenditures for directly promoting private industry quintupled, from $412,000 in 1949–50 to $2,056,000 in 1950–51. By fiscal 1960 over six million dollars were spent annually, taking on risks and advertising gains. The Puerto Rican government thus did not assume that private enterprise would attempt alert, adventurous cost-reducing, nor pay lip service to the Island tradition of social radicalism. The strategy was to treat the American business community as if it were poorly informed and timid, to give it liquidity and a sales pitch, not excluding a bit of reinterpretation about the early experiments with government-owned factories ("just wartime pressure").[63]

[62] *Annual Statistical Report of E.D.A. Manufacturing Plants: 1959–60* (San Juan: Economic Development Administration, 1961), p. 42.
[63] "Investment Group Hears Governor Review Puerto Rican Economy," excerpts from an address by Luis Muñoz Marin in New York, Jan. 27,

About three million dollars were spent a year during the late 1950's to coax businessmen to visit Puerto Rico in a mood receptive to tax exemption "prehearings" and the signing of leases. Advertisements in trade journals and direct mail campaigns adapted to industrial suborders and screened for credit ratings resulted in "leads" for Puerto Rican industrial representatives in New York, Chicago, and other cities. The prospect was given a glossy handbook on wages, payrolls, sales, profits, and other data about firms similar to his own but already operating in Puerto Rico. When he was persuaded to visit, he was encouraged to inspect these same plants.

Risks were reduced by the availability of government-owned sites and plants worth almost fifty million dollars, of which a large fraction were not in use, but which nevertheless provided over half the floor space of exempt firms. Annual rent charges varied from $.50 to $.95 per square foot. The Puerto Rico Industrial Development Company's gross annual rent (before depreciation and expenses) on its industrial property was less than 6 per cent which, together with the low returns on loans by the Company and the Development Bank, meant relinquishment of at least $1,300,000 on interest income in fiscal 1959. Nevertheless, the share of government capital in the new firms had fallen from a third in 1951 to one-tenth, partly because local firms (also tax exempt) now built most plants for lease in the San Juan area. Startup uncertainties were further reduced by the expenditure of $1.2 million for labor selection and training and a variety of technical and research services, plus $1.4 million in other subsidies such as ocean freight reimbursement for industries considered fraught with external economies. Exclusive of the promotion of rum production and

1961, *Quarterly Report to Investors in Puerto Rican Securities, June 1961* (San Juan: Government Development Bank for Puerto Rico, 1961), pp. 1–2. Ruth Gruber; *Puerto Rico: Island of Promise* (New York: Hill and Wang, 1960), pp. 61–62. *Annual Report of the Economic Development Administration: 1959–60* (San Juan, 1960), Statistical Appendix, Table 2.

sales, government economists thought returns to the Commonwealth treasury from the development program exceeded costs by half. That risk was very real is shown by the fourth of firms that operated at an average loss of 37.8 per cent of average equity in 1959 and by the 30 per cent of promoted enterprises abandoned through 1960 (half of these within two years), a rate that is roughly comparable to mainland United States experience. On the other hand only 47 plants had shut down by mid-1967 after their exemptions had expired, yet 218 plants with expired tax exemptions remained in operation.[64]

As in the discussion of Mexican development policy, many features of a complex program have been ignored. Worth mentioning, before concluding, however, is that Puerto Rican development had a trace of planning for a more integrated industrial structure. A sizeable part of direct financial assistance was given to "core industries," those either using Puerto Rican mineral and plant inputs or importing and processing crude materials formerly bought in more finished form, especially if the output would be bought by several other industries. Outstanding examples were the bagasse-using paper mill, a flour and feed mill, a meat packing plant, and ammonia and ethylene glycol plants associated with local petroleum refineries—all based on preliminary E.D.A. "feasibility studies" applying the linkage aspects of location theory. By mid-1967, the chemical industry was thought to have the greatest potential for industrial integration and expansion, and government officials cheerfully forecast over a billion dollars of investment in petrochemicals within a decade. Two additional petroleum refineries were already under construction; also on the way

---

[64] Barton, *op. cit.*, pp. 19–27; "Analysis of Discontinuances of Operations: 1960," pp. 1–3. See also the statistical appendices of the *Annual Reports* of the Economic Development Administration and the Puerto Rico Industrial Development Company; the *Annual Statistical Reports of E.D.A. Manufacturing Plants;* and *New York Times*, Aug. 3, 1967, p. 47.

were plants for making oxo-alcohols, polyvinyls, nylon 66, para-xylene, and other intermediate products, including petrochemical aromatics, perhaps in the world's largest such plant.[65] These industries would supply, not only each other, but also the next wave of new factories, makers of chemical consumer goods.

[65] *Industry in Puerto Rico* (New York: Chase Manhattan Bank, Economic Research Division, July, 1967), p. 27.

APPENDIX B

Table 21. Comparison of labor productivity, capital productivity, and labor efficiency in selected industries in Mexico (1961) and the United States (1958)

Industry	Average labor productivity in Mexico (USA=100)	Average capital productivity in Mexico (USA=100)	Capital-labor ratio in Mexico (USA=100)	Labor efficiency in Mexico: Apparent productivity with the U.S. capital-labor ratio under alternate Cobb-Douglas elasticities with respect to Mexican capital inputs. (USA labor productivity=100)			Indicated output per worker in Mexico with U.S. capital-labor ratios compared with actual labor productivity.		
	(1)	(2)	(3)	(4) k=.5	(5) k=.4	(6) k=.3	(7) k=.5	(8) k=.4	(9) k=.3
1. Meat packing (plants)	28	72	39	45	41	37	1 60	1 46	1 33
2. Fluid milk	05	19	27	10	08	07	1 92	1 69	1 48
3. Canned fruits and vegetables	30	86	35	51	46	41	1 69	1 52	1 37
4. Chocolate and cocoa products	13	42	31	23	21	18	1 80	1 60	1 42
5. Cane sugar	21	68	31	38	34	30	1 80	1 60	1 42
6. Confectionery products	22	67	33	38	34	31	1 74	1 56	1 39
7. Chewing gum	27	90	30	49	44	39	1 83	1 62	1 44
8. Prepared feeds for animals	30	75	40	47	43	39	1 58	1 44	1 32
9. Wines and liquors	32	80	40	51	46	42	1 58	1 44	1 32
10. Flour	19	45	42	29	27	25	1 54	1 41	1 30
11. Bread and bakery products	14	56	25	28	24	21	2 00	1 74	1 52
12. Beer	51	1 13	45	76	70	65	1 49	1 38	1 27
13. Cigarettes	28	47	60	36	34	33	1 29	1 23	1 17
14. Cigars	17	33	40	27	25	22	1 58	1 44	1 32
15. Cotton cloth	27	96	28	51	45	40	1 89	1 66	1 47
16. Wool cloth	23	1 28	18	54	46	38	2 36	1 99	1 67
17. Synthetic fibers	32	53	60	41	39	37	1 29	1 23	1 17
18. Women's under garments	27	53	51	38	35	33	1 40	1 31	1 22

19. Wood household furniture	19	60	32	34	30	27	1 77	1 58	1 41
20. Metal furniture	18	44	41	28	26	24	1 56	1 43	1 31
21. Pulp and paper (mills)	35	92	38	57	52	47	1 62	1 47	1 34
22. Paperboard (mills)	14	1 27	11	42	34	27	3 02	2 42	1 94
23. Paper products	22	60	61	28	27	26	1 28	1 22	1 16
24. Newspapers and periodicals	26	60	43	40	36	33	1 52	1 40	1 29
25. Commercial printing	19	58	33	33	30	26	1 74	1 56	1 39
26. Leather and leather products	26	1 16	31	47	42	37	1 80	1 60	1 42
27. Tires and inner tubes	57	1 16	49	81	76	71	1 43	1 33	1 24
28. Industrial chemicals	14	78	18	33	28	23	2 36	1 99	1 67
29. Paints and varnishes	16	67	24	33	28	25	2 04	1 77	1 53
30. Drugs	20	71	28	38	33	29	1 89	1 66	1 47
31. Soap and detergents	13	59	22	28	24	20	2 13	1 83	1 57
32. Agricultural chemicals	58	2 00	29	1 08	95	84	1 86	1 64	1 45
33. Flat glass	30	88	34	51	46	41	1 71	1 54	1 38
34. Glassware, pressed or blown	23	72	32	41	36	32	1 77	1 58	1 41
35. Clay products	20	71	28	38	33	29	1 89	1 66	1 47
36. Cement	39	1 22	32	69	62	55	1 77	1 58	1 41
37. Iron and steel, primary and secondary	27	51	53	37	35	33	1 37	1 29	1 21
38. Copper, primary and secondary	39	78	50	55	51	48	1 41	1 32	1 23
39. Metal cans	17	90	19	39	33	28	2 29	1 94	1 65
40. Bolts, nuts, screws, rivets	19	49	39	30	28	25	1 60	1 46	1 33
41. Farm machinery and equipment	25	83	30	46	40	36	1 83	1 62	1 44
42. Household appliances	33	53	46	49	45	42	1 47	1 36	1 26
43. Truck and bus bodies	25	96	26	49	43	37	1 96	1 71	1 50
44. Motor vehicles and parts	59	2 51	23	1 23	1 06	92	2 09	1 80	1 55
Unweighted average	26	81	35	45	40	36	1 76	1 57	1 40

Source: The index numbers of columns 1–3 were calculated by Edmar L. Bacha for three- and four-digit census classifications for the United States in 1958 and Mexico in 1961. The recession year unfortunately distorts the ratios for products like motor vehicles (Edmar L. Bacha, "Comparación entre la Productividad Industrial de México y Los Estados Unidos," *El Trimestre Económico*, Oct.–Dec. 1966, pp. 657–73). Estimates in the remaining columns were made by Professor Einar Hardin and myself as described in Chapter 3, Section V.

The Sample of Firms

Since observing technical decisions and results in a modern setting was the aim of the field work, only firms with new plants or great expansions, built after 1945, were considered. The sample is not representative of new plants since only twenty-two (43 per cent) of the fifty-one Mexican firms were selected at random. The remainder was chosen because of innovations, reputed progressive management, or simply to cover most two-digit industrial classifications—that is, various types of ownership (local, national, immigrant, government, and foreign) as well as broad size distribution, classified by employment (small, 5–99; medium, 100–499; large, over 500). Eleven out of the nineteen Puerto Rican firms were chosen because their products were identical to those of Mexican firms already studied. Forty-two per cent of all plants made simple commodities with less than five component parts in uniform production runs lasting a week or more which were sold to final buyers at less than one U.S. dollar, or its equivalent, per meter, pound, or other unit. Only three firms made the reverse combination of complex, high-cost, custom-built products. Of the fifty-one Mexican firms, twenty-five were located in and around Monterrey, a city famous for its thrifty and progressive business elite. Twenty-six were on the Central Plateau, for the most part in and around Mexico City.

Interviews were usually arranged by personal visits without

preceding correspondence. Only five times was I unable to obtain the cooperation of previously selected firms. At all other plants generosity with time and information was notable.[1] Interviews usually lasted from one to three hours, were preceded or followed by tours of the plant, and were based on substantial previous research about the history of the firm, its executives, production methods, employment record, and financial condition. In forty enterprises the highest ranking person interviewed was the president or general manager (often the leading owner), and in twenty-five cases it was an executive who specialized in production problems such as the technical director, production manager, or general superintendent. More than one person was interviewed at one-third of the firms, mostly at the larger ones; and repeated visits were made at thirteen to obtain additional information and to resolve doubtful points. The interviews, conducted in Spanish, English, and three times in German, covered questions on antecedents of investment decisions, instructions to designing engineers, finance, markets, labor relations, and experience with the plant in operation. Notes were taken freely, but the questionnaire (reproduced in Appendix D) was not used overtly. Only three respondents asked if a questionnaire were involved and were given copies. Needless to say, the order of questions was altered or expanded in many interviews to make the most of unexpected disclosures. As in all intensive interviews, the richness

[1] James J. Berna reports a similar experience with interviewing in his *Industrial Entrepreneurship in Madras State* (Bombay: Asia Publishing House, 1960): "One of the reasons for the generally friendly reception accorded the writer seems to be the simple fact that the entrepreneurs as a group are rather proud of the enterprises they have succeeded in building up ... Most of them also seemed a little flattered that a student would travel all the way from America to study their background and problems. The writer also had the definite impression that most of these men were glad of the opportunity to talk to some disinterested person about their situation" (p. 227).

of detail is partly offset by the selective filtering of perception, interpretation, and memory.[2]

Sixteen of the Mexican firms were founded during the 1940's and twenty-two during 1950–61. Three that antedate the Revolution of 1911 and ten others founded during the 1920's and 1930's bring the average age at the time of interviewing up to eighteen years. Thirty-one of the Mexican firms were either founded or undertook major plant expansions in 1955 or later.

Only three of the Puerto Rican firms were manufacturing on the Island before 1950. In fact, at the time of interviewing, the average age of firms was somewhat less than seven years, and construction or major expansion had occurred within the preceding four years.

The products manufactured by the seventy firms range from sugar and cheese to industrial equipment. Only one printing and publishing enterprise was selected and only one that made petroleum products. In fourteen other two-digit categories three or more firms were studied. Because of the heterogeneity of the products involved, seven firms were included in chemicals; in stone, clay, and glass products; and in both electrical and nonelectrical machinery. In each of five four-digit industries in Mexico, two firms making the same product were selected, and in two four-digit categories, there are three firms. Eleven Puerto Rican firms have Mexican counterparts, and two Puerto Rican firms almost duplicate each other. In short, forty-nine four-digit categories were represented: one category four times; three categories three times; twelve categories twice; and thirty-three categories once.

As shown in Table 22, ten firms in Puerto Rico produced nondurables and nine firms manufactured durables. In Mexico, twenty-six enterprises produced durables and twenty-five non-

2 Cf. Herbert A. Simon, "New Developments in the Theory of the Firm," *American Economic Review, Papers and Proceedings*, May 1962, pp. 7–12.

Table 22. Distribution of sample by industry and location

Industry	SIC*	ISIC†	Nuevo Leon	Central Plateau	Puerto Rico	Total
Processed foods, beverages, tobacco	20–21	20–22	1	3	2	6
Textiles	22	23	1	1	1	3
Apparel	23	243	—	2	1	3
Wood products	24–25	25, 26	1	1	1	3
Paper products	26	27	1	2	1	4
Printing and publishing	27	28	—	1	—	1
Chemicals	28	31	1	4	2	7
Petroleum products	29	32	—	1	—	1
Rubber and plastics	30	30, 399	1	2	1	4
Leather products	31	29, 241	—	2	1	3
Nondurables total			6	19	10	35
Stone, clay, glass products	32	33	3	—	3	6
Primary metal products	33	34	4	2	1	7
Fabricated metal products	34	35	1	2	1	4
Nonelectrical machinery	35	36	5	—	2	7
Electrical machinery and equipment	36	37	4	1	2	7
Transportation equipment	37	38	2	2	—	4
Durables total			19	7	9	35
Total			25	26	19	70
Percentage distribution			35.7	37.2	27.2	100

* U.S. Standard Industrial Classification.
† U.N. International Standard Industrial Classification.

durables. This even division does not apply, however, to the two regions studied within Mexico, Nuevo Leon and the Central Plateau. In Nuevo Leon, nineteen firms, or three out of four, produced durables; and on the Central Plateau, nineteen produced nondurables. Fifteen of the Nuevo Leon firms were located in the city of Monterrey, and ten in adjacent communities. Ten of the Central Plateau firms were located in the Federal District; ten in adjacent *municipios* of the State of Mexico, and six farther away in several other states. Twelve of the Puerto Rican firms were located in San Juan; three in Ponce; and four in as many other cities.

The number of employees was used as the index of size in classifying the enterprises. This index has certain well-known disadvantages compared with the value of fixed assets or annual production, but information about assets and production is less generally available and often unreliable.[3] Table 23 shows that median employment of sample enterprises in Nuevo Leon and Puerto Rico was between 100 and 249 employees. On the Central Plateau, it was between 250 and 499 employees. Almost all of the fifteen enterprises with more than 1,000 employees were located in Mexico. Three multiplant enterprises were studied in Puerto Rico and ten in Mexico. But, except for four enterprises, all Mexican employment figures and other information apply to one plant only. In the four exceptions, the executives interviewed preferred not to single out any one plant as typical of the company's policy and experience. Each of these four was a very large company. Two were Mexican owned, and two were American subsidiaries.

The eight categories of Table 23 have been reduced to three in Table 24: small, medium, and large with 5 to 99, 100 to 499, and 500 and more employees, respectively. Even with this classification, there is a bias in favor of medium- and large-sized firms. Three-quarters of the firms are distributed almost evenly between these categories; twenty-six medium, and twenty-seven large, and only seventeen firms which employed fewer than 100 workers. But these seventeen are fairly well scattered among sixteen industrial classifications and are about evenly divided among foreign subsidiaries and locally-owned firms. Yet, only two were selected in the Central Plateau region.

Comparison of the policies and experience of firms with varying amounts of foreign influence was an important objective of the study. Hence, an effort was made to include pairs of firms comparable in all aspects except ownership. In Mexico 69 per

[3] Bert L. Hoselitz, "Small Industry in Underdeveloped Countries," *Journal of Economic History*, Dec. 1959, p. 601n.

Table 23. Distribution of sample by location, ownership, and number of employees

Location and ownership	Number of employees							
	4–19	20–49	50–99	100–249	250–499	500–999	1,000–2,499	2,500 and more
Nuevo Leon	—	4	3	5	4	3	5	1
Central Plateau	1	—	1	5	4	7	5	3
Puerto Rico	1	3	4	5	3	2	—	1
U.S. subsidiaries	1	4	2	6	5	5	2	2
European subsidiaries	—	—	1	1	—	—	—	—
Immigrant	—	1	—	3	4	1	—	1
Private national	1	2	5	4	2	5	6	1
Public national	—	—	—	1	—	1	2	1
Total	2	7	8	15	11	12	10	5

Table 24. Distribution of sample by industry, number of employees, and ownership

Industry	SIC*	ISIC†	Total	Number of employees			Ownership				
				5–99 (small)	100–499 (medium)	500 and more (large)	U.S. subsid-iaries	Euro-pean subsid-iaries	Immi-grants	Private national	Public national
Processed foods, beverages, tobacco	20–21	20–22	6	2	1	3	3	—	1	1	2
Textiles	22	23	3	—	1	2	1	—	1	1	—
Apparel	23	243	3	1	2	—	1	—	1	1	—
Wood products	24–25	25, 26	3	2	1	—	—	—	1	2	—
Paper products	26	27	4	—	2	2	3	—	—	1	—
Printing and publishing	27	28	1	—	—	1	—	—	—	1	—
Chemicals	28	31	7	3	2	2	4	1	—	1	1
Petroleum products	29	32	1	—	—	1	—	—	—	1	—
Rubber and plastics	30	30, 399	4	—	2	2	2	—	1	1	—
Leather products	31	29, 241	3	1	2	—	1	—	1	2	1
Nondurables total			35	9	13	13	15	1	5	11	4
Stone, clay, glass products	32	33	6	1	3	2	—	—	2	4	—
Primary metal products	33	34	7	—	4	3	3	—	1	3	—
Fabricated metal products	34	35	4	1	2	1	1	—	1	2	—
Nonelectrical machinery	35	36	7	5	1	1	3	—	—	4	—
Electrical machinery and equipment	36	37	7	1	2	4	5	1	—	1	—
Transportation equipment	37	38	4	—	1	3	1	—	—	2	1
Durables total			35	8	13	14	13	1	4	16	1
Total			70	17	26	27	28	2	9	26	5
Percentage distribution			100	24.3	37.2	38.5	40.0	2.9	12.9	37.2	7.2

* U.S. Standard Industrial Classification.
† U.N. International Standard Classification.

cent of the enterprises were locally owned, and thirty-one per cent were foreign subsidiaries (see Table 25). Of the thirty-five locally-owned enterprises, five were owned and operated by the Mexican government. In Mexico eight were owned and operated by non-Spanish speaking immigrants or their descendants, who, by language and culture, appeared more foreign than Mexican. The remaining twenty-two firms, or 43 per cent, were private firms owned and largely operated by invariably Spanish-speaking Mexicans. I have called them "private national" in the tables. Seventeen of these were located in Nuevo Leon.

Of the sixteen foreign subsidiaries in Mexico, two were European and the rest American. Nine were on the Central Plateau and seven in Nuevo Leon. In Puerto Rico, fourteen of the total of nineteen plants were American subsidiaries. Table 23 shows that both locally-owned private firms and foreign subsidiaries are widely distributed according to size; and Table 24 indicates that both types are found in almost all of the two-digit industrial classifications.

In spite of the broad diversity of the sample, a large proportion of the enterprises shared important features. Seventy-nine per cent produced their output in *uniform production runs* that lasted one week or more and involved at least two hundred units of output. Fifty-four per cent produced *simple* commodities of less than five component parts, packaging excluded. Fluid mixtures were included in this category. The output of 53 per cent could be purchased in single units—meters, pounds, etc., by the final buyer at a *low* price, meaning less than the equivalent of one U.S. dollar. In fact, 42 per cent of the firms produced commodities with all three of these features.

At the other extreme, 24 per cent of enterprises produced *complex* commodities of more than fifteen components. Twenty per cent of the commodities produced were *high priced* and could only be purchased with outlays of the equivalent of one

Table 25. Distribution of sample by ownership and location

Type of firm	Nuevo Leon		Central Plateau		Mexico total		Puerto Rico		Total	
	No.	Per cent	No.	Per cent	No.	Per cent	No.	Per cent	No.	Per cent
U.S. subsidiaries	6	24.0	8	30.8	14	27.4	14	73.7	28	40.0
European subsidiaries	1	4.0	1	3.9	2	3.9	—	—	2	2.9
Immigrant	1	4.0	7	26.9	8	15.7	1	5.3	9	12.9
Private national	17	68.0	5	19.2	22	43.2	4	21.0	26	37.2
Public national	—	—	5	19.2	5	9.8	—	—	5	7.2
Total	25		26		51		19		70	

hundred U.S. dollars or more. Only 7 per cent of the firms, however, produced *custom-built* commodities, that is, in production runs of less than twenty units, according to the classification used. Only three firms selected made the combination of complex, high-cost, custom-built products; and each of these was Mexican owned, located in Nuevo Leon, and producing capital goods.

Only ten firms produced capital goods, including heavy transportation equipment. All but two of these were located in Nuevo Leon, the region in which this type of production had progressed the most. They came in all three sizes. One was government owned and two were foreign subsidiaries. Of the sixty remaining firms, thirty-one produced final consumer goods, and twenty-nine produced various types of intermediate products. Seventy per cent of the enterprises bought intermediate products for further processing, and 30 per cent mainly processed primary materials from mine, well, forest, or farm. Four of the five government-owned plants visited were in this latter class. In general, the extent of vertical integration of stages of production within a plant approached a level typical of American practice in about two-thirds of the plants, especially among medium and large producers of nondurable goods. All but two of the plants that were less integrated either produced durables, employed less than one hundred workers, were foreign subsidiaries, or were some combination of these.

The range of vertical integration that is economically feasible is reflected in the extent to which capacity can vary. Integration and capacity are usually positively related. Where the economies of integration and scale are great, as in continuous-flow chemical plants, Mexican and Puerto Rican plant capacity differed little from that in the United States. At the opposite extreme are complex, assembled products which permit a wide range of integration possibilities. In the case of such plants, Mexican executives claimed that their plants produced somewhere between a twentieth and a hundredth of the output they considered typical in the United States. Semicontinuous-flow industries, such as textiles, paper, steel cans, light bulbs, and the like, were produced at a level between one-tenth and one-half of American practice. Small firms, producing commodities with limited possibilities for vertical integration anywhere, but in which various levels of specialization and mechanization were nevertheless possible, typically seemed to have about one-fifth the annual volume of output in Mexico compared with the United States.

One should not assume that the comparatively small size of the Mexican market, combined with the technological indivisibilities, always implies limited competition in industries protected from imports. True enough, 35 per cent of the enterprises studied were sole producers, or in a group of five or fewer firms. On the other hand, 57 per cent had nine or more potential competitors, including 20 per cent with hundreds of possible competitors.

Two-thirds of the Mexican firms produced exclusively for the domestic market. Only three considered their export sales as important or more important than their domestic sales. One of these was a foreign subsidiary producing primary nonferrous metal products; another was an immigrant-owned tile producer; the third, a Mexican-owned publishing house. Executives of forty-three of the fifty-one Mexican enterprises commented on their firms' needs for import protection. As shown in Table 26, twenty-six believed they needed it, but seventeen thought they could manage without. Durable goods producers were somewhat more frequently concerned with protection. All of the enterprises not concerned about imports made goods naturally protected through perishability, transportation costs, raw material advantages, or the need for close contact with customers.

Nine of the Puerto Rican firms produced entirely for export,

Table 26. The need for tariff protection as seen by executives of fifty-one Mexican manufacturing enterprises

Type of firm	Definitely needed	Probably needed	Probably not needed	Definitely not needed	Undecided or "no" reply
Small	2	3	2	—	2
Medium	9	—	1	5	3
Large	10	2	5	4	3
U.S. subsidiaries	8	2	2	1	1
European subsidiaries	1	—	—	1	—
Immigrant	5	—	1	1	1
Private national	6	3	3	4	6
Public national	1	—	2	2	—
Nondurable producers	10	2	2	6	5
Durable producers	11	3	6	3	3
Nuevo Leon	9	3	3	4	6
Central Plateau	12	2	5	5	2
Total	21	5	8	9	8

largely for the mainland United States market; eight produced only for the Island market; and two said their sales were about evenly divided. According to the Economic Development Administration, with one exception, these plants were established at least partly as a result of its efforts in such matters as promotion, provision of a building, loans, help in selecting and training workers, and other assistance. The one exception, after it had been established, had also received E.D.A. help. Fifteen enterprises were exempt from Commonwealth (and, of course, U.S. Federal) taxes, and this number includes the eleven firms producing for export.

APPENDIX D

Questionnaire

ENGLISH	SPANISH
I. *Introduction*	I. *Introducción*
1. When was the new plant built? Number of employees? Number of shifts?	1. Cuándo fué construída la nueva fábrica? Número de empleados? Número de turnos?
2. Who designed the plant?	2. Por quién fué diseñado la fábrica?
3. Who else was consulted?	3. A quién además hubo necesidad de consultar?
4. What part of your past experience could you apply?	4. Fué posible emplear alguna experiencia anterior de usted?
5. Was the practice of similar firms elsewhere investigated? (Mexico, U.S., Europe, Japan)	5. Se tomó ejemplo de práctica de otras firmas similares? (México, E.U., Europa, Japón)
II. *Instructions to Designing Engineers*	II. *Instructivo para Ingenieros de Diseño*
1. For what capacity was the plant designed? Units/production run; no. of runs/year, month, week?	1. Para qué capacidad ha sido diseñada la fábrica? Unidades por lote, lotes por año, mes, semana?
2. How are your plans for im-	2. Cómo se inicia un plan de

provement initiated, developed, and approved within the firm?

3. Were the engineers told to design the plant with sufficient flexibility to allow easy shifts to other products?

4. What other products could you produce that you are not producing?

5. What alterations would still have to be made before changing to the other product?

6. Were the engineers given a time limit within which they had to complete the plans?

7. Would the engineers have preferred more time? Why? Why not?

8. Was the choice of equipment left primarily to the engineering firm?

9. If partly yes, for which types of machines?

10. How were the actual suppliers of equipment finally chosen? Who were they?

11. Can the materials processed be bought in a more (less) finished form?

12. Could the output have been

ampliación o mejora en esta empresa? Cómo se desarolla y quién se encarga de autorizarlo finalmente?

3. Mandó usted a los ingenieros que diseñaran la fábrica de tal modo que pueda tener cambios a otro tipo de productos?

4. Qué otros productos se podrían lograr aparte de los que ahora se producen?

5. Qué cambios sería necesario hacer, para lograr ese otro tipo de productos?

6. Se dió a los ingenieros algún plazo fijo para la realización del diseño?

7. Hubieran preferido los ingenieros tener más tiempo? Por qué? Por qué no?

8. Permitió usted que los ingenieros diseñadores seleccionaran la maquinaria? Completamente?

9. De ser en parte así, para qué tipo de maquinaria?

10. Cómo fueron elegidos finalmente los fabricantes de la maquinaria? Quienes fueron ellos?

11. Puede usted comprar los materiales en un estado más (o menos) elaborado?

12. Pueda la fábrica elaborar

processed to a greater (less) extent? Would that be profitable?

13. What factor seems to you to have been the most important in determining the production process employed here?

III. *Financial Considerations Affecting the Characteristics of the Investment*

1. Was the cost of the plant accurately estimated by the engineers? Was it what you had planned?

2. Was equipment recommended by engineers ever considered too costly by management so that plans had to be changed?

3. The plant was built in 19___. By what year did you expect to recover the original capital investment?

4. Could you tell me the general method you use in estimating capital cost per year (the depreciation formula)?

5. What rate of interest do you assume in these calculations?

6. If the rate of interest were _____ (50% more or less),

una etapa más (o menos) avanzada que la actual? Sería eso lucrativo?

13. Cuál le parece a usted el factor más importante que determina el proceso que aquí se emplea?

III. *Consideraciones Financieras que Influyen en el Tipo de Inversión*

1. Fué estimado con precisión por los ingenieros el costo de las instalaciones? Fué este costo el que usted había proyectado?

2. Ha pasado jamás que el equipo recomendado por los ingenieros resultó alto para los directivos de la empresa, y por consiguiente cambiaron los planes?

3. Se construyó la planta en 19___. Para qué año se esperaba recuperar la inversión original?

4. Podría usted decirme cúal es el método que usted emplea para presuponer el costo del capital por año (la fórmula de depreciación)?

5. Qué tipo de interés emplea usted en estos cálculos?

6. Si el tipo de interés fuera _____ (50% más o menos),

would that make much difference in the choice of equipment?

7. If large amounts of money could be borrowed at 4-5 per cent (or preferred stock issued) would you have specified different equipment? For example? What if no bank or financiera loans were available under 20%, or 2% per month?

8. Did any suppliers of capital or credit influence the choice of equipment? (Ex-im credit, manufacturers etc.) Does lower interest offset higher price—or is it the mere availability that counts?

9. Is it known who supplied most of the capital for the plant? Did this group suggest any change in the general plans? (For example, the rate of recovery)
    (Individual stockholders, parent companies, banks, government sources)

10. Did tax policy influence the choice of equipment? (Special exemptions)

11. To what extent was the ex-

importaría mucho en la selección de equipo?

7. Si hubiera sido posible prestar mucho dinero a un tipo de interes de 4–5% (o vender acciones prvilegiadas), habría usted comprado equipo distinto? Por ejemplo? Y si no hubiera sido disponible prestamos de un tipo de interes de menos de 20% o 2% el mes, habría sido necesario cambiar el equipo?

8. Influyeron en la selección del equipo, los provedores del capital o del crédito? (Ex-im Bank, fabricantes, etc.) Compensó un tipo de interés más bajo para un precio más alto? O es la sola disponibilidad lo que cuenta?

9. Se sabe quién aportó la mayor parte del capital para la fábrica? Propuso este grupo algún cambio en el proyecto? (Por ejemplo, la tasa de recuperación)
    (Accionistas individuales, matriz de la empresa, bancos, gobierno)

10. Influyó en la selección de maquinaria la política de impuestos? (Exenciones especiales)

11. Hasta que punto fué finan-

pansion financed by rein-
vesting earnings? Would the
investment have been af-
fected if it were not deducti-
ble from taxable income?

12. Did problems of import
licenses influence the choice
of equipment?

13. If there had been access to
fifty per cent more capital—
or if that much could have
been borrowed at very low
interest rates—would that
have made much difference
in plant design?

14. To get a better understanding of the situation, I would
like to know in what else the
investors could have safely
invested if they had not
chosen to manufacture these
products? Would they have?

IV. *Economic Factors
Influencing the Manner
of Operating the Plant*

1. Did you plan to set up and
operate the plant exactly as
would be done in a Euro-
pean or American firm of
comparable size? What was
to be done differently? Why?

2. Which processes and machines are most important in
your plant? What was the

ciada la expansión con util-
idades reinvertidas? Sería
afectada la inversión, si no
fuera deducible del ingreso
gravable?

12. Afectaron a la selección del
equipo, los problemas de li-
cencias de importación?

13. Si hubiera habido disponible
el capital a un 50% más, o
de haberse conseguido ello
por medio de prestamos a
bajo interés, habría esto
cambiado el diseño de la
fábrica?

14. Para tener un conocimiento
mejor de la situación, me
gustaría saber que otro tipo
de inversión hubieran elegido los inversionistas, de no
haber elegido hacer estos
productos? Es ésto posible?

IV. *Factores Económicos que
Influyen en el Modo de
operación de la fábrica*

1. Se tiene planteado establecer
y operar la fábrica exacta-
mente como operan una fábrica de este volumen en
Europa o los Estados Uni-
dos? Que iban a hacer de
otro modo? Por qué?

2. Cuáles procesos y máquinas
son los más importantes en
su fábrica? Cuáles fueron

best alternative to the process you finally selected? Why did you reject it?

3. For any part of your operations, were you forced to choose machinery that was not really well adapted to (the economic realities of Mexico today) your problems?

4. Have you ever replaced production equipment in less than 10 years solely because of obsolescence?

5. Is there novel equipment especially suited to this firm?

   a. What were the circumstances of its development?

   b. If no such equipment is present, what are the risks and gains that would have been involved in ordering equipment especially designed for your needs?

   c. Does it seem to you that the government or equipment manufacturers could profitably take these risks? Could they later cover their research expenses by charging manufacturers like you a sufficiently higher price?

las alternativas mejores de los procesos que al cabo, usted seleccionó? Por qué las rechazó usted?

3. Para algún aspecto de la operación, fué usted obligado a elegir maquinaria no muy bien acomodada a (las realidades económicas de México de hoy) sus problemas?

4. Ha reemplazado usted la maquinaria en menos de 10 años, sólamente por ser ésta anticuada?

5. Hay máquinas originales en su fábrica, diseñadas para esta compañía?

   a. Cúales fueron las circunstancias de su desarollo?

   b. Si no hay tal equipo, cuáles serían los riesgos y las ganancias de pedir equipo diseñado especialmente para sus exigencias?

   c. Le parece a usted que el gobierno o las fabricantes de las máquinas puedan tomar los riesgos con ganancia para ellos? Podrían ellos recuperar los gastos de las investigaciones con un precio elevado suficientemente?

6. Do you have equipment made in Mexico?

7. Have you ever contracted for technological research of any type by an outside research institute?

6. Tiene usted equipo hecho en México?

7. Ha usted jamás contratado para una investigación tecnológica, de algún instituto de investigación especializado?

V. *Labor Skills and Wages*

1. Were you limited in your choice of equipment because of uncertainties with respect to labor skills?

2. Do you know how the productivity of your workers compares with productivity elsewhere with the type of equipment you have?

3. In this industry is it necessary to pay very high salaries to good supervisors? Would you say the scarcity of these is an important problem?

4. Did regulations and union policies about wage increases, social welfare (fringe) benefits, modernization, and lay-off procedures influence your choice of equipment?

5. If the planners could have been sure that wages would rise only very slowly, if at

V. *El Trabajo Calificado y los Salarios*

1. Fué usted constreñido en la selección de maquinaria por incertidumbres de la disponibilidad de trabajadores calificados?

2. Sabe usted como se compara la productividad de sus obreros con la productividad de obreros en otra parte?

3. En esta industria es necesario pagar salarios muy altos a buenos supervisores? Diríase que la escasez de ellos es un problema de importancia?

4. Influyeron en la selección de maquinaria las leyes sobre el trabajo y la política sobre la subida de los salarios, beneficios sociales, prestaciones, modernización, y separaciones del trabajo?

5. Si los proyectadores hubieran podido asegurarse que los salarios no subirán

all, would it have made any difference in the choice of equipment?

sino muy lentamente, hubiera influido eso en la selección de la maquinaria?

VI. *The Influence of Markets*

VI. *La Influencia de los Mercados*

1. Are there special advantages in the present location, not found elsewhere?

1. Hay aquí ventajas especiales en fabricar que usted no puede encontrar en otra parte?

2. Do you make standard production runs for stock or do you produce to order? Did you know who would be your customers?

2. Fabrica usted de lotes de productos corrientes (de tamaños normales) o produce usted a órdenes de trabajo? Supo usted quienes serían sus clientes (compradores)?

3. How did you estimate the probable rate of growth of sales? (first year, fifth year) When did you expect to require your full capacity? Was this expectation correct?

3. Cómo estimó usted el crecimiento probable de las ventas? (año 1, año 5) Para cuándo creyó usted necesitar usar la plena capacidad? Resultó acertada esta creencia?

4. Did you expect competition? Did it materialize?

4. Anticipó usted competencia? Ha sucedido así?

5. Is tariff protection etc. important in this industry? Could you break even without it?

5. Son importantes en esta industria los impuestos y derechos de aduana? Puede usted recuperar sus gastos sin ellos?

VII. *Experience with the Plant in Operation*

VII. *La Experiencia Con la Planta en Operación*

1. Did the extra expense (sav-

1. Cree usted que los gastos

ing) of using _____ equipment instead of _____, the
alternative, pay off?

(economías) extraordinarias
de emplear ——— máquinas
en lugar de ———————,
la alternativa, le han recom-
pensado completamente?

2. Was it thought that local
availability of power, water,
transportation . . . would
impose special methods of
operation?

2. Creyó usted que la disponibilidad aquí de fuerza, agua,
del transporte . . . impusiera
un método de operación especial?

3. Was it thought that uncertainty of delivery time, costs,
and quality of materials
would impose special methods of operation?

   a. If access to materials were
   more reliable would that
   have made any difference
   in plant design?

3. Creyó usted que la incerti-
dumbre del tiempo de en-
tregas de materiales, de su
costo y calidad, impusiera
un método de operación especial?

   a. Si la disponibilidad de
   materias hubiera sido
   digno de más confianza,
   cree usted que eso habría
   influido el diseño del
   equipo?

4. Was there to be a special
emphasis on maintenance to
allow more intensive or
longer use of equipment?
How many years do your
principal machines last?

4. Había usted proyectado un
énfasis especial en mantenimiento de equipo para ganar
un uso más intensivo o pro-
longado? Cuántos años de
vida le parece a usted que
tienen sus máquinas princi-
pales?

   a. Could the machinery design easily be improved to
   facilitate Mexican maintenance needs?

   b. At this location must you

   a. Sabe usted si sea fácil
   cambiar el diseño del
   equipo para facilitar el
   mantenimiento como es
   mejor hacerlo en México?

keep an extra large inventory of spare parts?

5. Do you have second-hand equipment? For which processes?
   a. Was it available for all processes?
   b. What percentage of equipment cost does one save by buying used machinery?
   c. What risks does one take?
   d. If you had to buy all new equipment, would this plant still be a profitable investment?

6. May I ask what is the relative importance in the total cost of wages, materials, machinery, and plant overhead? (Percentages)

7. Does the way auxiliary processes (materials handling, storage, packaging) can or must be operated, on balance, constitute an advantage for the local firm—or a disadvantage?
   a. What percentage are these expenditures of total costs?
   b. What alternatives were

b. En este lugar es necesario retener un inventario de repuestos extraordinariamente grande?

5. Tiene usted equipo usado (reacondicionado)? En qué procesos?
   a. Fue ésto disponible para todos los procesos?
   b. Cuál porcentaje del costo del equipo se puede ahorrar así?
   c. Cuáles son los riesgos que toma uno en comprar equipo reacondicionado?
   d. Si usted tuviera que comprar todo el equipo nuevo, sería lucrativo invertir en esta planta?

6. Sería oportuno preguntarle el porcentaje en el costo total de los salarios, los materiales, la maquinaria, y los gastos generales?

7. Es la manera en que usted puede o tiene que explotar las actividades auxiliares (manejo, transporte dentro de la fábrica, envasar el producto, almacenaje) principalmente una ventaja o una desventaja de fabricar aquí?
   a. Cuál es el porcentaje que estos gastos son del costo total?

considered here? (Packaging, handling)

c. What criterion was most important in making the final choice? What else was considered?

8. Could you profitably install additional equipment to facilitate your current volume of production? If so, why was it not installed previously?

9. Would it have been possible to reduce costs by using less mechanization and more labor?

10. Did the equipment or the manner of its use have to be modified on the basis of experience? Why?

a. How was the need to change operations discovered?

11. How do you evaluate the performance of the equipment?

a. Frequency of breakdowns?

b. Percentage of idle time? Machine hours per pro-

b. Cuáles fueron las alternativas consideradas por usted en estos casos? (Banda o cadena transportadora, grúas, carretillas . . . el envasar . . .)

c. Cuál criterio fué lo mas importante en la selección final? Cuáles otros consideró usted?

8. Quiere usted instalar máquinas para esta capacidad que la fábrica aún no tiene? Por qué no las ha comprado antes?

9. Hubiera sido posible bajar los costos con menos mecanización y mas trabajadores?

10. Fué necesario modificar las máquinas a causa de su experiencia aquí? Por qué? Ha cambiado usted la manera de usarlas?

a. Cómo se encontró la necesidad de cambiar las operaciones así?

11. En esta compañía cómo estiman el rendimiento de una máquina?

a. La frecuencia de fallas?

b. El porcentaje de tiempo ocioso (vacío)? Dan cuenta en detalle de las

duction run reported in detail?

c. I would be interested in the detailed manner in which you allocate labor, material, and factory expenses to specific products and departments.

d. How often do you receive reports on these matters?

12. If you had to set up a plant to produce the same volume of production in (the United States or other industrialized country), what would you do differently?

horas de trabajo por máquina por lote?

c. Yo tendría interés en saber precisamente como esta compañía asigna los costos del trabajo, de los materiales, y de gastos generales a los productos específicos y a los varios departamentos.

d. Con qué frecuencia recibe usted informes de este tipo?

12. Si usted tuviera que proyectar una fábrica como ésta en (los Estados Unidos o otro país industrializado), que haría usted distinto?

Index of Persons

Index of Topics